Health & Safety *for* Management

A Text for Health & Safety Courses

Jeremy W. Stranks
MSc, FCIEH, FIOSH, RSP

PUBLISHED BY

©HIGHFIELD.CO.UK LTD

"Vue Pointe", Spinney Hill, Sprotbrough,
Doncaster, DN5 7LY, UK
Tel: +44 0845 2260350
Fax: +44 0845 2260360
E-mail: richard@highfield.co.uk

Websites:
www.highfield.co.uk
www.foodsafetytrainers.co.uk

ISBN 1-904544-00-2

First published 2003

©HIGHFIELD.CO.UK LTD

ISBN 1-904544-00-2

Printed by Apple Tree Print • Telephone: 01302 314011

Contents

Preface

Health and safety at work is a multi-disciplinary area of knowledge. It covers subjects as diverse as the law, human factors, engineering, ergonomics and fire prevention, each of which is an area of study in its own right. On this basis, it is perceived by some managers as something of a minefield, particularly in terms of its actual management in the workplace.

This book endeavours to provide managers with a structured approach to the development of management systems for health and safety. It deals with, for instance, the criminal and civil aspects of the law, systems for managing health and safety, the structural design of the workplace, occupational health and hygiene and hazardous substances. A number of standard forms have been incorporated to assist managers with monitoring activities such as safety auditing and risk assessment. The book includes a chapter on stress at work, bearing in mind the increasing significance attached to this subject.

Health & Safety for Management has also been prepared for use as a reference text for both accredited and in-house management health and safety training courses. Trainers will find its structured approach helpful in the design of courses targeted at all levels of management together with specialists, such as engineering management and safety officers.

1 Fundamentals of Health & Safety Law

Health and safety law covers many areas of the law – common, criminal, civil and contract law. The origins of health and safety law can be traced to the Industrial Revolution and the appalling conditions in which people worked, for instance, the cotton, pottery and match-making industries.

This chapter covers the sources of health and safety law, the range of people who have duties under this law, the criminal and civil liabilities of employers and others, the hierarchy of the courts, together with the procedures of courts and tribunals.

SOURCES OF HEALTH AND SAFETY LAW

Common Law

Common law is that body of law based on the decisions of the courts going back many hundreds of years. It is, fundamentally, unwritten law in that it is not written in the form of Acts of Parliament (statutes) or regulations (Statutory Instruments). It is based on the decisions of the courts that have been bound by the doctrine of precedent into a body of authoritive rules and principles. It is essentially judge-made law and accounts for the greater part of the law of contract and tort, both of which have played a significant role in the development of civil liability relating to occupational health and safety.

Common law is synonymous with case law and its rules, principles and doctrines are to be found in the various Law Reports, such as the All England Reports (AER). Case law is, fundamentally, a self-endorsing process, being perpetuated either by previous binding cases or by the interpretation of legislation.

The main contribution of common law to health and safety law is the body of rules developed in conjunction with the right of an employee and his dependants to sue an employer for damages for personal injury, disease or death sustained at work. This is the civil liability of an employer, which is to be found mainly in the rules of tort.

Criminal Law

A crime is defined as 'an offence against the State'. The commission of a crime can result in an individual being charged with an offence and prosecution in a criminal court, such as the Magistrates' Court, by an official enforcement organisation, such as the Police and Health and Safety Executive (HSE). Criminal cases are heard in the Magistrates' Court and in the Crown Court, where serious cases are heard before a judge and jury.

The burden of proof with regard to a criminal charge rests with the prosecution. Such a charge must be proved **beyond reasonable doubt**. The main sanctions that a criminal court can impose are a fine and/or imprisonment. These sanctions are intended as a punishment, to deter and to reform, but not to compensate an injured party.

Civil Law

Civil law is concerned with the liability arising from an act or omission, which the law regards as giving an individual or organisation the right to present a legal claim against another. Civil claims are heard in the civil courts, notably the county courts or the High Court. The two areas of civil law most relevant to occupational health and safety are **torts**, a collective name for certain rights of action, especially negligence, breach of statutory duty and breach of contract. Where a civil claim in respect of injury, disease or death is presented, the following features are present:

- the proceedings are brought by an individual, the claimant; and
- the purpose of the claim is to secure an award of damages, ie financial compensation, for suffering and disablement.

The objective is, therefore, compensatory, the degree or level of compensation being related to factors such as loss of livelihood, loss of mobility, anticipated cost of future care and the loss of enjoyment of certain activities previously carried out, such as dancing or playing a particular sport.

Contract Law

A contract is an agreement between two parties. To be legally enforceable, certain basic features are required in a contract. It must be certain in its wording, that is, unambiguous, and consist of an offer made by one party that must be accepted unconditionally by the other party. The great majority of contracts need not necessarily be in writing. There must, however, be consideration that flows from one party to another. This is the legal ingredient that changes an informal agreement into a legally binding contract, for instance, the carrying out of work for wages or the provision of goods and services for money.

There are three types of contract, those of record or deed, or a simple contract that may be oral, written or implied. For a contract to be valid, all of the following must be accepted and agreed by the parties involved:

- an offer and its acceptance;
- an intention to create a legal status;
- the capacity to enter into a contract;
- a consent to the contract without duress;
- an agreed consideration;
- the actions are legal; and
- fulfilment of the contract is actually possible.

Two essentials for a valid contract are that the parties must intend to enter into a legally binding agreement and both parties must have the legal capacity to make the contract. 'Capacity' to contract means that the parties must be sane, sober and over the age of 18 years as a rule.

THE CRIMINAL AND CIVIL LIABILITIES OF EMPLOYERS AND OTHERS

Breaches of health and safety law can incur both criminal and civil liability on the party or parties committing the breaches.

Criminal Liability

Criminal liability refers to the duties and responsibilities of individuals and organisations under statute, principally the Health and Safety at Work etc Act (HSWA) 1974, together with regulations made under the Act, and the penalties that can be imposed by the criminal courts, namely fines, imprisonment and remedial orders, on offenders.

There are two categories of conviction, namely:

♦ **Summary conviction** – for offences regarded as less serious, which, in practice, applies to most health and safety-related offences, and where the case is brought before a Magistrates' Court. The maximum penalty for certain of these offences, such as failing to undertake a suitable and sufficient risk assessment, is £20,000 and/or six months imprisonment; for other health and safety-related offences, £5,000.

♦ **Conviction on indictment** – where the case is tried before a judge and jury in a Crown Court. This form of trial is reserved for the more serious offences, such as corporate manslaughter, and offenders can be sentenced to up to two years' imprisonment with fines being unlimited.

Thus the criminal courts in question are:

♦ The Magistrates' Courts and, in Scotland, the Sheriff Courts, which handle the majority of health and safety offences.

♦ The Crown Courts, which deal with the more serious offences.

Appeals can be made to the High Court and beyond, to the Court of Appeal (Criminal Division) and, assuming leave is given, to the House of Lords. Subject to certain criteria, a case may pass to the European Court of Justice.

Criminal law is based on a system of enforcement. Its statutory provisions are enforced by the state's enforcement agencies, such as the police, HSE, local authorities and fire authorities.

Civil Liability

A civil action generally involves negligence and/or breach of a statutory duty. In such actions a claimant sues a defendant for a remedy or remedies beneficial to the claimant. In most cases this remedy takes the form of damages, ie financial compensation for injury, damage or loss sustained. In a substantial number of cases, the claimant will agree to settle out of court personally or through his insurers.

Civil liability refers, therefore, to the penalty that can be imposed by a civil court, for example, the County Court, High Court, Court of Appeal (Civil Division) or House of Lords and consists of an award of damages in most cases.

SOURCES OF LAW

EU Directives

These are European Community instruments of legislation that are legally binding on the governments of all member states. On this basis they must introduce national legislation, or use administrative procedures where applicable, to implement the requirements of Directives. For example, the 'Heavy Loads' Directive was implemented in the UK as the Manual Handling Operations Regulations 1992.

Acts of Parliament (Statutes)

Acts of Parliament may be **innovatory**, ie introducing new legislation, or **consolidating**, ie reinforcing, with modifications, existing law. Statutes, in most cases, empower the Minister or Secretary of State to make regulations (delegated or subordinate legislation) known as Statutory Instruments. Typical examples are the HSWA and the Fire Precautions Act 1971.

Regulations (Statutory Instruments)

Regulations are generally more detailed than the parent Act, which lays down the framework and objectives of the legislation. Typical examples are the Control of Substances Hazardous to Health (COSHH) Regulations and the Health and Safety (Display Screen Equipment) Regulations.

Approved Codes of Practice

The Health and Safety Commission (HSC) is empowered under the HSWA to approve and issue Codes of Practice for the purpose of elaborating on health and safety duties and other matters laid down in statute or regulations. A Code of Practice may be drawn up by the HSC or HSE. In every case, however, the relevant government department or other body must be consulted beforehand and approval of the Secretary of State obtained. Any such Code of Practice approved in this way is an Approved Code of Practice (ACOP).

An ACOP enjoys a special status under the HSWA. Although failure to comply with any provision of the code is not in itself an offence, in criminal proceedings a failure may be taken by a court as proof that a defendant has contravened the legal requirement to which the provision relates. In such a case it will be open to the defendant to satisfy the court that he /she has complied with the requirement in some other way, for instance, through carrying out works of an equivalent nature.

Examples of ACOPS are those issued with the COSHH Regulations entitled 'Control of Substances Hazardous to Health', 'Control of Carcinogenic Substances' and 'Control of Substances Hazardous to Health in Fumigation Operations'.

Case Law

Case law is, traditionally, derived from the common law as judges have progressively formulated the rules and principles of law as the cases occur for decisions before the courts. Criminal law also has its own case law based on decisions by judges in the criminal courts over many years.

What is important in a decision is the **ratio decidendi** (the reason for the decision). This decision is binding on courts of equal rank who may be considering the same point of law. Ratio decidendi is the application of such an established principle to the facts of a given case, for instance, in the case of negligence, which consists of omitting to do what a 'reasonable man' would do in order to avoid causing injury to others.

Case law is found in Law Reports, for example, the All England Law Reports, the Industrial Cases Reports, the current Law Year Book and in professional journals, for example, Law Society Gazette, Solicitors Journal. In addition, many newspapers carry daily law reports, for example, The Times, Financial Times and Daily Telegraph. Decisions of the European Court of Justice are carried in The Times.

HSE Series of Guidance Notes

The HSE issues Guidance Notes, some of which accompany regulations. Guidance Notes have no legal status and are issued on a purely advisory basis. There are five series of HSE Guidance Notes:

- general;
- chemical safety;
- plant and machinery;
- medical; and
- environmental hygiene.

THE DUTIES OF EMPLOYERS AT COMMON LAW

As stated earlier in this chapter, the common law is based on the doctrine of precedent under which, in the vast majority of cases, a court must follow the earlier decisions of the courts at its own level and of the superior courts. This is known as **binding precedent**. The doctrine of binding precedent is based on the concept of **stare decisis**, that is, 'keep to the decisions of past cases', 'let the decision stand'.

Under the common law employers owe a general duty towards their employees to take reasonable care to avoid injuries, disease or death at work (the common duty of care).

More specifically, all employers must:

♦   provide and maintain a safe place of work with safe means of access and egress;
♦   provide and maintain safe appliances and equipment and plant for doing the work;
♦   provide and maintain a safe system for doing the work;
♦   provide competent and safety conscious personnel.

[Wilson's & Clyde Coal Co. Ltd. v English (1938) 2 AER 628]

TORTS

A tort is a civil wrong. It concerns the legal relationship between parties generally in the everyday course of their affairs, the duties owed by one to another and the legal effect of a wrongful act or omission of one party causing harm to the person, property, reputation or economic interests of another. Torts are of universal application compared with the law of contract, which applies only to the specific parties involved.

Torts of particular significance in the field of occupational health and safety are those of negligence, breach of statutory duty, nuisance and trespass. The common law duties of employers form part of the general law of negligence and, as such, are specific aspects of the duty to take reasonable care.

NEGLIGENCE

Negligence is defined in case law as:

♦   the existence of a duty of care owed by a defendant to a claimant (plaintiff);
♦   breach of that duty; and
♦   damage, loss or injury resulting from or caused by that breach.

[Lochgelly Iron & Coal Co.Ltd v M'Mullan (1934) AC1)]

These three facts must be established by an injured employee before he is entitled to bring a claim for damages. It is essential that the breach of duty caused the injury or occupational disease (causation). Breach of duty need not be the exclusive cause, but it must be a substantial one, ie materially contribute to the injury or ill-health condition.

The legal process involving the tort of negligence is for a claimant to sue a defendant, for example, an employer, for damages.   If the action is successful, the claimant will be awarded damages.

Defences in Actions for Negligence

There are two defences available to an employer or other person who may be sued for a breach of a common law duty.

'Volenti non fit injuria'

This term means 'to one who is willing, no harm is done'. It is a complete defence and means that no damages will be payable. It has a very limited application, for instance, where an employee, who has received training and instruction in the dangers involved in not following the laid down safety procedures and statutory duties, is fully aware of the risks and suffers injury, disease and/or death as a result of non-compliance. In such situations, it is open to an employer to submit that the employee concerned voluntarily agreed to run the risk of the injury involved, ie voluntary assumption of risk.

Contributory Negligence

The Law Reform (Contributory Negligence) Act 1945 provides that where injury is caused by the fault of two or more persons, liability or fault and, in consequence, damages must be apportioned in accordance with the extent to which both or more persons were to blame.

On this basis, an employer, when sued by an employee as a result of injury, may be able to claim that the employee contributed to his accidental injuries through his failure to follow safety procedures, a safe system of work, safe working practice or that he was careless with regard to the use of machinery and equipment. Much will depend upon the circumstances of the case, however. Once the level of damages has been established, a judge would commonly apportion liability on, for instance, a 60% employer:40% employee basis, 30% employer:70% employee basis, etc. with the resultant award of damages being modified accordingly.

BREACH OF STATUTORY DUTY

The courts have sometimes recognised that a breach of a duty imposed by a statute may give rise to a civil claim for damages. This applies in cases where a statute may impose a duty but makes no reference to civil liability for any injury or loss caused by the breach. In these cases, the approach of the courts has been that of ascertaining whether the duty imposed was for the protection of a specific class of person, for example, an employee, or for the general public.

In particular, the courts have, in the past, viewed the safety provisions of the Factories Acts, particularly those relating to the safeguarding of machinery, as being protective to a particular class of person, namely employees and, in many cases, have allowed a civil action for damages as a result of a breach of that statutory duty. Civil actions based on the tort of breach of statutory duty have been particularly successful in the case of claims involving injury from dangerous machinery.

It should be noted that section 47 of the HSWA provides that:
♦ a breach of any of the general duties in section 2 to 8 will not give rise to civil liability; and
♦ breach of any duty imposed in regulations under the Act will give rise to civil liability, unless the regulations state otherwise.

It should be noted that civil liability is expressly excluded from the Management of Health and Safety at Work Regulations (MHSWR), whereas in other regulations this exclusion is not made. This implies that a breach of, for instance, the Workplace (Health, Safety and Welfare) Regulations (WHSWR) 1992 and the Provision and Use of Work Equipment Regulations (PUWER) 1998, both of which do not incorporate a specific exclusion of civil liability, may give rise to a claim for breach of statutory duty where there is a clear-cut breach of the regulations resulting in injury to a claimant.

THE TORT OF TRESPASS

Trespass implies some form of wrongdoing by one person against another. Trespass may be to a person, to land or to goods.

Trespass to the Person

This may take the form of assault, battery or false imprisonment.

An **assault** involves an attempt to offer to apply unlawful force on another person. There must be an ability to carry out the threat as the basis of the wrong is that the claimant is placed in present fear of violence being offered. The mere making of threats cannot be an assault, although they may prevent an action becoming an assault, unless the words imply immediate action. Generally, there must be active conduct although an omission can be an assault.

A **battery** is the unlawful application of force, however slight, to the person of another against his will. The charge of battery is usually combined with assault and becomes **assault and battery**. Examples of battery are striking a man, throwing water at him, throwing a squib at him or even applying a tone rinse to the scalp of a customer, which was not ordered and caused hair and scalp damage.

False imprisonment is the unauthorised bodily restraint of a person without justification. The imprisonment must be total: if he is restrained in three directions, but free to go in a fourth, no false imprisonment exists. If a person is contractually on premises and not given facilities to leave, that is not false imprisonment. Moreover the claimant need not be aware of his imprisonment.

Trespass to Land

This may take four forms:

♦ entry on to the land of another;
♦ remaining on the land of another;
♦ placing or throwing any material object upon the land of another; and
♦ unlawful use of the public highways.

The tort is actionable per se and it is not necessary to prove actual damage or loss.

Trespass to Goods

Here there must be direct interference with goods and this may consist of moving the chattel or throwing something at it.

Section 1 of the Torts (Interference with Goods) Act 1977 defines 'wrongful interference with goods' as including conversion of goods, trespass to goods, negligence or any other tort so far as it results in damage to goods or to an interest in goods. 'Goods' is defined as 'in general, all chattels personal other than things in action or money'.

THE TORT OF NUISANCE

'Halsbury's Laws of England' states that 'nuisances are divisible into common law and statutory nuisances'. 'A common law nuisance is one that apart from statute violates the principles that the common law lays down for the protection of the public and of individuals in the exercise and enjoyment of their rights'. A 'nuisance' has further been defined as 'an act not warranted by law, or an omission to discharge a legal duty, which act or omission obstructs or causes inconvenience or damage to the public in the exercise of rights common to all Her Majesty's subjects'. Nuisances at common law may be **private nuisances** or **public nuisances.**

A private nuisance can take many forms, but in all cases it constitutes some form of act, or failure to act, on the part of an individual or group that results in obstruction, inconvenience or damage to another individual or group.

An action for private nuisance lies where there has been interference with the enjoyment of land. Such interference need not be intentional, however. Private nuisances are associated with, for instance, the keeping of animals, the playing of loud music, the emission of smoke and gases from the burning of refuse. Interference must be sufficiently significant and unreasonable, ie without thought for a neighbour or other persons who could be affected, for a claim for nuisance to be successful.

Action in respect of a private nuisance may be brought by a person injured by the nuisance and he may make a claim for damages and/or obtain an **injunction** restraining someone from committing further nuisance. In appropriate cases, he may abate the nuisance himself, for instance, by lopping overhanging trees.

Public nuisances, on the other hand, have a direct effect on the public at large. Typical examples include obstruction of a public right of way, failure to make secure an excavation in a car park and hosing down brickwork where the spray falls on members of the public in close proximity.

In the case of public nuisances, the person primarily responsible for the initiation of action is the Attorney General, who has complete discretion in the matter. However, a private individual may bring an action in his own name if he has suffered some direct and substantial injury, different in kind from that suffered by the rest of the public, or if the act is also a private nuisance against his land.

COURTS AND TRIBUNALS

There are two distinct systems whereby the courts deal with criminal cases and civil actions. Some courts have both criminal and civil jurisdiction, however.

CRIMINAL COURTS

Magistrates' Court

This is the lowest of the courts and deals principally with summary offences, mainly criminal offences. The jurisdiction of this court is limited. Lay Justices of the Peace (JPs) determine and sentence for many of the less serious offences. Fines that can be imposed and terms of imprisonment are limited. JPs also hold preliminary examinations into other offences to ascertain whether the prosecution can show a prima facie case on which the accused may be committed for trial at a higher court. The Sheriff Court performs a parallel function in Scotland, although procedures differ from those of the Magistrates' Courts.

Crown Court

Serious indictable criminal charges and cases where the accused has right to jury trial are heard on indictment in the Crown Court before a judge and jury. The Crown Court is empowered to impose unlimited fines and/or a maximum of two years' imprisonment for health and safety-related offences. This court also hears appeals from the Magistrates' Court.

CIVIL COURTS

County Court

These courts operate on an area basis and deal in the first instance with a wide range of civil matters. They are limited, however, in the remedies that can be applied. Cases are generally heard before a circuit judge or registrar, the latter having limited jurisdiction. A judge can award compensation up to £50,000.

High Court of Justice

More important civil matters, because of the sums involved or legal complexity, will start in the High Court of Justice before a High Court judge. The High Court has three divisions:

- **Queen's Bench** deals with contract and torts, claims in excess of that of the County Court's power.
- **Chancery** deals with matters relating to, for instance, land, wills, bankruptcy, partnerships and companies.
- **Family** deals with matters involving, for instance, adoption of children, marital property and disputes.

In addition, the Queen's Bench Division hears appeals on matters of law:

- from the Magistrates' Courts and Crown Courts on a procedure called 'case stated' and;
- from some tribunals, for example, the finding of an industrial tribunal on an enforcement notice under the HSWA.

Queen's Bench Division also has some supervisory functions over the lower courts and tribunals in cases where they exceed their powers or fail to undertake their functions properly.

The High Court of Justice, the Crown Court and the Court of Appeal are known as 'the Supreme Court of Judicature'.

THE COURT OF APPEAL

The Court of Appeal has two divisions:

- the Civil Division, which hears appeals from the County Courts and the High Court;
- the Criminal Division, which hears appeals from the Crown Court.

THE HOUSE OF LORDS

The Law Lords deal with important matters of law only, following appeal to the House of Lords from the Court of Appeal and, in restricted circumstances, from the High Court.

THE EUROPEAN COURT OF JUSTICE

This is the supreme law court, whose decisions and interpretations of European Community law are final. Such decisions are enforceable through the network of courts and tribunals in all member states. Cases can only be brought before this court by organisations or individuals representing organisations.

The European Court of Justice may also give advisory opinion to the Council of Ministers and the European Commission on legal matters.

TRIBUNALS

Tribunals deal with many industrial and work-related matters, including industrial relations issues, together with cases involving unfair dismissal, equal pay and sex discrimination.

Each tribunal consists of a legally qualified chairman appointed by the Lord Chancellor and two lay members, one from management and one from a trade union, selected from panels maintained by the Department of Employment following nominations from employers' organisations and trade unions. When all three members are sitting the majority view prevails.

Industrial tribunals deal with the following health and safety issues:

♦ appeals against improvement and prohibition notices served by enforcement officers (Health and Safety at Work etc Act 1974);

♦ time off for training of safety representatives (Safety Representatives and Safety Committees Regulations 1977);

♦ failure by an employer to pay a safety representative for time off to undertake his functions and for training (Safety Representatives and Safety Committees Regulations 1977);

♦ failure of an employer to make a medical suspension payment (Employment Protection (Consolidation) Act 1978);

♦ dismissal, actual constructive, following a breach of health and safety law, regulation and/or term of employment contract (Employment Protection (Consolidation) Act 1978);

The Employment Appeals Tribunal, although not a formal court, is presided over by a judge, who hears appeals on points of law from industrial tribunals.

COURT PROCEDURES

Civil Actions

In a civil action, a claimant sues a defendant. Most civil actions involve an action in tort, commonly negligence and/or breach of statutory duty, and a claim for damages in respect of personal injury, death and/or damage to property.

The first stage of a civil action is the issue of a Writ of Summons, which must be acknowledged by the defendant following service by returning a completed form of acknowledgement of service to the issuing court office, ie the Central Office of the High Court or the District Registry. Where a defendant fails to acknowledge service of a writ within the specified time limit, judgement may be entered against him.

Where an issue goes for trial, the counsel representing the claimant commences by outlining the allegations against the defendant, as indicated in the Statement of Claim previously delivered to the defendant. Witnesses may be called including designated expert witnesses. In most cases a civil action will be heard by a judge sitting alone.

A defence counsel has a choice of several submissions, namely:

♦ 'no case to answer' – in this case, following a reply from the claimant's counsel, the judge gives his verdict, or

♦ 'no evidence to be called' – the claimant's counsel addresses the court, followed by the defence counsel, or

♦ 'defence with evidence' – the defendant's counsel submits the case for the defence, calling witnesses as appropriate.

The judge will then find for or against the claimant. If successful, the claimant is awarded damages. Costs are generally paid by the losing party. In certain cases a claimant may be required to pay his own costs, particularly where a court feels such an action should never have been brought.

Standard procedure in the County Court is covered by the Courts and Legal Services Act 1990. County Court actions generally involve actions where damages not exceeding £50,000 are involved. In these actions, a summons, which sets out the details of the parties to the action and the nature and amount of the claim, is requested by the claimant. The Registrar, an officer of the court, prepares the summons and serves it on the defendant, which the defendant or his solicitor must accept.

The Registrar frequently carries out a Pre-Trial Review with the objective of identifying the key issues of the claim and any points of contention. The actual trial is taken by a county court judge alone. Where the claim is admitted by the defendant, or where the defendant does not present himself to answer the claim, judgement is made in favour of the claimant. In case of dispute, the trial proceeds on lines similar to those in the High Court.

Criminal Prosecutions

Any breach of the HSWA or the 'relevant statutory provisions' is a criminal offence and proceedings are taken in a criminal court. Offences may be summary offences, indictable offences or those that are 'triable either way'.

Summary offences include:

♦ contravening a requirement under section 14 of HSWA (power of HSC to direct investigations and inquiries);
♦ contravening a requirement of an inspector; and
♦ preventing a person from appearing before an inspector, or from answering a question asked by an inspector.

In the case of **indictable offences**, a Magistrates' Court can decide whether there is sufficient evidence to commit an offender to a Crown Court for trial. Where such evidence exists, namely a prima facie case, magistrates can install committal proceedings through issue of an indictment.

Offences triable only on indictment are:

♦ breaching any of the relevant statutory provisions through, for instance, undertaking a process without a licence from the HSE or breaching a term, condition or restriction attached to such a licence; and
♦ acquiring, or attempting to acquire, possessing or using an explosive article or substance.

Certain offences are triable either way and permit the accused to be heard either in a Magistrates' Court or Crown Court, depending upon the choice made by the accused and the severity of the offence.

Many offences are triable either way, including:

♦ breach of duties under sections 2 to 7 of the HSWA;
♦ breach of section 8 of the HSWA, ie intentionally or recklessly interfering with anything provided in the interests of health, safety and welfare;
♦ breach of section 9 of the HSWA, ie levying charges on employees in respect of anything done or provided in pursuance of any specific requirement of the relevant statutory provisions;

- breaching regulations made under the HSWA;
- obstructing an inspector intentionally;
- intentionally or recklessly making a false statement;
- intentionally making a false entry in a book, register, etc required to be maintained;
- impersonating an inspector; and
- breach of any requirement or prohibition imposed by an Improvement Notice or Prohibition Notice.

LEGAL ROUTES FOLLOWING AN ACCIDENT AT WORK FIG. 1

ACCIDENT		
CRIMINAL	**CIVIL**	
Prosecution by the enforcement authority for a breach of duty under statute and/or Regulations.	Civil action by injured person for a breach of common law or statutory duty.	Injured person claims industrial injuries benefit under Social Security Act etc.
Fine and/or imprisonment if convicted.	Court awards damages if the claim is successful.	Benefit awarded where claim is successful.
Criminal appeal procedure.	Civil appeal procedure.	DWP appeal procedure.

OCCUPIERS' LIABILITY

People who occupy land and premises, such as private individuals, local authorities, organisations and companies, shopkeepers and operators of commercial premises, have a range of liabilities. Their land and premises are visited by people for a variety of purposes, such as to undertake work, for business purposes, for recreation, to settle accounts and to receive information.

Under the criminal law, the HSWA (section 4) requires those people in control of premises to take reasonable care towards these other persons. A failure to comply with this duty can lead to prosecution and a fine on conviction.

In the case of civil law, anyone who is injured whilst visiting or working on land or premises may be in a position to sue the occupier for damages, even though the injured person may not be his employee.

What is 'occupation'?

Lord Gardner in Commissioner for Railways v McDermott (1967) 1 AC 169 ruled on the situation relating to the occupation of premises thus:

'Occupation of premises is a ground of liability and is not a ground of exemption from liability. It is a ground of liability because it gives some control over and knowledge of the state of the premises, and it is natural and right that the occupier should have some degree of responsibility for the safety of persons entering his premises with his permission…there is 'proximity' between the occupier and such persons and they are his "neighbours". Thus arises a duty of care.'

CRIMINAL AND CIVIL LAW PROCEDURES – THE DISTINCTION FIG. 2

CRIMINAL LAW	CIVIL LAW
Remedy – prosecution by the state in a criminal court.	Action for damages in a civil court.
Purpose – to punish.	Purpose – to compensate.
Prosecutor and defendant.	Claimant and respondent.
Withdrawal – only by leave from the court.	Withdrawal – at any time.
Innocent until proved guilty beyond reasonable doubt.	No presumption or favour; case decided on the balance of probabilities.
Indictable cases tried before a judge and jury.	Normally heard before a judge alone.
Limitations Act does not normally apply.	Limitations Act does apply.

Thus was established the concept of the 'Neighbour Principle'. Occupier's liability is, therefore, an area of civil law concerned with the duties of occupiers of land and premises to all those who may enter or come onto those premises. The legislation covering this area of civil liability is the Occupiers' Liability Act (OLA) 1975 and, specifically in the case of trespassers, the OLA 1984.

OCCUPIERS' LIABILITY ACT 1957

Under the OLA 1957 an occupier owes a common duty of care to all lawful visitors. This common duty of care is defined as 'a duty to take such care as in all the circumstances of the case is reasonable to see that the visitor will be reasonably safe in using the premises for which he is invited or permitted by the occupier to be there'.

This duty owed by occupiers of premises to all persons lawfully on their premises is in respect of 'dangers due to the state of the premises or to things done or omitted to be done on them'.

Thus the OLA regulates the nature of the duty imposed in consequence of a person's occupation of premises. The duties are not personal duties but, rather, are based on the occupation of premises, and extend to a person occupying, or having control over, any fixed or movable structure, including any vessel, vehicle or aircraft.

Visitors

Protection is afforded to all lawful visitors, whether they enter for the occupier's benefit, such as customers or clients, of for their own benefit, such as a police officer, though not to persons exercising a public or private right of way over premises.

Warning Notices

Occupiers have a duty to erect notices warning visitors of imminent danger, such as a flooded access road or a dangerous building. However, under the OLA, the display of a warning notice does not, in itself, absolve the occupier from liability unless, in all the circumstances, it is sufficient to enable the visitor to be reasonably safe.

Moreover, whilst an occupier could excuse his liability by displaying a suitable prominent and carefully worded notice, the chance of avoiding liability is greatly reduced as a result of the Unfair Contract Terms Act 1977. This Act states that it is not permissible to avoid liability for death or injury due to negligence by contract or display of a notice, including a notice displayed in accordance with the OLA.

Trespassers

What is a trespasser? A trespasser is defined in common law as a person who:
- goes on premises without invitation or permission;
- although invited or permitted to be on premises, goes to a part of the premises to which the invitation or permission does not extend;
- remains on premises after the invitation or permission to be there has expired; and
- deposits goods on premises when not authorised to do so.

OCCUPIERS' LIABILITY ACT 1984

This Act imposes a duty on occupiers with regard to trespassers, namely persons who may have a lawful authority to be in the vicinity or not, who may be at risk of injury on the occupier's premises.

This duty can be discharged by issuing some form of warning, such as the display of formal hazard warning notices. However, such notices must be very explicit, stating:
- the hazard to which people may be exposed, such as the risk of slipping or falling; and
- the measures they must take to avoid the hazard, such as walking along designated footpaths or the use of non-slip footwear.

It is not sufficient, however, to merely display this form of notice. The requirements of the notice must be actively enforced by the occupier at all times.

Generally, the displaying of a notice, the clarity, legibility and explicitness of the notice, supported by evidence of regularly reminding people of the message outlined in the notice, may count to a certain extent as part of a defence when sued in the event of injury by a simple trespasser under the Act.

The Duty towards Children

From a legal viewpoint, children are deemed to be less responsible than adults, and the OLA 1957 is quite specific on this matter, requiring an occupier to be prepared for children being less careful than adults.

Children, by virtue of their lack of experience, understanding and maturity, may not appreciate the significance of hazards they encounter. Where, for instance, there is something, or a situation, on the premises that represents a lure or attraction to a child, such as a pond, a hole in the ground, a derelict building or scaffolding surrounding a building, this may constitute a 'trap' as far as a child is concerned. Should a child be injured as a result of coming into contact with this trap, for example, falling off a scaffold, the occupier could be liable. Much will depend upon the location of the premises, for instance, whether it is close to a residential area, school or footpath, or is in an isolated location, such as a farmyard. However, in all cases, occupiers must consider the potential for child trespassers and take appropriate precautions.

Contractors and their Employees

The relationship between occupiers of premises and contractors has always been tenuous. The OLA 1957 states that an occupier may expect that a person, in exercising his calling, such as a window cleaner, builder or house painter, will appreciate and guard against any risks ordinarily incident to that calling, for instance, the risk of falling, so far as the occupier gives them leave to do so. This means that the risks associated with the system of work are the responsibility of the contractor, as an employer, and not the occupier.

It should be appreciated, however, that while the above may be the case under the civil law, the situation at criminal law, namely the duties of employers towards non-employees under section 3 of the HSWA, is quite different.

Where work is being undertaken by a contractor, the occupier may not be liable if he:

♦ took care to select a competent contractor; and

♦ satisfied himself that the work was being properly done by the contractor.

However, in many cases, an occupier may not be competent or knowledgeable enough to ascertain whether work is being undertaken safely. For instance, he may presume that it is standard practice for a window cleaner to clean the external window surfaces of a fourth floor office without operating from a suspended scaffold or safety harness! In such cases the occupier might need to be advised by an architect or safety specialist in order to be satisfied that the work is being done properly and safely.

This relationship between occupiers and contractors has been substantially clarified through the provisions of the Construction (Design and Management) (CDM) Regulations 1994.

VICARIOUS LIABILITY

The doctrine of vicarious liability is based on the fact that an employee acts on behalf of an employer in a range of situations, for example, laying bricks, producing products and collecting money. Thus, if an employee, whilst acting in the course of his employment, negligently injures another employee, the employee of another contractor or even a member of the public, the employer, rather than the employee, will be liable for that injury.

This form of liability rests on the employer simply because he is the employer and is deemed to have ultimate control over his employees in a 'master–servant relationship', a concept in law that goes back to Victorian times.

This liability must be insured against under the Employers' Liability (Compulsory Insurance) Act 1969 and the Employers' Liability (Compulsory Insurance) Regulations 1998. Employers are unable to contract out of this liability as such practices are prohibited by the Law Reform (Personal Injuries) Act 1948 and the Unfair Contract Terms Act 1977.

The key to liability is that the accident causing the injury or death arises, firstly, out of and, secondly, in the course of, employment. This does not normally include the time travelling to and from work, although it might if the mode of transport was within the employer's control, such as a contractor's bus, or was provided by the employer or in arrangement with the employer.

KEY POINTS

♦ An employer or occupier of premises may be prosecuted by the enforcement agencies in the criminal courts and sued by a claimant in the civil courts.

- Most modern protective legislation is driven by European Directives.
- The majority of civil claims are based on negligence but, in certain cases, a breach of a statutory duty may give rise to civil liability.
- Case law is an important area of the law, based on the doctrine of precedent.
- Criminal law is based on a system of enforcement, whereas civil law operates on the basis of a claimant making a claim against another person, a defendant, with a view to securing an award of damages.
- The function of the criminal courts is, fundamentally, to punish offenders, whereas that of the civil courts is to compensate people who may have suffered some form of wrong at the hands of another.
- Industrial tribunals are empowered to deal with certain health and safety-related issues.
- Occupiers of premises owe a common duty of care to all lawful visitors and, in certain cases, to trespassers.
- The 'master', ie an employer, is vicariously liable for the actions of his 'servants', ie his employees.

2 The Principal Criminal Law

A person who breaks the criminal law, such as the Road Traffic Act, may be prosecuted, namely, brought before a criminal court to answer a charge or charges. If found guilty, he can be fined or imprisoned or have some form of order made against him.

This chapter deals with the principal criminal law with regard to occupational health and safety, namely, the HSWA 1974 and the MHSWR 1999, together with enforcement procedures under the Act. Provisions relating to compulsory employer's liability insurance are also covered.

THE EUROPEAN DIMENSION

Whilst subordinate or delegated legislation, such as specific regulations, is made under the Act through the Secretary of State for Employment, it must be appreciated that, during the 1990s, most regulations were based on European Union Directives, which have been implemented by successive governments of the UK as specific regulations.

Moreover, all post-1993 regulations, such as the PUWER 1998, do not stand alone but must be read in conjunction with the general duties of employers and others under the MHSWR 1999, in particular those relating to risk assessment, management systems and the appointment of competent persons.

HEALTH AND SAFETY AT WORK ETC ACT 1974

The HSWA brought in a radically new approach to dealing with the risks to people at work. The Act covers 'all persons at work' – employers, employees, the self-employed, occupiers of premises and controllers of premises – other than domestic workers in private employment. It is aimed at people and their activities, rather than premises and processes, which was the case with former legislation, such as the Factories Act 1961.

The HSWA incorporates provisions for both the protection of people at work and the prevention of risks to the health and safety of the general public, which may arise from work activities.

Objectives of the HSWA
- To secure the health, safety and welfare of all persons at work.
- To protect others against the risks arising from workplace activities.
- To control the obtaining, keeping and use of explosive or highly flammable substances.
- To control emissions into the atmosphere of noxious or offensive substances.

Under the HSWA various groups of people, such as employers, employees, occupiers of premises and people who manufacture and design articles and substances for use at work, have both general and specific duties, which are outlined below. All these duties are of a 'reasonably practicable' nature. (See **The hierarchy of duties** later in this chapter.)

Section 2 – General duties of employers to their employees

It is the duty of every employer, so far as is reasonably practicable, to ensure the health, safety and welfare at work of all his employees.

The matters to which that duty extends include in particular:

♦ the provision and maintenance of plant and systems of work that are, so far as is reasonably practicable, safe and without risks to health;

♦ arrangements for ensuring, so far as is reasonably practicable, safety and absence of risks to health in connection with the use, handling, storage and transport of articles and substances;

♦ the provision of such information, instruction, training and supervision as is necessary to ensure, so far as is reasonably practicable, the health and safety at work of his employees;

♦ so far as is reasonably practicable as regards any place of work under the employer's control, the maintenance of it in a condition that is safe and without risks to health and the provision and maintenance of means of access and egress from it that are safe and without such risks; and

♦ the provision and maintenance of a working environment for his employees that is, so far as is reasonably practicable, safe, without risks to health, and adequate as regards facilities and arrangements for their welfare at work.

Statements of health and safety policy

It shall be the duty of every employer to prepare and as often as may be appropriate revise a written statement of his general policy in respect of the health and safety at work of his employees and the organisation and arrangements for the time being in force for carrying out that policy, and to bring the statement and any revision of it to the notice of all his employees.

Section 3 – General duties of employers and self-employed to persons other than their employees

Every employer must conduct his undertaking in such a way as to ensure, so far as is reasonably practicable, that persons not in his employment who may be affected thereby are not thereby exposed to risks to their health or safety. (Similar duties are imposed on self-employed persons.)

Every employer and self-employed person must give to persons (not being his employees) who may be affected by the way in which he conducts his undertaking the prescribed information about such aspects of the way in which he conducts his undertaking as might affect their health or safety.

Section 4 – General duties of persons concerned with premises to persons other than their employees

This section has effect for imposing on persons duties in relation to those who:

♦ are not their employees, but;

♦ use non-domestic premises made available to them as a place of work.

Every person who has, to any extent, control of premises must ensure, so far as is reasonably practicable, that the premises, all means of access thereto or egress therefrom, and any plant or substances in the premises or provided for use there, is or are safe and without risks to health.

Section 5 – General duty of persons in control of certain premises in relation to harmful emissions into atmosphere

Any person having control of any premises of a class prescribed for the purposes of section 1(1)(d) must use the best practicable means for preventing the emission into the atmosphere from the premises of noxious or offensive substances and for rendering harmless and inoffensive such substances as may be so emitted.

Section 6 – General duties of manufacturers, etc as regards articles and substances for use at work

Any person who designs, manufactures, imports or supplies any article for use at work:

♦ must ensure, so far as is reasonably practicable, that the article is so designed and constructed as to be safe and without risks to health when properly used;

♦ must carry out or arrange for the carrying out of such testing and examination as may be necessary to comply with the above duty; and

♦ must provide adequate information about the use for which it is designed and has been tested to ensure that, when put to that use, it will be safe and without risks to health.

Any person who undertakes the design or manufacture of any article for use at work must carry out or arrange for the carrying out of any necessary research with a view to the discovery and, so far as is reasonably practicable, the elimination or minimisation of any risks to health or safety to which the design or article may give rise.

Any person who erects or installs any article for use at work must ensure, so far as is reasonably practicable, that nothing about the way it is erected or installed makes it unsafe or a risk to health when properly used.

Any person who manufactures, imports or supplies any substance for use at work:

♦ must ensure, so far as is reasonably practicable, that the substance is safe and without risks to health when properly used;

♦ must carry out or arrange for the carrying out of such testing and examination as may be necessary; and

♦ must take such steps as are necessary to ensure adequate information about the results of any relevant tests is available in connection with the use of the substance at work.

Section 7 – General duties of employees

It shall be the duty of every employee while at work:

♦ to take reasonable care for the health and safety of himself and of other persons who may be affected by his acts or omissions at work; and

♦ as regards any duty or requirement imposed on his employer, to cooperate with him so far as is necessary to enable that duty or requirement to be performed or complied with.

Section 8 – Duty not to interfere with or misuse things provided pursuant to certain provisions

No person shall intentionally or recklessly interfere with or misuse anything provided in the interests of health, safety or welfare in pursuance of any of the relevant statutory provisions.

Section 9 – Duty not to charge employees for things done or provided pursuant to certain specific provisions

No employer shall levy or permit to be levied on any employee of his any charge in respect of anything done or provided in pursuance of any specific requirement of the relevant statutory provisions.

'The relevant statutory provisions'

This term refers to:

♦ duties under the statute, ie the HSWA;

♦ duties under regulations made under HSWA, such as the Noise at Work Regulations 1989; and

♦ any other duties under statutes and regulations still in force, such as parts of the Factories Act 1961, and regulations made under that statute.

The term is used extensively in modern health and safety legislation.

CORPORATE LIABILITY

Under the HSWA directors, managers, company secretaries and similar officers of the body corporate have both general and specific duties. Breaches of these duties can result in both the organisation and the individual concerned being prosecuted.

Section 37 – Offences by bodies corporate

Where a breach of one of the relevant statutory provisions on the part of a body corporate is proved to have been committed with the consent or connivance of, or to have been attributable to any neglect on the part of, any director, manager, secretary or other similar officer of the body corporate or a person who was purporting to act in any such capacity, he as well as the body corporate shall be guilty of that offence and shall be liable to be proceeded against and punished accordingly.

Note: Breach of this section can have the following outcomes:

♦ where an offence is committed through neglect by a board of directors, the organisation can be prosecuted as well as the directors individually who may have been to blame;

♦ where an individual functional director is guilty of an offence, he may be prosecuted as well as the organisation; and

♦ an organisation can be prosecuted even though the act or omission was committed by a junior official or executive or even a visitor to the organisation.

Section 36 – Offences due to fault of other person

This section makes provision for dealing with offences committed by corporate officials, such as technical managers, human resources managers, health and safety managers, etc.

Where the commission by any person of an offence under any of the relevant statutory provisions is due to the act or default of some other person, that other person shall be guilty of the offence, and a person may be charged with and convicted of the offence by virtue of this subsection whether or not proceedings are taken against the first-mentioned person.

THE HIERARCHY OF DUTIES UNDER CRIMINAL LAW

Statutory duties, such as those under the HSWA and regulations, give rise to criminal liability. There are three distinct levels of statutory duty, namely, that which are of an absolute or strict nature, and those duties qualified by the terms 'so far as is practicable' and 'so far as is reasonably practicable'.

Absolute or strict requirements

Where risk of injury or disease is inevitable if safety requirements are not followed, a statutory duty may well be strict or absolute. An example of an absolute duty is in Regulation 5 of the PUWER 1998 which states:

♦ every employer shall ensure that work equipment is so constructed or adapted as to be suitable for the purpose for which it is to be used or provided.

Absolute duties are accompanied by the terms 'shall' or 'must' and there is little or no defence available when charged with such an offence.

Most of the duties under, for instance, the MHSWR 1999, the WHSWR 1992 and the PUWER 1998 are of an absolute nature, which implies a higher level of duty than that indicated in, for instance, the HSWA, where the duties of employers and others are qualified by the term 'so far as is reasonably practicable'.

'Practicable' requirements

A duty qualified by the term 'so far as is practicable' implies that 'if in the light of current knowledge or invention', 'if in the light of the current state of the art', it is feasible to comply with the requirement then, irrespective of cost, inconvenience or sacrifice involved, such a requirement must be complied with. [Schwalb v Fass H & Son (1946) 175 LT 345]

Thus 'practicable' means more than physically possible and implies a higher duty of care than a duty qualified by the term 'so far as is reasonably practicable'.

'Reasonably practicable' requirements

A duty qualified by this term implies that a computation must be made in which the quantum of risk is placed on one scale and the sacrifice involved, in terms of time, effort and money to avert the risk, is placed in the other. If it can be shown that there is gross disproportion between these two factors, ie the risk being insignificant in relation to the sacrifice, then the defendant discharges the onus upon himself. [Edwards v National Coal Board (1949) 1 AER 743]

Most duties under the HSWA and many regulations are qualified by the term 'so far as is reasonably practicable'.

'Reasonable care'

This term is present in section 7 of the HSWA whereby every employee has a duty to take 'reasonable care' for the safety of himself and others. But what is reasonable in the circumstances and what is a reasonable person?

The mythical 'reasonable man' was interpreted by one judge in the past by comparing him with 'the man who travels to work every day on the top deck of the No 57 Clapham omnibus'. As such, the term is flexible and changes with time according to society and the norms present at the time.

ENFORCEMENT PROCEDURES UNDER THE HEALTH AND SAFETY AT WORK ACT

The enforcing authorities in respect of the HSWA and regulations made under same are:

- the HSE, which is split into a number of inspectorates;
- local authorities, principally through their environmental health departments; and
- fire authorities, for certain fire protection-related legislation.

Actual enforcement is undertaken by inspectors appointed under the HSWA and authorised by written warrant from the enforcing authority.

POWERS OF INSPECTORS

Under section 20 of the HSWA, an inspector has the following powers:

- to enter premises at any reasonable time and, where obstruction is anticipated, to enlist the support of a police officer;
- on entering a premises:
    - to take with him any person duly authorised by his enforcing authority;
    - any equipment or materials required for any purpose for which the power of entry is being exercised;
    - to make such examination and investigation as may be necessary;
- to direct that premises or any part of such premises, or anything therein, shall remain undisturbed for so long as is reasonably necessary for the purposes of examination or investigation;
- to take such measurements and photographs and make such recordings as he considers necessary for the purposes of any examination or investigation;
- to take samples of articles or substances found in any premises, and of the atmosphere in or in the vicinity of such premises;
- where it appears to him that an article or substance has caused or is likely to cause danger to health or safety, to cause it to be dismantled or subjected to any process or test;
- to take possession of any article or substance and to detain same for so long as is necessary:
    - to examine same; and
    - to ensure it is not tampered with before his examination is completed;
- to ensure it is available for use as evidence in any proceedings for an offence under the relevant statutory provisions;
- to require any person whom he has reasonable cause to believe to be able to give any information relevant to any examination or investigation to answer such questions as the inspector thinks fit and to sign a declaration of truth of his answers;
- to require the production of, inspect and take copies of, an entry in:
    - any books or documents, which by virtue of the relevant statutory provisions are required to be kept;
    - any other books or documents, which it is necessary for him to see for the purposes of any examination or investigation;
- to require any person to afford him such facilities and assistance with regard to

any matter or things within that person's control or in relation to which that person has responsibilities as are necessary to enable the inspector to exercise any of the powers conferred on him by this section; and

♦ any other power that is necessary for the purpose of carrying into effect the relevant statutory provisions.

After an inspector has completed an examination or investigation, he has a duty to inform safety representatives of the actual matters he has found and must give the employer similar information.

NOTICES

Enforcement officers are empowered to serve two types of notice.

Improvement Notices

If an inspector is of the opinion that a breach of the relevant statutory provisions has occurred, or is likely to occur, he may serve an Improvement notice on the employer, occupier of premises or an employee. The notice must state which statutory provision the inspector believes has been contravened and the reason for this belief. The notice should also indicate a time limit within which the contravention(s) should be remedied.

Prohibition Notices

Where an inspector is of the opinion that a work activity involves or will involve a serious risk of personal injury, he may serve a Prohibition Notice on the owner and/or the occupier of the premises or on the person having control of that activity.

Such a notice will direct that the activities specified in the notice shall not be carried on by or under the control of the person on whom the notice is served unless certain specified remedial measures have been complied with. It should be appreciated that it is not necessary for an inspector to believe that a legal provision is being or has been contravened. A Prohibition Notice is served where there is an immediate threat to life and in anticipation of danger.

A Prohibition Notice may have an immediate effect after its service by an inspector. Alternatively, it may be deferred, thereby allowing the person time to remedy the situation quickly. The duration of a deferred Prohibition Notice is stated on the notice, for example, 48 hours.

PROSECUTION

Prosecution is frequently the outcome of a failure to comply with an Improvement Notice or Prohibition Notice. Conversely, an inspector may simply institute legal proceedings in the Magistrates' Court without service of a notice.

Whilst the majority of cases are heard in a Magistrates' Court, there is provision in the HSWA on indictment (in the Crown Court). Much depends upon the gravity of the offence.

PENALTIES

In a Magistrates' Court the maximum fine that can be imposed per offence is £20,000 for breaches of sections 2 to 6 of the HSWA and for breach of an Improvement Notice or Prohibition Notice. The maximum fine for other offences is £5,000.

In the higher courts, fines are unlimited with a maximum two year prison sentence for offences concerning explosives, licensing regimes and for breach of either type of notice.

FOLLOW-UP ACTION BY AN ENFORCEMENT OFFICER

In most cases, a person is charged with an offence or offences as a result of:
◆ an inspection of the workplace;
◆ a formal complaint by someone, for example, employee, member of the public;
◆ an investigation following an accident;

After considering the situation, an inspector must take a decision to:
◆ take no further action;
◆ issue a form of written caution following a verbal caution at the time of the visit;
◆ serve an Improvement Notice;
◆ serve an immediate or deferred Prohibition Notice; and
◆ instigate criminal proceedings in the Magistrates' Court.

Anyone who has been served with a notice, or who has been summonsed to appear to answer charges in a court, cannot afford to disregard these matters. It is important to recognise that an inspector has resorted to such action for one or more reasons, such as
◆ flagrant disregard for the law;
◆ failure to heed advice provided by an inspector or to cooperate with an inspector with a view to bringing about improvement;
◆ where there may be imminent or serious risk of personal injury to employees, non-employees and members of the public; and
◆ there is clear-cut evidence of a breach of one or more of the relevant statutory provisions, which has resulted in an accident at work.

Where such a situation has arisen, employers must endeavour to obtain further information from managers and employees about the circumstances prevailing that resulted in the offence.

Written statements should be taken from witnesses in accordance with the Police and Criminal Evidence Act (PACE) procedures, including the use of the statutory caution, as soon as possible after, particularly, a serious or fatal accident. In most cases a solicitor specialising in criminal health and safety law should be consulted well ahead of any court appearance.

MANAGEMENT OF HEALTH AND SAFETY AT WORK REGULATIONS 1999

The original 1992 version of these regulations implemented the European Framework Directive 'on the introduction of measures to encourage improvements in the safety and health of workers at work'. The regulations are accompanied by an ACOP produced by the HSC and, as such, represent a significant change in the approach to health and safety law.

A number of important features are incorporated in these regulations, namely:
◆ the duties on employers are of an absolute or strict nature, compared with duties under, for instance, the HSWA, which are qualified by the term 'so far as is reasonably practicable'; in fact, this has been the case with the majority of regulations; produced since 1993;

- other regulations produced after 1992, such as the WHSWR 1992, must be read and interpreted in conjunction with the general duties under the MHSWR; and
- the MHSWR introduced the concept of risk assessment and the requirement for formally documented health and safety management systems.

Regulation 3 – Risk assessment

This regulation placed an absolute duty on every employer and self-employed person to make **a suitable and sufficient assessment** of the risks to the health and safety of:

- his employees to which they are exposed whilst at work, and
- persons not in his employment arising out of or in connection with the conduct by him of his undertaking.

For the purpose of identifying the measures he needs to take to comply with the requirements and prohibitions imposed upon him by or under the relevant statutory provisions and Part II of the Fire Precautions (Workplace) Regulations (FPWR) 1997.

Specific provisions with regard to risk assessment apply in the case of the employment of young persons (ie those persons between 16 and 18 years).

Information on risk assessment procedures is incorporated in the ACOP to the MHSWR and in the HSE publication 'Five Steps to Risk Assessment'.

Regulation 4 – Principles of prevention to be applied

Where an employer implements any preventive and protective measures he shall do so on the basis of the principles specified in Schedule 1 to the regulations.

Regulation 5 – Health and safety arrangements

This regulation places an absolute duty on employers to actually manage their health and safety-related activities thus:

Every employer shall make and give effect to such arrangements as are appropriate, having regard to the nature of his activities and the size of his undertaking, for the **effective planning, organisation, control, monitoring and review** of the preventive and protective measures.

These arrangements must be recorded where five or more employees are employed.

Regulation 6 – Health surveillance

Every employer shall ensure that his employees are provided with such health surveillance as is appropriate having regard to the risks to their health and safety that are identified by the assessment.

Regulation 7 – Health and safety assistance

An employer must appoint one or more **competent persons** to assist him in undertaking the measures he needs to take to comply with the requirements and prohibitions imposed upon him by or under the relevant statutory provisions and by Part II of the FPWR.

Regulation 8 – Procedures for serious and imminent danger and for danger areas

Employers must:

- establish and where necessary give effect to appropriate procedures to be followed

in the event of serious or imminent danger to persons at work;
- nominate a sufficient number of competent persons to implement these procedures; and
- prevent any employee being given access to a danger area unless he has received adequate health and safety instruction.

Regulation 9 – Contacts with external services

Every employer shall ensure that any necessary contacts with external services are arranged, particularly as regards first aid, emergency medical care and rescue work.

Regulation 10 – Information for employees

Every employer shall provide his employees with comprehensible and relevant information on:
- the risks to their health and safety identified by the assessment;
- the preventive and protective measures;
- the procedures referred to in Regulation 8(1)(a) and the measures referred to in Regulation 4(2)(a) of the FPWA; and
- the identity of the competent persons nominated in accordance with Regulation 8(1)(b) and the measures referred to in Regulation 4(2)(b) of the FPWR 1997, and the risks notified to him in accordance with Regulation 11(1)(c) (shared workplaces).

Specific provisions apply prior to the employment of a child.

Regulation 11 – Cooperation and coordination

This regulation concerns the duties of employers who share a workplace, whether on a temporary basis, for example, a construction site, or permanent basis, for example, an office block, an industrial development. Each employer must:
- cooperate with other employers to enable them to comply with current legal requirements;
- take all reasonable steps to coordinate the steps he takes with the steps taken by other employers to comply with legal requirements; and
- take all reasonable steps to inform other employers of risks to their employees' health and safety arising from his activities.

Note: These duties should be read in conjunction with the requirements of the CDM Regulations 1994 where a construction project or construction work may involve several employers.

Regulation 12 – Persons working in host employers' or self-employed persons' undertakings

This regulation covers the situation where employees of another employer may be required to work in an employer's premises, business activity or operations. It largely extends the duties of employers to non-employees under section 3 of the HSWA with regard to the giving by 'host' employers of information, instruction and training to non-employees working on their premises or in their business activity.

Every employer and self-employed person shall ensure that the employer of any employees from an outside undertaking who are working in his undertaking is provided with comprehensible information on:

♦ the risks arising in the undertaking; and
♦ the measures taken by the first-mentioned employer to comply with legal requirements and to protect those employees.

These measures include details of emergency and evacuation procedures and the competent persons nominated to implement the procedures.

Regulation 13 – Capabilities and training

Every employer shall, in entrusting tasks to his employees, take into account their capabilities as regards health and safety.

Note: This requirement implies a need to match the individual to the task, both mentally and physically, from a health and safety viewpoint. It requires a good understanding of the human factors area of health and safety, in particular ergonomic considerations, the physical and mental limitations of people and the potential for human error.

Every employer shall ensure that his employees are provided with adequate health and safety training:

♦ on their being recruited into the employer's undertaking;
♦ on their being exposed to new or increased risks because of:
    ♦ their being transferred or given a change of responsibilities within the employer's undertaking;
    ♦ the introduction of new work equipment into or a change regarding work equipment already in use within the employer's undertaking;
    ♦ the introduction of new technology into the employer's undertaking, or
    ♦ the introduction of a new system of work or a change regarding a system of work already in use within the employer's undertaking.

Training shall:

♦ be repeated periodically where appropriate;
♦ be adapted to take account of new or increased risks; and
♦ take place during working hours.

Regulation 14 – Employees' duties

Every employee shall use any machinery, equipment, dangerous substance, transport equipment, means of production or safety device provided to him by his employer in accordance both with any training in the use of the equipment concerned, which has been received by him, and the instructions regarding that use, which have been provided to him by the said employer in compliance with the requirements imposed upon that employer by or under the relevant statutory provisions.

Every employee shall inform his employer or any other employee with specific responsibility for the health and safety of his fellow employees:

♦ of any work situation that a person with the first-mentioned employee's training and instruction would reasonably consider represented a serious and immediate danger to health and safety; and
♦ of any matter that a person with the first-mentioned employee's training and

instruction would reasonably consider represented a shortcoming in the employer's protection arrangements for health and safety.

Regulation 15 – Temporary workers

This regulation places an absolute duty on employers to provide any person working under a fixed term contract of employment or who is employed in an employment business with comprehensible information on:

- any special occupational qualifications or skills required to be held by that employee if he is to carry out his work safely; and
- any health surveillance required, before the employee concerned commences his duties.

Regulation 16 – Risk assessment in respect of new or expectant mothers

Where:

- the persons working in an undertaking include women of child-bearing age;
- the work is of a kind that could involve risk, by reason of her condition, to the health and safety of a new or expectant mother, or to that of her baby, from any processes or working conditions, of physical, biological or chemical agents; and
- the assessment required by Regulation 3(1) shall include an assessment of such risk.

Where, in the case of an individual employee, the taking of any other action the employer is required to take under the relevant statutory provisions would not avoid the risk referred to above, the employer shall, if it is reasonable to do so, and would avoid such risks, alter her working conditions or hours of work.

If it is not reasonable to alter her working conditions or hours of work, or if it would not avoid such risk, the employer shall, subject to section 67 of the Employment Rights Act (ERA) 1996, suspend the employee from work so long as is necessary to avoid such risk.

Reference to risk, in relation to risk from any infectious or contagious disease, are references to a level of risk that is in addition to the level to which a new or expectant mother may be expected to be exposed outside the workplace.

Regulation 17 – Certificate from a registered medical practitioner in respect of new or expectant mothers

Where:

- a new or expectant mother works at night;
- a certificate from a registered medical practitioner or registered midwife shows that it is necessary for her health or safety that she should not be at work for any period of such work identified in the certificate; and
- the employer shall, subject to section 67 of the ERA 1996, suspend her from work so long as is necessary for her health or safety.

Regulation 18 – Notification by new or expectant mothers

Nothing in paragraph 2 or 3 of Regulation 16 shall require the employer to take any action in relation to an employee until she has notified the employer in writing she is pregnant, has given birth within the previous six months, or is breastfeeding.

Regulations 18 contains further specific provisions on this matter.

Regulation 19 – Protection of young persons

Every employer shall ensure that young persons (ie those aged between 16 and 18 years) employed by him are protected at work from any risks to their health or safety that are a consequence of their lack of experience, or absence of awareness of existing or potential risks or the fact that young persons have not yet fully matured.

Subject to paragraph 3, no employer shall employ a young person for work:

- that is beyond his physical or psychological capacity;
- involving harmful exposure to agents that are toxic or carcinogenic, cause heritable genetic damage or harm to the unborn child or that in any other way chronically affect human health;
- involving harmful exposure to radiation;
- involving the risk of accidents, which it may reasonably be assumed cannot be recognised or avoided by young persons owing to their insufficient attention to safety or lack of experience or training;
- in which there is a risk to health from:
    - extreme cold or heat;
    - noise, or
    - vibration;
- and in determining whether work will involve harm or risks for the purpose of this paragraph, regard shall be had to the results of the assessment.

Nothing in paragraph 2 shall prevent the employment of a young person who is no longer a child for work:

- where it is necessary for his training;
- where the young person will be supervised by a competent person; and
- where any risk will be reduced to the lowest level that is reasonably practicable.

Regulation 21 – Provisions as to liability

Nothing in the relevant statutory provisions shall operate so as to afford an employer a defence in criminal proceedings for a contravention of those provisions by reason of any act or default of:

- an employee of his, or
- a person appointed by him under regulation 7 (competent person).

Regulation 22 – Exclusion of civil liability

Breach of a duty imposed by these regulations shall not confer a right of action in any civil proceedings.

SCHEDULE 1
GENERAL PRINCIPLES OF PREVENTION

This Schedule specifies the general principles of prevention set out in Article 6(2) of Council Directive 89/391/EEC thus:

- avoiding risks;
- evaluating the risks that cannot be avoided;
- combating the risks at source;

- adapting the work to the individual, especially as regards the design of the workplace, the choice of work equipment and the choice of working and production methods, with a view, in particular, to alleviating monotonous work and work at a pre-determined work rate and reducing their effect on health;
- adapting to technical progress;
- replacing the dangerous by the non-dangerous or the less dangerous;
- developing a coherent overall prevention policy that covers technology, organisation of work, working conditions, social relationships and the influence of factors relating to the working environment;
- giving collective protective measures priority over individual protective measures; and
- giving appropriate instructions to employees.

EMPLOYERS' LIABILITY INSURANCE

The Employers' Liability (Compulsory Insurance) Act 1969 deals with the duties of employers in terms of ensuring themselves against claims that may be made by employees.

Under section 1 every employer carrying on business in Great Britain shall insure and maintain insurance against liability for bodily injury or disease sustained by his employees, and arising out of and in the course of their employment in Great Britain in that business.

This insurance must be provided under one or more 'approved policies', ie a policy of insurance not subject to any conditions or exceptions prohibited by Regulations.

Cover

Cover is required in respect of liability to employees who either:
- are ordinarily resident in Great Britain; or
- though not ordinarily resident in Great Britain, are present in Great Britain in the course of employment here for a continuous period of not less than 14 days.

Issue and display of certificate of insurance

The insurer must issue the employer with a certificate of insurance. This certificate must be issued not later than 30 days after the date on which the insurance was commenced or renewed. The certificate must be prominently displayed.

The Employers Liability (Compulsory Insurance) Regulations 1998 amended the former regulations thus:
- the sum to be insured must be not less than £5,000,000;
- the prescribed wording on the certificate of insurance must give specific information on the cover provided;
- certificates must be kept for 40 years; and
- authorised inspectors can require the production of not just a current certificate but also past certificates of insurance.

KEY POINTS

- The HSWA is the principal statute covering health and safety at work in the United Kingdom.
- The HSWA is an enabling Act, thereby enabling the Secretary of State for

Employment to make regulations, for example, Health and Safety (Display Screen Equipment) Regulations 1992.

♦ Duties under the HSWA are qualified by the term 'so far as is reasonably practicable' whereas those under the MHSWR are of an absolute or strict nature.

♦ The HSWA requires employers to prepare a written Statement of Health and Safety Policy, which must be brought to the attention of all employees.

♦ Under the HSWA enforcement officers have extensive powers, including the power to serve Improvement Notices and Prohibition Notices and to instigate proceedings in the courts.

♦ The MHSWR place an absolute duty on employers to undertake a suitable and sufficient assessment of the risks to their own employees and to other persons affected by their activities.

♦ Employers must install health and safety management systems and appoint competent persons to oversee the implementation of those management systems.

♦ Employers have particular responsibilities towards new or expectant mothers, young persons and children.

♦ All employers must carry employers' liability insurance cover.

3 Health & Safety Management

The duty on employers under the MHSWR to actually manage health and safety within the organisation is well established. This chapter examines the proactive and reactive features of health and safety management systems, Statements of Health and Safety Policy, safe systems of work, the role of competent persons, joint consultation and documentation requirements.

CURRENT TRENDS IN HEALTH AND SAFETY LEGISLATION

Before considering the very important aspect of health and safety management, it is appropriate to consider the way the approach to health and safety legislation in the United Kingdom changed in the latter half of the 20th century. The earlier legislation, such as the Factories Acts 1937 – 61 laid down prescriptive standards and as long as an employer complied with these standards then it was presumed that he complied with the law.

In 1975, the HSWA came into operation, establishing the HSC and the HSE. As such, the HSWA is an enabling Act, giving the Secretary of State for Employment power to make regulations. Draft regulations pass before the HSC, who eventually recommend their implementation to the government. The HSC are also empowered to make ACOPs to supplement regulations.

All modern health and safety legislation is largely driven by European Directives, which are largely implemented as specific regulations in the UK. For instance the Directive 'on the health and safety of workers at work' was originally implemented in the UK as the MHSWR 1992.

Regulations produced since 1993 do not, in most cases, stand on their own and must be read in conjunction with the general duties on employers under the MHSWR, in particular the duties relating to:

- risk assessment;
- the operation and maintenance of safety management systems;
- the appointment of competent persons;
- development and implementation of emergency procedures;
- provision of information, instruction and training;
- assessment of human capability prior to allocating tasks; and
- specific provisions for pregnant workers and young persons.

What is important is that the level of duty imposed on employers under regulations produced post-1993 is largely of a strict or absolute nature, compared with those duties qualified by the terms 'so far as is practicable' and 'so far as is reasonably practicable' as with the HSWA and Regulations produced in the 1970s and 1980s.

Risk assessment, taking into account the requirements and prohibitions imposed by or under the relevant statutory provisions and Part II of the FPWR 1997, is an essential element in the design of all health and safety management systems.

Out of these requirements has come the need for organisations to produce and maintain a wide range of documents, details of which will be covered later in this chapter.

THE DUTY TO MANAGE HEALTH AND SAFETY

The MHSWR place an absolute duty on employers to actually manage the health and safety of their employees, as opposed to merely complying with the minimum legal requirements, through the installation and implementation of 'health and safety arrangements'. These arrangements must be written down, perhaps as a series of internal codes of practice incorporated in an organisation's health and safety manual. Procedures for ensuring compliance with these 'arrangements', for establishing performance objectives and for measuring actual performance against agreed objectives, should also be put into operation.

What is 'management'?

Before considering this issue further, it would be appropriate at this stage to define the term 'management'. One definition is 'the effective use of resources in the pursuit of organisational goals'. Employees, in terms of their skills, loyalties and commitment to the success of the organisation, are, perhaps, the most important resource, a matter that many managers fail to consider.

Health and safety management

The ACOP to the MHSWR goes into considerable detail on this matter as follows.

Planning

Employers should set up an effective health and safety management system to implement their health and safety policy, which is proportionate to the hazards and risks. Adequate planning includes:

- adopting a systematic approach to the completion of risk assessment. Risk assessment methods should be used to decide on priorities and to set objectives for eliminating hazards and reducing risks. This should include a programme, with deadlines for completion of the risk assessment process, together with suitable deadlines for the design and implementation of the preventive and protective measures that are necessary;
- selecting appropriate methods of risk control to minimise risks; and
- establishing priorities and developing performance standards both for the completion of risk assessment(s) and the implementation of preventive and protective measures, which at each stage minimises the risk of harm to people. Wherever possible, risks are eliminated through selection and design of facilities, equipment and processes.

Organisation

This includes:

- involving employees and their representatives in carrying out risk assessments, deciding on preventive and protective measures and implementing those requirements in the workplace. This may be achieved by the use of formal health and safety committees, where they exist, and by the use of teamworking, where employees are involved in deciding on the appropriate preventive and protective measures and written procedures, etc;
- establishing effective means of communication and consultation in which a positive approach to health and safety is visible and clear. The employer should have

adequate health and safety information and make sure it is communicated to employees and their representatives, so informed decisions can be made about the choice of preventive and protective measures. Efficient communication will ensure that employees are provided with sufficient information so that control measures can be implemented effectively; and

♦ securing competence by the provision of adequate information, instruction and training and its evaluation, particularly for those who carry out risk assessments and make decisions about preventive and protective measures. Where necessary, this will need to be supported by the provision of adequate health and safety assistance or advice.

Control

Establishing control includes:

♦ clarifying health and safety responsibilities and ensuring that the activities of everyone are well coordinated;

♦ ensuring everyone with responsibilities understands clearly what they have to do to discharge their responsibilities, and ensure that they have the time and resources to discharge them effectively;

♦ setting standards to judge the performance of those with responsibilities and ensure they meet them.   It is important to reward good performance as well as to take action to improve poor performance; and

♦ ensuring adequate and appropriate supervision, particularly for those who are learning and who are new to a job.

Monitoring

Employers should measure what they are doing to implement their health and safety policy, to assess how effectively they are controlling risks, and how well they are developing a positive health and safety culture. Monitoring includes:

♦ having a plan and making adequate routine inspections and checks to ensure that preventive and protective measures are in place and effective. Active monitoring reveals how effectively the health and safety management system is functioning; and

♦ adequately investigating the immediate and underlying causes of incidents and accidents to ensure that remedial action is taken, lessons are learnt and longer term objectives are introduced.

In both cases it may be appropriate to record and analyze the results of monitoring activity, to identify underlying themes or trends that may not be apparent from looking at events in isolation.

Review

Review involves:

♦ establishing priorities for necessary remedial action that were discovered as a result of monitoring, to ensure that suitable action is taken in good time and is completed;

♦ periodically reviewing the whole of the health and safety management system including the elements of planning, organisation, control and monitoring to ensure that the whole system remains effective.

This proactive approach is one that many organisations need to consider, sooner than their merely reactive response following accidents or ill-health associated with work activities.

MANAGEMENT SYSTEMS

There are a number of management systems that need consideration and implementation in order to ensure compliance with the recommendations outlined in the ACOP above. These include the following.

Safety monitoring arrangements

The procedures for undertaking workplace safety inspections, safety surveys, safety sampling exercises and other forms of safety monitoring along with the investigation of the causes of accidents, incidents and occupational ill-health. This will include the preparation of statistical information indicating trends in accident and ill-health experience for use in the design of future health and safety strategies.

Risk assessment procedures

Risk assessment procedures for the workplace, work activities, work groups, work equipment, personal protective equipment (PPE), substances hazardous to health, noise, manual handling operations and work with display screen equipment (DSE).

Planned preventive maintenance systems

Formal systems for ensuring the workplace, equipment, systems and devices are maintained in an efficient state, in efficient working order and in good repair.

Cleaning schedules

Formal schedules for ensuring the workplace, furniture, furnishings and fittings are kept sufficiently clean, including procedures for the removal and disposal of waste materials.

Emergency procedures

Formal emergency procedures, including the training and appointment of competent persons to oversee evacuation procedures.

Health surveillance

The provision of health surveillance where employees may be exposed to risks to the health identified by risk assessments.

Competent persons

The training and appointment of competent persons to assist the employer in ensuring compliance with legal requirements and for overseeing the preventive and protective measures arising from risk assessments.

Instruction and training

The provision of on-going health and safety training at all levels within the organisation, including directors and senior managers.

Human capability assessment

Consideration of the need to ensure that the demands of the job do not exceed the employees' ability to carry out the work without risks to themselves or others. This may include the assessment of both physical and mental capability to undertake tasks safely.

Information

Information provided to employees to ensure safe working practices should be comprehensible to the people concerned and relevant to the operations undertaken.

Consultation procedures

There should be a formal system for consultation on health and safety issues, the information to be provided to employees, health and safety training arrangements and the consequences of new technologies. This may take place through consultation with trade union-appointed safety representatives (SR), representatives of employee safety and through the operation of a formally constituted safety committee. Employers must take the lead in this area.

The key elements of effective health and safety management systems can be found in **Successful health and safety management,** (HSE, 1991) and the **Guide to occupational health and safety management systems** (British Standards Institute, 1996).

These systems are dealt with later in this chapter.

STATEMENTS OF HEALTH AND SAFETY POLICY

Under Section 2(3) of the HSWA every employer has a duty to 'prepare and as often as appropriate revise a written statement of his general policy with regard to the health and safety at work of his employees and the organisation and arrangements for the time being in force for carrying out that policy, and to bring the statement and any revision of it to the notice of his employees'.

The Statement of Health and Safety Policy is, fundamentally, the key document for detailing the management systems and procedures necessary for ensuring sound levels of health and safety performance. It should be revised at regular intervals prior to, particularly, changes in the structure of the organisation, the introduction of new articles and substances, and changes in legal requirements affecting the organisation. It must be signed by the most senior person in the organisation, for example, chief executive, managing director, and dated.

Fundamentally, the statement must be seen as a 'living document', which reflects the current organisational arrangements, the hazards and precautions necessary on the part of employees and others, the individual responsibilities of people from the chief executive downwards and systems for monitoring performance. Many statements incorporate sub-policies, such as those covering smoking at work, sickness absence, asbestos and health surveillance.

Objectives of the Statement of Health and Safety Policy
- It should affirm long-range purpose.
- It should commit management at all levels and reinforce this purpose in the decision-making process; and
- It should indicate the scope left for decision-making by junior managers.

Scope of a Statement of Health and Safety Policy
This document should cover the following aspects:

- management intent;
- the 'arrangements' for implementing the policy;
- individual accountabilities of directors, line managers, employees and other groups, such as contractors and their employees;
- details of the organisational structure with regard to both line and staff functions; and
- the role and function of health and safety specialists, for example, health and safety advisers, occupational health nurses, occupational physicians, SRs.

Principal features of a Statement of Health and Safety Policy

A Statement of Health and Safety Policy should incorporate the following features:

- a general statement of intent, which states the basic objectives of the organisation and its overall philosophy in relation to the management of health and safety; and
- the organisation for health and safety, including a broad outline of the chain of command, how accountabilities are set, how policy implementation is to be monitored and how individual job descriptions should reflect health and safety responsibilities and associated accountabilities.

The arrangements for putting the policy into practice, including procedures, systems, rules and procedures. This may include arrangements for training, risk assessment, fire safety, liaison with enforcement officers and many other matters. It is common practice for the detailed arrangements to be incorporated in a health and safety manual incorporating codes of practice on topics such as accident reporting, recording and investigation, risk assessment procedures, PPE, etc. with a view to ensuring consistency of approach across the organisation.

Effective Policies for Health and Safety at Work (HSE, 1980) recommends that a Statement of Health and Safety Policy should incorporate the following elements:

- A written safety policy that states the basic objectives and is supplemented by more detailed rules and procedures to cater for specific hazards.
- Definition of both the duties and extent of responsibility of specified line management levels for safety and health, with identification made at the highest level of an individual with overall responsibility.
- Clear definition of the function of the safety officer/adviser and his relationship with line management made clear.
- The system for monitoring safety performance and publishing information about such performance.
- An identification and analysis of hazards, together with the precautions necessary on the part of staff, visitors, contractors, etc.
- An information system that will be sufficient to produce an identification of needs and can be used as an indicator of the effectiveness of the policy.
- A training policy for all management and staff levels.
- A commitment to consultation on health and safety and to a positive form of worker involvement.

The HSE further suggests that it is not sufficient to publish a policy, however comprehensive it may be, unless the policy is translated into effective action at all levels within the organisation. Success, in terms of acknowledged and continuing commitment at all management levels, is more likely where the policy is underwritten by the Board, who must make adequate financial provision for bringing the policy into effect.

Framing a Statement of Health and Safety Policy

Many employers have difficulty in deciding the actual format and layout for a Statement of Health and Safety Policy. Bearing in mind the points made above, such a statement can incorporate the following elements:

Part I   The Statement of Intent

Part II   The organisation for making the policy effective at all levels

Part III   The Arrangements for putting the policy into practice and linked to the organisation's Health and Safety Manual

This can be followed by a series of Appendices, which are of particular relevance to the organisation and can include:

Appendix A   A list of the relevant statutory provisions applying to the organisation

Appendix B   Specification of the duties and responsibilities of people at all levels from the chief executive downwards, together with an organisation chart indicating the different levels of responsibility

Appendix C   Duties and responsibilities of the safety adviser and local safety officers; functions of SRs

Appendix D   Statement of Policy on Risk Assessment

Appendix E   Statement of Policy on Smoking at Work

Appendix F   Statement of Policy on Sickness Absence

Appendix G   Statement of Policy on Drugs in the Workplace

Appendix H   Statement of Policy on Stress at Work

Appendix I   The hazards arising at work and the precautions necessary

Appendix J   Safety Committee Constitution

INTERNAL SAFETY CODES, RULES AND INSTRUCTIONS

The employer has a duty under the HSWA to ensure the provision of information, instruction and training for all employees, and to identify the hazards and precautions necessary on the part of employees and other persons, for example, the employees of contractors.

Compliance with these requirements may be through the preparation of internal codes of practice and rules of a general and specific nature.

Inadequate and/or ineffective internal information and instructions to employees contribute to the causes of accidents and ill-health at work. In some cases, rules and instructions may be ambiguous, badly worded or simply not available to the people to whom they are directed.

Safety codes of practice, rules and instructions complement the 'arrangements' outlined in a Statement of Health and Safety Policy.

Codes of Practice

An internal code of practice is, fundamentally, directed at standardizing the approach to a particular matter throughout an organisation. It should provide guidance to managers on legal requirements and procedures to be followed on, for instance, the operation of Permit to Work Systems, accident reporting and recording and the carrying out of health risk assessments under the COSHH Regulations.

Internal codes should, preferably, be incorporated in a Health and Safety Manual maintained by managers. Codes of practice should be reviewed and updated on a regular basis in line with current legislation and industry recommendations.

Rules and instructions

Rules and instructions are best covered in a form of employee Health and Safety Handbook, which is issued to all employees at the induction training stage. The handbook should be written in comprehensible style and extensively illustrated. It should incorporate, for instance, individual responsibilities for ensuring safe working practices, the principal hazards that could arise, the procedure for reporting hazards, accidents, incidents, ill-health and 'near misses' to line managers, basic 'DOs' and 'DON'Ts' with regard to safe working and arrangements for welfare.

THE RIGHT SAFETY CULTURE

Clearly, there is more to the maintenance of sound health and safety standards than mere legal compliance. Increasingly, enforcement agencies are paying attention to the existence or otherwise of a safety culture within organisations.

Establishing a safety culture – the principles involved

The HSE Director General's submission to the Piper Alpha Inquiry (Rimington, 1989) identified a number of important principles involved in the establishment of a safety culture, which is accepted by everyone and observed generally. These principles are:

- ♦ the acceptance of responsibility at and from the top, exercised through a clear chain of command, seen to be actual and felt throughout the organisation;
- ♦ a conviction that high standards are achievable through proper management;
- ♦ the setting and monitoring of relevant objectives/targets based upon satisfactory internal information systems;
- ♦ the systematic identification and assessment of hazards and the devising and exercise of preventive systems that are subject to audit and review; in such approaches, particular attention must be given to the investigation of error;
- ♦ immediate rectification of deficiencies; and
- ♦ promotion and reward of enthusiasm and good results.

Developing a safety culture – the essential features

'Developing a Safety Culture' (Confederation of British Industries, 1991), takes the above points further. This publication is based on a study undertaken by that organisation which, identifies a number of features that are essential to a sound safety culture. An organisation wishing to improve its performance will need to judge its existing practices against them.

The publication recommends:

- there should be leadership and commitment from the top, which is genuine and visible; this is the most important feature;
- there should be acceptance that improving health and safety performance is a long term strategy that requires sustained effort and interest;
- there should be a policy statement of high expectations that conveys a sense of optimism about what is possible supported by adequate codes of practice and safety standards;
- health and safety should be treated as other corporate aims and properly resourced;
- it must be a line management responsibility;
- 'ownership' of health and safety must permeate at all levels of the work force; this requires employee involvement, training and communication;
- realistic and achievable targets should be set and performance measured against them;
- incidents should be thoroughly investigated;
- consistency of behaviour against agreed standards should be achieved by auditing, and good safety behaviour should be a condition of employment;
- deficiencies revealed by an investigation or audit should be remedied promptly; and
- management should receive adequate and up-to-date information to be able to assess performance.

HEALTH AND SAFETY MANAGEMENT SYSTEMS

In the 1990s a number of health and safety management systems have been put forward with a view to assisting employers to comply with duties under the MHSWR. These systems are reviewed below.

Occupational Health and Safety Management Systems (BS 8800: 1996)

BS 8800 offers an organisation the opportunity to review and revise its current occupational health and safety arrangements against a standard that has been developed by industry, commerce, insurers, regulators, trade unions and occupational health and safety practitioners.

The standard offers all the essential elements required to implement an effective occupational health and safety management system. It is equally applicable to small organisations as it is to large complex organisations.

The aims of the standard are 'to improve occupational health and safety performance of organisations by providing guidance on how management of occupational health and safety may be integrated with the management of other aspects of business performance in order to:

- minimise risks to employees and others;
- improve business performance; and
- assist organisations to establish a responsible image in the workplace.'

The benefits to be derived

Whilst organisations recognise that they have a duty to manage health and safety, their senior managers may also believe the management of same is a financial burden that gives very little positive return, e.g. VAT and PAYE. This lack of belief frequently results in a lack of, or limited, commitment to health and safety by these managers.

Conversely, those organisations that do subscribe with commitment usually find enormous benefit. Apart from the obvious effect on staff morale, they find a positive contribution to the bottom line of their operational costs. The following benefits can be gained:

- improved commitment from staff (and positive support from trade unions);
- reduction in staff absenteeism;
- improved production output, through reductions in downtime from incidents;
- reduction in insurance premiums;
- improved customer confidence;
- reduction in claims against the organisation; and
- reduction in adverse publicity.

Achieving progress

The way forward for successful health and safety management is to involve everyone in the organisation, using a proactive approach to identify hazards and to control those risks that are not tolerable. This ensures that those employees at risk are aware of the risks that they face and of the need for the control measures.

In order to achieve positive benefits, health and safety management should be an integral feature of the undertaking, contributing to the success of the organisation. It can be an effective vehicle for efficiency and effectiveness, encouraging employees to suggest improvements in working practices. In an ideal environment, health and safety is an agenda item alongside production, services, etc at any senior management review of the undertaking, rather than an inconvenient add-on item.

Status review of the health and safety management system

As an integral feature of a review of an organisation's health and safety management system, BS 8800 recommends the following four aspects:

- requirements of relevant legislation dealing with occupational health and safety management issues;
- existing guidance on occupational health and safety management within the organisation;
- best practice and performance in the organisation's employment sector and other appropriate sectors (for example, from relevant HSC's industry advisory committees and trade association guidelines); and
- efficiency and effectiveness of existing resources devoted to occupational health and safety management.

Policies on health and safety

According to BS 8800 there are nine important areas that should be addressed in a policy, each of which allows visible and identifiable objectives to be set, thus:

- recognizing that occupational health and safety is an integral part of its business performance;

♦ achieving a high level of occupational health and safety performance, with compliance to legal requirements as the minimum and continual cost-effective improvement in performance;
♦ provision of adequate and appropriate resources to implement the policy;
♦ the publishing and setting of occupational health and safety objectives, even if only by internal notification;
♦ placing the management of occupational health and safety as a prime responsibility of line management, from most senior executive to the first-line supervisory level;
♦ ensuring understanding, implementation and maintenance of the policy statement at all levels in the organisation;
♦ employee involvement and consultation to gain commitment to the policy and its implementation;
♦ periodic review of the policy, the management system and audit of compliance to the policy; and
♦ ensuring that employees at all levels receive appropriate training and are competent to carry out their duties and responsibilities.

Approaches to health and safety management

There are two recommended approaches depending upon the organisational needs of the business and with the objective that such an approach will be integrated into management systems.

The first approach is based on **Successful health and safety management** (Health and Safety Executive, 1991) and the second on ISO 14001, **Environmental management systems**.

Successful health and safety management

The key elements of successful health and safety management are set out in **FIG. 3.**

Policy

Organisations that are successful in achieving high standards of health and safety have health and safety policies that contribute to their business performance, their responsibilities to people and the environment in a way that fulfils both the spirit and the letter of the law. In this way they satisfy the expectations of shareholders, employees, customers and society at large. Their policies are cost-effective and aimed at achieving the preservation and development of physical and human resources and reductions in financial losses and liabilities. Their health and safety policies influence all their activities and decisions, including those to do with the selection of resources and information, the design and operation of working systems, the design and delivery of products and services, and the control and disposal of waste.

Organizing

Organisations that achieve high health and safety standards are structured and operated so as to put their health and safety policies into effective practice. This is helped by the creation of a positive culture, which secures involvement and participation at all levels. It is sustained by effective communications and the promotion of competence, which enables all employees to make a responsible and informed contribution to the health and safety effort. The visible and active leadership of senior managers is necessary to develop and maintain a culture that is supportive of health and safety management. Their aim is not simply to avoid accidents, but to motivate and empower people to work safely. The vision, values and beliefs of leaders become the shared 'common knowledge' of all.

KEY ELEMENTS OF SUCCESSFUL HEALTH AND SAFETY MANAGEMENT FIG. 3

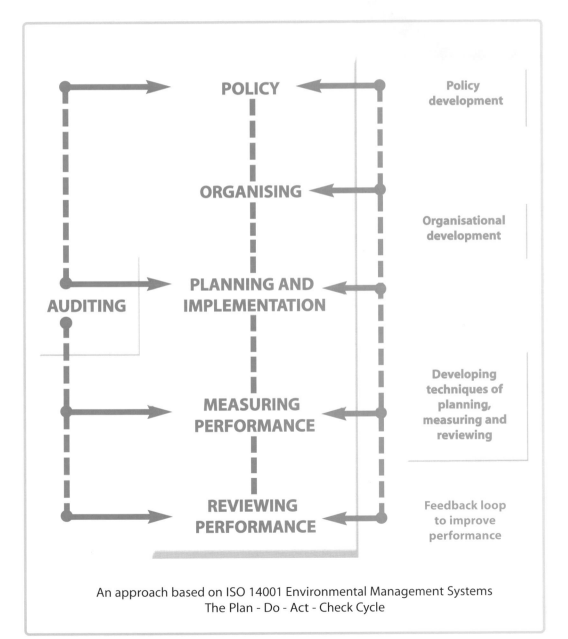

An approach based on ISO 14001 Environmental Management Systems
The Plan - Do - Act - Check Cycle

Planning

Successful organisations adopt a planned and systematic approach to policy implementation. Their aim is to minimise the risks created by work activities, products and services. They use risk assessment methods to decide priorities and set objectives for hazard elimination and risk reduction. Performance standards are established and performance is measured against them. Specific actions needed to promote a positive health and safety culture and to eliminate and control risks are identified. Wherever possible, risks are eliminated by the careful selection and design of facilities, equipment and processes or minimised by the use of physical control measures. Where this is not possible systems of work and PPE are used to control risks.

Measuring performance

Health and safety performance in organisations that manage health and safety successfully is measured against pre-determined standards. This reveals when and where action is needed to improve performance. The success of action taken to control risks is assessed through active self-monitoring involving a range of techniques. This includes an examination of both hardware (premises, plant and substances) and software (people, procedures and systems), including individual behaviour. Failures of control are assessed through reactive monitoring, which requires the thorough investigation of any accidents, ill-health or incidents with the potential to cause harm or loss. In both active and reactive monitoring the objectives are not only to determine the immediate causes of sub-standard performance but, more importantly, to identify the underlying causes and the implications for the design and operation of the health and safety management system.

Auditing and reviewing performance

Learning from all relevant experience and applying the lessons learned are important elements in effective health and safety management. This needs to be done systematically through regular reviews of performance based on data from monitoring activities and from independent audits of the whole health and safety management system. These form the basis for self-regulation and for' securing compliance with Sections 2 to 6 of the HSWA. Commitment to continuous improvement involves the constant development of policies, approaches to implementation and techniques of risk control. Organisations that achieve high standards of health and safety assess their health and safety performance by internal reference to key performance indicators and by external comparison with the performance of business competitors. They also often record and account for their performance in their annual reports.

ISO 14001: ENVIRONMENTAL MANAGEMENT SYSTEMS

Initial status review

This first stage of the process is, fundamentally, a review and assessment of the 'current state of play' with regard to both proactive and reactive health and safety management systems. Proactive factors to be considered include the presence of written safe systems of work, joint consultation procedures, an integrated approach to risk assessment, documented planned preventive maintenance systems and a procedure for providing information, instruction and training at all levels within the organisation.

Reactive systems include those for accident reporting, recording and investigation, accident and incident costing and means for the provision of feedback following the investigation of accidents, incidents and occupational ill-health.

Occupational health and safety policy

This stage entails a review of the current Statement of Health and Safety Policy and other sub-policies covering, for instance, sickness absence, contractors' activities and the use of hazardous substances.

Planning

Feedback from the Initial Status Review and the effectiveness of the Statement of Health and Safety Policy will identify areas for planning for future actions. This stage may entail the setting up of management systems to cover:

- future safety monitoring operations;
- the preparation of contractors' regulations;
- systems for raising the awareness of employees;
- the provision of information, instruction and training;
- planned preventive maintenance;
- health surveillance of specific groups of employees; and
- a review of risk assessment procedures.

Implementation and operation

Once the strategy and objectives for future health and safety activities has been established at the planning stage, the process of implementing these objectives must be put into operation, perhaps on a phased basis. These written objectives should specify:

- the actual objective;
- the manager responsible for achieving this objective;
- the financial arrangements where appropriate;
- the criteria for assessing successful achievement of the objective; and
- a date for completion of the objective.

Checking and corrective action

Procedures should be established for checking that agreed objectives are being achieved within the timescale allocated and for ensuring specific corrective action is taken in the event of failure or incomplete fulfillment of the objective.

Management review

Any phased programme of improvement must be subject to regular management review. The dates for review, and the management responsible for same, should be established before the implementation stage. In most cases a review team assess the success in achievement of the pre-determined objectives and make recommendations for future action, including any monitoring arrangements necessary.

Continual improvement

As a result of undertaking this phased approach to health and safety management, there should be a continual improvement in health and safety performance including:

♦ improved attitudes and awareness on the part of management and employees;

♦ greater commitment to, and recognition of, the need to incorporate health and safety in management procedures;

♦ regular revisions of policy based on feedback from reviews;

♦ a developing health and safety culture within the organisation;

♦ improved systems for ensuring corrective action is dealt with quickly; and

♦ ease of integration of environmental management systems with health and safety management systems.

ISO 14001 has much to offer as a model for health and safety management systems. As with any other system, there must be senior management commitment to the process along with active demonstration of support, recognition of successes achieved and constant review of progress.

SAFE SYSTEMS OF WORK

The requirement on employers to provide and maintain plant and systems of work that are, so far as is reasonably practicable, safe and without risks to health is well-established. [HSWA Sec2(2)(a)] At common law, an employer must ensure a safe system of work for his employees. [Wilsons & Clyde Coal Co Ltd v English (1938) 2 AER 628]

What is a safe system of work?

There are various definitions of this term:

♦ the integration of people, machinery and equipment in a correct environment to ensure the safe possible working conditions in a particular work situation or area; and

♦ a formal step-by-step description of any task or process that takes into account the hazards likely to be encountered.

In the design of safe systems of work, the following factors may need to be considered:

♦ a safe layout of the working area with adequate space between machinery, plant, equipment and other installations and for undertaking the task;

♦ a correct sequence of operations, using mechanical handling equipment where practicable;

♦ analysis of tasks and the provision of clear instructions on tasks;

♦ the specification of safe working procedures, perhaps on a step-by-step basis; and

♦ the provision of a healthy working environment to include control over heating, lighting and ventilation systems, airborne contaminants and levels of noise and vibration.

Job safety analysis

This is defined as the identification of all the accident prevention measures appropriate to a particular job or area of work activity and the behavioural factors that most significantly influence whether or not these measures are taken. Job safety analysis is a technique used in the design of safe systems of work and may be:

♦ job-based, for example, machinery operators, cleaners, drivers; and

♦ activity-based, for example, roof work, assembly of parts, loading vehicles.

Job safety analysis is, fundamentally, based on work study technique and takes place in the following stages, based on the mnemonic SREDIM

SELECT	–	the work to be studied
RECORD	–	the method of doing the work
EXAMINE	–	the total operating system
DEVELOP	–	the optimum methods for doing the work
INSTALL	–	the method into the organisation's activities
MAINTAIN	–	the defined and measured method of work

The SREDIM principle can be applied to job safety analysis, thus:

♦ **SELECT** the job to be analyzed;
♦ break the job down into an ordered sequence of job steps; **RECORD** these steps;
♦ critically observe and **EXAMINE** each step to identify the risk of accident or ill-health;
♦ **DEVELOP** control measures to eliminate or reduce the risks;
♦ formulate written safe systems of work and job safety instructions; **INSTALL** these systems through the provision of information, instruction and training; supervise regularly to ensure compliance with the safe system of work; and
♦ **MAINTAIN** these systems through regular reviews of working practices involving the safe system of work.

Job safety instructions

These are a direct outcome of the design of a safe system of work and are a means of communicating the safe system of work to the operators. Job safety instructions should be covered during induction training and during orientation training of employees who have moved to new jobs.

PERMIT TO WORK SYSTEMS

A Permit to Work system is a formally documented safe system of work designed to prevent accidental injury to operators and damage to plant, premises and product where work with a foreseeably high level of risk is to be undertaken, for example, work involving entry into confined spaces, on electrical equipment or involving the use of highly flammable substances.

A Permit to Work document sets out:
♦ the work to be undertaken, and
♦ the precautions necessary at each stage of the work.

It is a clear record that all foreseeable risks have been identified in advance and that all precautions are specified and taken in a correct sequence. Operation of a Permit to Work system requires a high degree of supervision and control.

The following principles should be observed in the operation of Permit to Work systems:
- the Permit to Work document must provide concise and accurate information about:
  - the work to be undertaken;
  - the timescale for completion of the work;
  - individual responsibilities for various stages of the operation;
- until cancelled, it is the principal instruction, which overrides all other instructions;
- no one must, under any circumstances, work at a place or on equipment not indicated as safe in the permit;
- only work indicated or described in the permit must be undertaken;
- only the originator may amend or cancel a permit;
- anyone taking over the work must be adequately briefed;
- the person accepting the permit is fully responsible for complying with the terms of the permit;
- the boundary or limits of the working area must be clearly defined; and
- contractors and their employees must be trained in the procedure prior to undertaking any specific work incorporated in the permit.

Permit to Work situations

The decision to operate a Permit to Work system is dependent on the risks inherent in the work involved. Typical Permit to Work situations include:
- entry into confined spaces, closed vessels and vessels containing agitators;
- work involving the breaking of lines or the opening of plant containing steam and hazardous substances under pressure;
- work on electrical systems;
- welding and cutting operations (hot work) in areas other than workshops;
- work in isolated locations, locations with difficult access and at high level;
- work in the vicinity of, or requiring the use of, highly flammable, explosive or toxic substances;
- work resulting in potential atmospheric pollution of the workplace;
- certain fumigation operations involving hazardous dusts, gases, fogs, vapours or mists; and
- work involving contractors in any of the above.

Stages of a Permit to Work system
Assessment
Consideration of the work necessary, the methods and materials to be used, the hazards that could arise and precautions necessary.

Withdrawal from service
In the case of plant this may entail physical locking off of machinery, valves and other items to prevent inadvertent operation of same whilst work is in progress. Warning notices and safety signs should be displayed at this stage.

Isolation
After the plant has been withdrawn from service, it may need to be physically isolated, by means of barriers and displaying warning notices, along with electrical and mechanical

isolation. In certain cases, it may be necessary to carry out atmospheric monitoring where personnel may be required to enter a confined space. Specific requirements, in this case, are outlined in the Confined Spaces Regulations 1997.

Cancellation of the Permit to Work

On completion of the work specified in the permit, it should be cancelled by completion of the appropriate section. Cancellation should incorporate a declaration to the effect that all personnel and equipment have been removed from the plant or area in question. The permit should then be returned to the originator.

Return to service

Following completion of the work and cancellation of the permit, the plant can be returned to service. The person in charge of the process or operation should ensure that the permit has been cancelled and make the final entry to the effect that he/she accepts responsibility for same.

Administrative procedures

A Permit to Work must be raised before the work, or a particular phase of the work, requiring the Permit to Work is commenced by the senior person responsible for carrying out the work. Work should be carefully pre-planned to cause the least possible interference with other work. In some cases, it may be necessary to refer to internal and external sources of advice, for example, manufacturers of plant. Under no circumstances should a Permit to Work be issued, even in an emergency situation, without careful consideration of the risks and the precautions necessary. Where an isolation procedure, for instance, is particularly complicated, it is common practice to attach this procedure to the permit.

Authority for the issue of Permits to Work should be restricted to named senior managers, and the criteria for authorization must be based on skill, knowledge and experience of the individuals concerned.

Documentation, record keeping, training and supervision

In most cases, Permits to Work are printed in triplicate, self-carbonned and serial numbered. The original is handed to the person undertaking the work, the first copy to the manager in the area where the work is being undertaken and the third copy retained by the originator. On completion of the work and final clearance of the Permit to Work, the original and first copy should be returned to the originator.

A record of permits issued should be maintained. This provides useful feedback for the future design of safe systems of work, specification of plant and equipment and in the identification of training needs. Completed Permits to Work should be retained for a period of not less than two years.

Employees and other persons, for example, contractors' employees involved in implementing Permit to Work systems, need training prior to undertaking this work. Supervision should ensure that all stages of a Permit to Work system are completed satisfactorily.

EMERGENCY PROCEDURES

The duties of employers and occupiers of premises under fire safety legislation with regard to the emergency evacuation of premises in the event of fire are well known.

However, in many organisations, a well-documented and practised emergency procedure may be necessary for other reasons. This may arise due to the nature of the work, such as the manufacture or use of hazardous substances, work underground or in confined spaces, work involving risk of exposure to radiation or work involving demolition of structures.

Regulation 8 of the MHSWR requires employers to establish 'procedures for serious and imminent danger and for danger areas'. A 'danger area' is defined in the ACOP as 'a work environment which must be entered by an employee where the level of risk is unacceptable without special precautions being taken'. A danger area could be a confined space, a flammable substances storage area or an area that has been structurally damaged as result of fire.

A risk assessment should identify the significant risks arising out of work. This could include, for example, the potential for a major escalating fire, explosion, building collapse, pollution incident or, perhaps, one of the scheduled dangerous occurrences listed in Reporting of Injuries, Diseases and Dangerous Occurrences Regulations (RIDDOR), such as the collapse or bursting of a closed pressure vessel.

All these events could result in a major incident, ie one that may:
- affect several departments within an undertaking;
- endanger the surrounding communities;
- be classed as a dangerous occurrence under RIDDOR; and
- result in adverse publicity for the organisation with ensuing loss of public confidence and marketplace image.

Establishing emergency procedures

The ACOP to the MHSWR makes the following points with regard to the establishment of emergency procedures:
- the aim must be to set out clear guidance on when employees and others at work should stop work and move to a place of safety;
- the risk assessment should identify the foreseeable events that need to be covered by these procedures;
- many workplaces or work activities will pose additional risks. All employers should consider carefully in their risk assessment whether such additional risks might arise;
- the procedures may need to take account of responsibilities of specific employees, for example, in shutting down the plant;
- the procedures should set out the role, identity and responsibilities of the competent persons nominated to implement the detailed actions;
- where specific emergency situations are covered by particular regulations, procedures should reflect any requirements laid on them by these regulations;
- the procedure should cater for the fact that emergency events can occur and develop rapidly, thus requiring employees to act without waiting for further guidance;
- emergency procedures should normally be written down, clearly setting out the limits of action to be taken by all employees;
- work should not be resumed after an emergency if a serious danger remains. Consult the emergency authorities if in doubt;
- in shared workplaces, separate emergency procedures should take account of others in the workplace and, as far as is appropriate, should be coordinated.

Implementing the emergency procedure

When putting an emergency procedure into action the following factors should be considered:

- liaison with external authorities, for example, police, fire service and other organisations;
- the appointment of an emergency controller;
- establishment of an emergency control centre;
- responsibility for initiating the emergency procedure;
- notification to local authority;
- call out of key personnel;
- immediate action on site;
- evacuation procedure;
- access to records of people on site;
- public relations;
- catering and temporary shelter;
- contingency arrangements; and
- training of employees in the procedure.

COMPETENT PERSONS

Traditionally, health and safety legislation has required an employer to appoint 'competent persons' to undertake a range of activities, such as the inspection of scaffolds and excavations prior to use, the examination and testing of pressure systems and supervision of the erection of cranes and lifting equipment.

Under the MHSWR an employer must appoint one or more competent persons:

- to assist him/her in undertaking the measures he/she needs to take to comply with the requirements and prohibitions imposed upon him by or under the relevant statutory provisions and Part II of FPWR 1997 (Regulation 7); and
- to oversee procedures for serious and imminent danger and for danger areas (Regulation 8).

The ACOP to the MHSWR makes the following points about competent persons.

Employers are solely responsible for ensuring that those they appoint to assist them with health and safety measures are competent to carry out the tasks they are assigned and are given adequate information and support. In making decisions on who to appoint, employers need to know and understand the work involved, the principles of risk assessment and prevention, and current legislation and health and safety standards. Employers should ensure that anyone they appoint is capable of applying the above to whatever tasks they are assigned.

Regulation 8(3) states that a person shall be regarded as competent for the purposes of paragraph 1(b) (nomination of competent persons to implement evacuation procedures) where he has sufficient training and experience or knowledge and other qualities to enable him properly to implement the evacuation procedures referred to in that sub-paragraph.

Case law definition

It should be noted that the term 'competent person' is not generally defined in statute or regulations. Therefore the onus is on the employer to decide whether persons are competent to undertake these duties. An employer might do this by reference to the person's training, qualifications and experience.

The term, however, is defined in case law. A competent person should have practical and theoretical knowledge as well as sufficient experience of the particular machinery, plant or procedure involved to enable him/her to identify defects or weaknesses during plant and machinery examinations, and to assess their importance in relation to the strength and function of that plant and machinery. [Brazier v Skipton Rock Company Limited (1962) 1 AER 955]

Health and safety specialists

Increasingly organisations have seen the need to appoint health and safety specialists to fulfil the competent person role on a general basis. But what should an employer take into account when making such an appointment?

Successful health and safety management (Health and Safety Executive, 1991) makes the following points with regard to the role and functions of health and safety advisers, be they internally appointed persons or consultants.

Organisations that successfully manage health and safety give health and safety advisers the status and ensure they have the competence to advise management and workers with authority and independence. Subjects on which they advise include:

♦ health and safety policy formulation and development;
♦ structuring and operating all parts of the organisation (including the supporting systems) in order to promote a positive health and safety culture and to secure effective implementation of policy;
♦ planning for health and safety, including the setting of realistic short- and long-term objectives, deciding priorities and establishing adequate performance standards;
♦ day-to-day implementation and monitoring of policy and plans, including accident and incident investigation, reporting and analysis; and
♦ reviewing performance and auditing the whole safety management system.

To fulfil these functions they have to:

♦ maintain adequate information systems on relevant law (civil and criminal) and on guidance and developments in general and safety management;
♦ be able to interpret the law and understand how it applies to the organisation;
♦ establish and keep up-to-date organisational and risk control standards relating to both 'hardware' (such as the place of work and the plant, substances and equipment in use) and 'software' (such as the procedures, systems and people); this task is likely to involve contributions from specialists, for example, architects, engineers, doctors and occupational hygienists;
♦ establish and maintain procedures for the reporting, investigating, recording and analysis of accidents and incidents;
♦ establish and maintain adequate and appropriate monitoring and auditing systems; and
♦ present themselves and their advice in an independent and effective manner, safeguarding the confidentiality of personal information such as medical records.

Competence of health and safety advisers

Competence implies a level of skill, knowledge and experience, which is appropriate to the hazards that may arise in an organisation. In the majority of cases, health and safety advisers should have successfully completed a recognised course of training. This training may be under the auspices of, for example, the National Examination Board in Occupational Safety and Health (NEBOSH), the Royal Society for the Prevention of Accidents (RoSPA), a university or college. It is recommended that health and safety advisers have corporate membership of a professional institution, such as the Institute of Occupational Safety and Health (IOSH).

Training should be complemented by a period of experience in the various aspects of workplace health and safety.

JOINT CONSULTATION ON HEALTH AND SAFETY

The duty on an employer to consult with trade union-appointed safety representatives on matters relating to health and safety at work is established in the HSWA and procedures for consultation are outlined in the Safety Representatives and Safety Committees Regulations (SRSCR) 1977. Where there is no form of trade union involvement an employer must comply with the Health and Safety (Consultation with Employees) Regulations 1996.

SAFETY REPRESENTATIVES AND SAFETY COMMITTEES REGULATIONS 1977

These regulations broadly require an employer to consult and cooperate with trade union-appointed SRs, and for SRs to cooperate with employers in connection with:
- the arrangements for health and safety at work;
- measures for ensuring satisfactory health and safety performance; and
- systems for checking the effectiveness of the above arrangements and measures.

The regulations, ACOP and HSE Guidance are incorporated in the HSC publication 'Safety representatives and safety committees', commonly known as the 'Brown Book'.

The principal objective of the regulations is to provide a basic framework within which each undertaking can develop effective working relationships. These relationships must cover a wide range of situations, ie different forms of workplace and work activity.

Appointment of SRs

A recognised trade union may appoint SRs from amongst the employees in all cases where one or more employees are employed by an employer by whom it is recognised. The employer must be notified by the trade union of the names of SRs. Each SR has prescribed functions (not duties).

Functions of SRs

SRs have the following functions:
- to represent employees in consultation with employers;
- to cooperate effectively in promoting and developing health and safety measures;
- to make representations to the employer on any general or specific matter affecting the health and safety of their members;
- to make representations to the employer on general matters affecting the health and

safety of other persons employed at the workplace;
- to carry out certain inspections;
- to represent members in consultation with inspectors;
- to receive information from inspectors; and
- to attend a safety committee if appropriate.

None of these functions, however, imposes a duty on SRs.

Inspections of the workplace

SRs are entitled to undertake workplace inspections every three months and employers must give them reasonable assistance. Notice in writing must be given by the trade union. They can also inspect:
- the scene of an accident;
- where there has been a substantial change in the conditions of work;
- where new information has been published by the HSC or HSE; and
- following a notifiable accident, disease or dangerous occurrence.

Inspection of documents

After giving an employer reasonable notice, SRs are entitled to inspect any document relevant to the workplace that an employer is required to keep by virtue of the relevant statutory provisions and that an employer has to maintain, other than documents relating to the health records of identifiable individuals.

An employer must make available to SRs such information within his knowledge that is necessary to enable them to fulfil their functions, other than:
- any information, the disclosure of which would be against the interest of national security;
- any information that they could not disclose without contravening a prohibition imposed by or under any enactment;
- any information relating specifically to an individual, unless he/she has consented to its disclosure;
- any information, the disclosure of which, for reasons other than its effect on health, safety and welfare at work, could cause substantial injury to the employer's undertaking or, where the information was supplied to them by some other person, to the undertaking of that person; and
- any information obtained by the employer for the purpose of bringing, prosecuting or defending any legal proceedings.

APPROVED CODE OF PRACTICE

Qualifications of SRs

So far as is reasonably practicable, SRs should have two years' experience with the employer or in similar employment.

Functions of SRs

SRs should:
- keep themselves informed of legal requirements;

- encourage cooperation; and
- undertake health and safety inspections and inform the employer of the outcome of inspections.

Obligations of employers

Employers must provide information on:

- the plans and performance of the undertaking with regard to health and safety;
- hazards and precautions necessary;
- the occurrence of accidents, dangerous occurrences and occupational disease; and
- any other information, including the results of any measurements taken.

SAFETY COMMITTEES

Basic objectives

These are:

- to promote cooperation; and
- to act as a focus for employee participation.

Functions

Safety committees have a range of functions to consider:

- the circumstances of individual accidents and cases of reportable disease;
- accident statistics and trends;
- the examination of safety audit reports;
- the examination of reports and information from the HSE;
- to assist in the development of safety rules and systems;
- to conduct periodic inspections;
- to monitor the effectiveness of health and safety training, communication and publicity; and
- to provide a link with the inspectorate.

Safety committee membership

Safety committees should be reasonably compact but allowing for representation of management and all employees. It should be recognised that a SR is not appointed by the safety committee and vice versa. Neither is responsible to or for the other. Management representation can include line managers, supervisors, engineers, human resources specialists, medical and safety advisers.

The committee must have authority to take action and specialist knowledge should be available.

Conduct

Meetings should be held as often as necessary; agendas and minutes should be provided.

Arrangements at individual workplaces

There should be:

- division of conduct of activities; and
- clear objectives/terms of reference for the committee.

Membership and structure of a safety committee should be clearly defined in writing (perhaps as an Appendix to the Statement of Health and Safety Policy). Matters notified by SRs should be published to the safety committee.

HEALTH AND SAFETY (CONSULTATION WITH EMPLOYEES) REGULATIONS 1996

Under these regulations employers must consult any employees who are not covered by the SRSCR. This may be by direct consultation with employees or through representatives elected by the employees they are to represent.

HSE Guidance

HSE Guidance accompanying the regulations details:
- which employees must be involved;
- the information they must be provided with;
- procedures for the election of representatives of employee safety;
- the training, time off and facilities they must be provided with; and
- their functions in office.

DOCUMENTATION REQUIREMENTS

Increasingly, the significance of well-written safety documentation becomes apparent, particularly where an employer may face criminal charges in the courts.

Preparation and maintenance of the following documents, where appropriate, is recommended:
- Statement of Health and Safety Policy [HSWA]

Risk assessments:
- general [MHSWR];
- workplace, work activity and work group [MHSWR, Workplace (Health, Safety and Welfare) Regulations 1992;
- work equipment [Provision and Use of Work Equipment Regulations 1998];
- PPE [Personal Protective Equipment at Work Regulations 1992];
- manual handling operations [Manual Handling Operations Regulations 1992];
- display screen equipment users [Health and Safety (Display Screen Equipment) Regulations 1992];
- noise exposure [Noise at Work Regulations 1989];
- substances hazardous to health [COSHH Regulations 1999].
- Contractors Regulations or Rules for the Safe Conduct of Project Work [Construction (Design and Management) Regulations 1994, Construction (Health Safety and Welfare) Regulations 1996 and Lifting Operations and Lifting Equipment Regulations 1998; and
- Instructions for safe working by employees [HSWA].

KEY POINTS

- All modern protective legislation is risk assessment-driven.
- The organisation's Statement of Health and Safety Policy is the starting point for the installation of management systems.

- Safe systems of work must be provided by employers under the HSWA.
- Establishing and promoting the right safety culture is an important feature of health and safety management.
- Employers are advised to adopt one of the current health and safety management systems.
- A competent person is a person appointed by an employer who has the appropriate levels of skill, knowledge and experience to recognise the risks and ensure the precautions are taken by the persons exposed to those risks.
- Procedures must be established and implemented in respect of serious and imminent danger and for danger areas.
- Increasingly, there is a need for health and safety specialists to be trained to a level commensurate with the risks associated with the organisation's activities.
- There must be a formal system for consultation with employees on health and safety issues.
- Documentation of health and safety policies and procedures is an essential element of good health and safety management.

4 Principles of Accident Prevention, Safety Monitoring & Risk Assessment

Safety monitoring is an important element of the proactive approach to health and safety management. It entails the on-going review of performance through the undertaking of inspections, audits, surveys and other forms of monitoring. Reactive strategies, such as accident and incident investigation, must also be considered with a view to producing feedback for incorporation in future proactive strategies.

Risk assessment is frequently an outcome of safety monitoring activities, entailing the identification of hazards, measurement and evaluation of risks and the implementation of preventive and protective measures, taking into account current legal requirements.

This chapter reviews the various forms of safety monitoring, accident reporting procedures and techniques of risk assessment, together with the principles of accident prevention.

PRINCIPLES OF ACCIDENT PREVENTION

What is an accident?

Most people would consider an accident to be an event that was unforeseeable and that, in many cases, resulted in some form of injury or loss. The term 'accident' can be defined in a number of ways:

♦ an unplanned and uncontrolled event that has led to, or could have caused, injury to persons, damage to plant or other loss (Royal Society for the Prevention of Accidents); and

♦ an unexpected, unplanned event in a sequence of events that occurs through a combination of causes. It results in physical harm (injury or disease) to an individual, damage to property, business interruption or any combination of these (Department of Occupational and Environmental Health, University of Aston in Birmingham).

The situation prior to an accident

Accidents are, fundamentally, concerned with two factors. First, they involve people and how, as individuals, they perceive risk and, second, the objective danger at that particular point in time.

Accident prevention, therefore, must take into account the objective danger in the workplace through the implementation of 'safe place' strategies, such as the maintenance of machinery guarding and safety devices. The perception of risk on the part of employees, together with the potential for human error, must also be considered by the use of a range of 'safe person' strategies, such as the provision of information, instruction and training aimed at increasing people's understanding of the hazards and the precautions they must take.

PROACTIVE STRATEGIES

'Safe place' strategies

'Safe place' strategies are directed at preventing contact with, or reducing, the dangers to which people are exposed whilst at work. They should, as far as possible, be used in preference to a 'safe person' strategy. They include the following.

Safe workplaces

The structural aspects of workplaces, such as floors and staircases, the stability of buildings, temperature, lighting and ventilation

Safe plant and equipment

The relative safety aspects of machinery, equipment and hand tools, together with pressure systems, electrical systems and other systems in use; the procedures for maintenance, examination and testing of work equipment, such as lifting equipment

Safe processes

Those elements incorporated in a manufacturing process, such as machinery, raw materials, loading and unloading procedures, storage requirements

Safe materials

Certain materials that may be dangerous, such as chemicals and raw materials of all types; handling procedures; the information requirements for hazardous substances

Safe systems of work

The design and operation of safe systems of work in a range of situations; information, instruction, training and supervision requirements; the use of Permits to Work in high-risk situations; the training and appointment of competent persons where appropriate

Safe access

The relative safety of external approaches to a workplace, including parking areas; roof work and work at heights; external lighting arrangements; designated pedestrian walkways; traffic speed controls

Supervision requirements

The need for regular supervision of employees to ensure safe working practices

Trained employees

The training of employees to ensure competence in the tasks they carry out, for example, lift truck drivers, electricians and machine operators; induction training for all employees; orientation training prior to the introduction of new processes and systems

'Safe person' strategies

In certain situations a 'safe place' strategy may not be possible to operate and the responsibility for safety may have to rest with the employee to some extent. This applies in the case of the correct use of PPE by employees and in the taking of specific measures to protect health by good standards of personal hygiene.

'Safe person' strategies include the following.

Personal hygiene

Employees exposed to the risk of skin conditions through exposure to substances such as adhesives, glues and skin sensitisers; the need for regular washing of exposed hands and forearms to prevent these conditions; in many cases, handwashing before eating food due to the risk of contaminating the food

Vulnerable groups

Certain groups at risk due to their condition, for example, pregnant workers, and their immaturity and lack of experience, for example, young persons; specific provisions to ensure the health and safety of these groups

PPE

The last resort, when all other protective measures have failed, or an interim measure until a 'safe place' strategy can be put into operation; PPE to be 'suitable' in terms of the risks it is designed to protect against and for the person for whom it is provided; employees to be made aware of the limitations of PPE

Safe behaviour

Regular supervision to ensure safe behaviour at work; disciplinary procedures in the event of unsafe behaviour, for example, horseplay, dangerous working practices, failure to use/wear PPE; potential for human error and the consequences

Raising and maintaining awareness

Induction training; measures to maintain awareness of hazards; information, instruction and training; use of safety propaganda, for example, safety posters; supervision requirements

REACTIVE STRATEGIES

Feedback

Information obtained following the investigation of accidents, incidents and ill-health; meaningful interpretation of accident and ill-health statistical information; incorporation of feedback information into future 'safe place' strategies.

Minimising the effects of injury

First aid provisions; arrangements for hospitalisation of injured employees; rehabilitation following injury.

Emergency planning

Arrangements for dealing with emergencies, such as a major escalating fire, explosion, sudden release of toxic substances, evacuation procedures; competent persons to oversee evacuation; disaster plan; liaison with external emergency services; shelter arrangements; dealing with casualties.

SAFETY MONITORING

Safety monitoring is a proactive strategy aimed at assessing and evaluating safety performance within an organisation. It implies the use of a range of techniques such as safety inspections, safety audits, safety surveys, safety tours and safety sampling exercises. In certain cases, the use of simple checklists to ensure conformance with safety standards prior to, and during, work activities may be sufficient. The various forms of safety monitoring are dealt with next.

Safety inspections

This form of monitoring is a scheduled or unscheduled inspection of a workplace or part of a workplace, such as a factory, office, workshop, construction site or a public building. It may be carried out by a manager, safety adviser, SR or an enforcement officer, such as an environmental health officer.

The principal objective of a safety inspection is to identify hazards with a view to making recommendations for the prevention or control of the risks arising from those hazards. This form of monitoring may also examine maintenance standards, working practices, environmental conditions and compliance with legal requirements and written safe systems of work.

A safety inspection is, in effect, a general examination of the situation in a workplace at a specific time rather than the in-depth approach taken by a safety survey. As with any form of safety monitoring, it is vital that the objectives of the monitoring system are clearly defined and the outcome of the inspection, in terms of recommendations for future action, is acted upon by management.

Trade-union appointed SRs are entitled to undertake safety inspections of the workplace at agreed frequencies and in specific situations under the SRSCR 1977.

Safety surveys

A safety survey can take a number of forms. It may involve the close scrutiny of a number of critical areas of operation, such as the implementation of defined electrical safety procedures, manual handling arrangements or procedures for dealing with hazardous substances across an organisation. Alternatively, it may take the form of an in-depth study of all health and safety-related activities in a workplace or within an organisation with a number of separate locations.

Safety surveys examine a range of issues, such as the effectiveness of health and safety management, environmental working conditions, occupational health and hygiene procedures, the very broad field of accident prevention and the current system for providing information, instruction, training and supervision.

At the completion of the survey, management are presented with a written safety survey report incorporating immediate, short-term, medium-term and long-term recommendations. Implementation of these recommendations is monitored on a regular basis by the safety surveyor, who produces progress reports for consideration by management.

Safety audits

Successful Health and Safety Management (Health and Safety Executive, 1991) defines a safety audit as 'the structured process of collecting independent information on the efficiency, effectiveness and reliability of the total safety management system and drawing up plans for corrective action'.

RoSPA defines a safety audit as 'the systematic measurement and validation of an organisation's management of its health and safety programme against a series of specific and attainable standards'.

Broadly, a safety audit subjects each area of an organisation's activities to a systematic critical examination with the objective of minimising injury and other forms of loss. It examines, for instance, the quality and extent of documentation, including the organisation's Statement of Health and Safety Policy, risk assessments, Permits to Work, contractors' safety regulations and procedures for providing employee safety information. Most particularly, an audit examines current health and safety management systems, management and employee attitudes to health and safety, prevention and control procedures and training arrangements.

Whilst there is no standard format for a safety audit, audits can be designed to cover aspects of particular significance to an organisation, such as the management of hazardous substances, safety procedures for employees working away from base and specific health protection arrangements, in addition to the more general issues that apply to all workplaces.

A specimen safety audit is shown at **FIG. 4**.

Safety tours

A safety tour is generally taken to mean an unscheduled examination of a workplace or work area, largely directed at assessing whether current safety procedures are being applied and maintained. A safety tour can be undertaken by a particular group of people, such as the immediate manager accompanied by SRs and/or safety committee members. The purpose of the exercise may be to ensure that fire protection and housekeeping measures are being observed, PPE is being worn correctly, safe systems of work are being implemented and display screen equipment users are using their workstations correctly.

A safety tour tends to be a spontaneous activity as opposed to a safety audit or survey, which may be planned some time ahead. It is common practice for members of a safety committee to undertake a safety tour prior to a meeting with a view to drawing attention to the activities of the committee and seeking views of employees on current issues relating to health and safety.

Safety sampling

This technique is designed to measure, by random sampling, the accident potential in a specific workplace, or at a particular process or work activity, by identifying safety defects or omissions. It entails the use of a safety sampling document that lists specific aspects to be observed and assessed, for example, machinery safety, electrical safety, housekeeping, the use of hazardous substances and lift truck operations. Each of these aspects for consideration is numerically ranked or graded according to its significance and a maximum number of points is awardable for each aspect.

This system of safety monitoring is particularly appropriate in organisations operating a number of comparable workplaces, such as shops, supermarkets, workshops, offices, manufacturing units, distribution centres and depots. By measuring specific aspects of safety performance and the allocation of points for same, it is possible to compare performance at individual locations and develop future strategies for improvement across the organisation. Safety sampling, fundamentally, monitors the overall effect of a safety programme.

A typical safety sampling document is shown at **FIG. 5**.

Checklist systems

Where there is a need to monitor specific aspects of safety performance, such as those relating to fire protection or the correct use of hazardous substances, perhaps on a daily basis, many organisations operate a simple checklist system. In this case, a trained person, such as a supervisor, undertakes this check in his area on a daily or weekly basis using the checklist. Such a system relies heavily on the conscientious use of the checklist, regular revisions to same, and the effectiveness of the action taken where there is a deviation from the items indicated in the checklist.

SPECIMEN SAFETY AUDIT FIG. 4

DOCUMENTATION

Legislation	YES	NO
1. Are all managers aware of the health and safety legislation applying to the organisation's activities and workplaces?		
2. Is this legislation available to management and employees?		
3. Have all relevant Approved Codes of Practice, HSE Guidance Notes and internal codes of practice been studied by managers with a view to ensuring compliance?		

Formal documentation	YES	NO
4. Is there are formally established Statement of Health and Safety Policy?		
5. Does the existing Statement of Health and Safety Policy meet current conditions in the workplace and/or work activities?		
6. Are the 'organisation and arrangements' to implement the Policy still adequate?		
7. Is there a named director or senior manager with overall responsibility for health and safety?		
8. Have the hazards and precautions necessary on the part of employees and other persons been identified and recorded?		
9. Do all job descriptions adequately describe individual responsibilities and accountabilities for health and safety, including appointed competent persons?		
10. Do written safe systems of work exist for hazardous activities?		
11. Is Permit to Work documentation available and used?		
12. Has a suitable and sufficient assessment of the risks to employees and other persons been undertaken, recorded and brought to the attention of other persons?		
13. Have risk assessors been trained in risk assessment techniques?		
14. Have other risk assessments in respect of: ♦ substances hazardous to health ♦ risks to hearing		

Formal documentation	YES	NO
♦ workplaces and/or work activities and/or work groups ♦ work equipment ♦ personal protective equipment ♦ manual handling operations ♦ display screen equipment ♦ fire been made, recorded where appropriate and brought to the attention of employees and other persons where necessary?		
15. Is there a current fire certificate?		
16. Is there a record of inspections of means of escape in the event of fire, fire appliances, fire alarms, warning notices, fire and smoke detection equipment?		
17. Are there records of inspection and maintenance of the workplace, equipment, including machinery guards and safety devices, safety systems and devices?		
18. Are all certificates of test and examination available, eg lifting equipment, pressure systems?		
19. Are all licences available eg to store petroleum spirit?		
20. Are there formal workplace health and safety rules and procedures which are promoted and enforced?		
21. Are these rules and procedures documented in a way which is comprehensible and relevant to employees and others?		
22. Are disciplinary procedures for unsafe behaviour clearly documented and known to employees and others?		
23. Is there a formal emergency procedure?		
24. Have competent persons been trained in implementing the emergency procedure?		
25. Is documentation available for the recording of injuries, near misses, damage only accidents, occupational diseases, ill-health and scheduled dangerous occurrences?		
26. Are health and safety instructions and training records maintained?		

Formal documentation	YES	NO
27. Are there documented procedures for regulating the activities of, contractors, visitors and other persons working on site?		
28. Is hazard reporting documentation available to employees and other persons?		
29. Is there a documented planned preventative maintenance system to cover the workplace, work equipment, systems and devices?		
30. Are written cleaning schedules produced and implemented?		

Health and Safety Systems	YES	NO
31. Have competent persons been appointed and adequately trained on the basis of identified and assessed risks?		
32. Are the roles, functions, responsibilities and accountabilities of, competent persons clearly identified in writing?		
33. Are there arrangements for specific forms of safety monitoring, e.g. safety inspections, safety tours, safety audits		
34. Is there an effective system for measuring and monitoring individual management performance on health and safety issues?		
35. Are systems established for the formal investigation of accidents, occupational ill-health, near misses and dangerous occurrences?		
36. Do investigation procedures produce results which can be used to prevent future accidents?		
37. Are the causes of accidents, ill-health, near misses and dangerous occurrences analysed in terms of failure of established systems of work?		
38. Is a hazard reporting system in operation?		
39. Are employees and other persons on site aware of the need to report hazards to management?		
40. Is a system for preventing and controlling damage to structural items, machinery, vehicles, etc in operation?		
41. Is the system for consultation with trade union safety Representatives and/or employees clearly established?		

Health and Safety Systems	YES	NO
42. Are the role, constitution and objectives of the safety committee clearly identified and established?		
43. Are procedures for appointing or electing safety committee members clearly identified?		
44. Are the available facilities, including training arrangements, known to committee members?		
45. Are the capabilities of employees as regards health and safety taken into account when entrusting them with tasks?		
46. Are First Aid arrangements adequate?		
47. Are all First Aid personnel adequately trained and retrained?		
48. Are formal procedures covering sickness absence known to all employees?		
49. Is there a procedure for regulating sickness absence?		
50. Are managers aware of the current sickness absence rate?		
51. Do current arrangements ensure that health and safety implications are considered at the design stage of projects?		
52. Is there a formally-established health and safety budget?		

Prevention and Control Procedures	YES	NO
53. Are formal inspections of workplaces, work equipment, access equipment, electrical equipment and appliances, storage equipment, warning systems, First Aid boxes, resuscitation equipment, welfare amenity areas, etc undertaken regularly?		
54. Are machinery guards and safety devices examined on a regular basis?		
55. Is a Permit to Work system operated where there is a high degree of foreseeable risk?		
56. Are fire and emergency procedures practised on a regular basis?		
57. Where specific fire hazards are identified, are they dealt with under current fire protection arrangements?		

Prevention and Control Procedures	YES	NO
58. Are all items of fire protection equipment and alarms tested, examined and maintained on a regular basis?		
59. Are all fire exits and escape routes marked, kept free from obstruction and operational?		
60. Are all fire appliances correctly labelled, sited and maintained?		
61. Are the requirements of cleaning schedules monitored?		
62. Is housekeeping of a high standard, eg material storage, waste disposal, removal of spillages?		
63. Are all gangways, stairways, fire exits, access and egress points to the workplace maintained and kept clear?		
64. Is environmental monitoring of temperature, lighting, ventilation, humidity, radiation, noise and vibration undertaken on a regular basis?		
65. Is health surveillance of persons exposed to assessed risks undertaken on a regular basis?		
66. Are local exhaust ventilation systems examined, tested and maintained according to legal requirements?		
67. Is monitoring of personal exposure to assessed health risks undertaken on a regular basis?		
68. Are arrangements for the storage and handling of hazardous substances adequate?		
69. Are all hazardous substances identified and correctly labelled, including transfer containers?		
70. Is the appropriate personal protective equipment available?		
71. Is the PPE worn or used by employees consistently when exposed to risks?		
72. Are storage facilities for items of PPE provided?		
73. Are welfare amenity provisions ie sanitation, hand washing, shower, clothing storage, facilities for taking meals, adequate?		

Information, Instruction and Training	YES	NO
74. Is the information provided by manufacturers and suppliers of articles and substances for use at work adequate?		
75. Do employees and other persons have access to this information?		
76. Is the means for promoting health and safety at work adequate?		
77. Is effective use made of safety propaganda eg posters?		
78. Do current safety signs meet the requirements of the Safety Signs Regulations 1980 and the Health and Safety (Safety Signs and Signals) Regulations 1996?		
79. Are safety signs adequate in terms of the assessed risks?		
80. Are fire instructions prominently displayed?		
81. Is the 'Health and Safety Law – What You Should Know' poster prominently displayed?		
82. Are hazard warning systems adequate?		
83. Are the individual training needs of employees are other persons assessed on a regular basis?		
84. Is health and safety training for employees undertaken: ♦ at the induction stage ♦ on their being exposed to new or increased risks because of: ♦ transfer or change in responsibilities ♦ the introduction of new work equipment or a change respecting existing work equipment ♦ the introduction of new technology ♦ the introduction of a new system of work or change in an existing system of work?		
85. Is the above training: ♦ repeated periodically ♦ adapted to take account of new or increased risks ♦ carried out during working hours?		
86. Is specific training undertaken regularly for First Aid staff, lift truck drivers, crane drivers and others exposed to risks?		
87. Are selected employees trained in the correct use of fire appliances?		

FINAL QUESTION	YES	NO
Are you satisfied that your organisation is as safe and healthy as you can reasonably make it, or that you know what action must be taken to achieve that state?		
ACTION PLAN		
1.*Immediate Action*		
2.*Short-term Action (1 month)*		
3.*Medium-term Action (6 months)*		
4.*Long-term Action (2 years)*		
Date_____ **Auditor**_____		

FIG. 5

SAFETY SAMPLING EXERCISE			LOCATIONS				
	EXERCISE	TIME	1	2	3	4	5
1.	Fire prevention	Max 20					
2.	Housekeeping	Max 20					
3.	Access & egress	Max 10					
4.	Welfare amenities	Max 20					
5.	Machinery and plant	Max 20					
6.	Electrical safety	Max 20					
7.	Personal protection	Max 10					
8.	Structural safety	Max 20					
9.	Environmental factors	Max 20					

FIG. 5

SAFETY SAMPLING EXERCISE			LOCATIONS				
EXERCISE		**TIME**	**1**	**2**	**3**	**4**	**5**
10.	Public protection	Max 10					
11.	Mechanical handling	Max 10					
12.	Manual handling	Max 10					
13.	Hazardous substances	Max 20					
14.	Work at heights	Max 10					
15.	Internal storage	Max 20					
16.	Hand tools	Max 10					
17.	Working practices	Max 20					
18.	Deliveries	Max 10					
19.	Office	Max 20					
20.	External	Max 10					
SCORES		**MAX 300**	**TOTALS**				

ACTION PLAN	YES	NO
1.Immediate Action		
2.Short-term Action (14 days)		
3.Medium-term Action (6 months)		
4.Long-term Action (2 years)		
Sampling Officer_____ **Date**_____		

ACCIDENT REPORTING, RECORDING AND INVESTIGATION

Apart from the duties on employers to report certain certain types of injury, occupational diseases and incidents to the enforcing authority, i.e. HSE, local authority, the investigation of all forms of loss-producing incident is an important strategy in accident prevention. Investigation provides feedback on the direct and indirect causes of these incidents, which can be integrated in future safety strategies.

REPORTING OF INJURIES, DISEASES AND DANGEROUS OCCURRENCES REGULATIONS 1995

These regulations lay down the requirements for the reporting of death, certain types of injury and occupational disease, incidents involving gas appliances and certain incidents listed in the Schedule to the regulations known as 'dangerous occurrences'.

Definitions

The following definitions are significant.

Specified major injury or condition

This means:
- (a) fracture of the skull, spine or pelvis;
- (b) fracture of any bone:
  - (i) in the arm or wrist, but not a bone in the hand; and
  - (ii) in the leg or ankle, but not a bone in the foot;
- (c) amputation of:
  - (i) a hand or foot; and
  - (ii) a finger, thumb or toe, or any part thereof, if the joint or bone is completely severed;
- (d) the loss of sight of an eye, a penetrating injury to the eye, or a chemical or hot metal burn to the eye;
- (e) either injury (including burns) requiring immediate medical treatment, or loss of consciousness, resulting in either case from an electric shock from any electrical circuit or equipment, whether or not due to direct contact;
- (f) loss of consciousness resulting from lack of oxygen;
- (g) decompression sickness (unless suffered during an operation to which the Diving Operations at Work Regulations 1981 apply) requiring immediate medical treatment;
- (h) either acute illness requiring medical treatment, or loss of consciousness, resulting in either case from absorption of any substance by inhalation, ingestion or through the skin;
- (i) acute illness requiring medical treatment where there is reason to believe this resulted from exposure to a pathogen or infected material; and
- (j) any other injury which results in the person injured being admitted immediately into hospital for more than 24 hours.

FIG. 6

Report of an injury or dangerous occurrence

Filling in this form
This form must be filled in by an employer or other responsible person.

Part A

About you
1 What is your full name?

2 What is your job title?

3 What is your telephone number?

About your organisation
4 What is the name of your organisation?

5 What is its address and postcode?

6 What type of work does the organisation do?

Part B

About the incident
1 On what date did the incident happen?

/ /

2 At what time did the incident happen?
(Please use the 24-hour clock, eg 0600)

3 Did the incident happen at the above address?

Yes ☐ Go to question 4

No ☐ Where did the incident happen?

☐ elsewhere in your organisation – give the name, address and postcode

☐ at someone else's premises – give the name, address and postcode

☐ in a public place – give details of where it happened

If you do not know the postcode, what is the name of the local authority?

4 In which department, or where on the premises, did the incident happen?

Part C

About the injured person
If you are reporting a dangerous occurrence, go to Part F.
If more than one person was injured in the same incident, please attach the details asked for in Part C and Part D for each person.

1 What is their full name?

2 What is their home address and postcode?

3 What is their home phone number?

4 How old are they?

5 Are they
☐ male?
☐ female?

6 What is their job title?

7 Was the injured person (tick only one box)
☐ one of your employees?
☐ on a training scheme? Give details:

☐ on work experience?
☐ employed by someone else?
Give details of the employer:

☐ self-employed and at work?
☐ a member of the public?

Part D

About the injury
1 What was the injury? (e.g. fracture, laceration)

2 What part of the body was injured?

3 Was the injury (tick the one box that applies)

☐ a fatality?

☐ a major injury or condition? (see accompanying notes)

☐ an injury to an employee or self-employed person that prevented them doing their normal work for more than three days?

☐ an injury to a member of the public, which meant they had to be taken from the scene of the accident to a hospital for treatment?

4 Did the injured person (tick all the boxes that apply)

☐ become unconscious?

☐ need resuscitation?

☐ remain in hospital for more than 24 hours?

☐ none of the above.

Part E

About the kind of accident
Please tick the one box that best describes what happened, then go to Part G.

☐ Contact with moving machinery or material being machined

☐ Hit by a moving, flying or falling object

☐ Hit by a moving vehicle

☐ Hit something fixed or stationery

☐ Injured while handling, lifting or carrying

☐ Slipped, tripped or fell on the same level

☐ Fell from a height
How high was the fall?

metres

☐ Trapped by something collapsing

☐ Drowned or asphyxiated

☐ Exposed to, or in contact with, a harmful substance

☐ Exposed to fire

☐ Exposed to an explosion

☐ Contact with electricity or an electrical discharge

☐ Injured by an animal

☐ Physically assaulted by a person

☐ Another kind of accident (describe it in Part G)

Part F

Dangerous occurrences
Enter the number of dangerous occurrence you are reporting. (The numbers are given in the Regulations and in the notes that accompany this form.)

Part G

Describing what happened
Give as much detail as you can. For instance:
• the name of any substance involved
• the name and type of any machine involved
• the events that led to the incident
• the part played by any people.
If it was a personal injury, give details of what the person was doing. Describe any action that has since been taken to prevent a similar incident. Use a separate piece of paper if you need to.

☐☐☐☐ ☐

Part H

Your signature

Signature

Date
/	/

Where to send the form
Please send it to the enforcing authority for the place where it happened. If you do not know the enforcing authority, send it to the nearest HSE office.

For official use
Client number   Location number   Event number

☐ INV REP ☐ Y ☐ N

Reportable disease

This is a disease specified in column 1 of Schedule 2 of the regulations and involving any one of the activities specified in the corresponding entry in column 2 of that Schedule.

TABLE 1 : EXAMPLES OF REPORTABLE DISEASES

	COLUMN 1	COLUMN 2
	DISEASE	**WORK ACTIVITY**
18.	**Hepatitis**	Work involving exposure to human blood products or body secretions or excretions
19.	**Legionellosis**	Work on or near cooling systems, which are located in the workplace and use water; or work on hot water service systems located in the workplace, which are likely to be a source of contamination
25.	**Tetanus**	Work involving contact with soil likely to be contaminated by animals
41.	**Occupational dermatitis**	Work involving exposure to any of the following agents: (a) epoxy resin systems (b) formaldehyde and its resins (c) metalworking fluids (d) chromate (hexavalent or derived from trivalent chromium) (e) cement, plaster or concrete (f) acrylates and methacrylates (g) colophony (rosin) and its modified products (h) glutaraldehyde (i) merecaptobenzothiazole, thiurams, substituted paraphenylene-diamines and related rubber processing chemicals (j) biocides, antibacterials, preservatives or disinfectants (k) organic solvents (l) antibiotics and other pharmaceuticals and therapeutic agents (m) strong acids, strong alkalis, strong solutions (e.g. brine) and oxidising agents including domestic bleach or reducing agents (n) hairdressing products including in particular dyes, shampoos, bleaches and permanent waving solutions (o) soaps and detergents (p) plants and plant-derived material including in particular especially the daffodil, tulip and chrysanthemum families, the parsley family (carrots and parsnips, parsley and celery), garlic and onion, hardwoods and the pine family (q) fish, shellfish or meat (r) sugar or flour (s) any other known irritant or sensitising agent including in particular any chemical bearing the warning "may cause sensitisation by skin contact" or "irritating to the skin"

Duties of the responsible person

The responsible person (see definition below) must forthwith send a report to the enforcing authority, i.e. HSE or local authority on the approved form (Form 2508A) wherever a person suffers from one of these diseases.

Dangerous occurrences

This is an occurrence that arises out of or in connection with work and is of a class specified in Part 1 of Schedule 1 of the regulations. Examples of dangerous occurrences are:

4. explosion, collapse or bursting of any pressure vessel, including a boiler or boiler tube, in which the internal pressure was above or below atmospheric pressure, which might have been liable to cause the death or, or any of the injuries or conditions covered by Regulation 3(2) to, any person or which resulted in stoppage of the plant involved for more than 24 hours; and

7. a collapse or partial collapse of any scaffold that is more than five metres high, which results in a substantial part of the scaffold falling or overturning; and where the scaffold is slung or suspended, a collapse or partial collapse of the suspension arrangements (including any outrigger) that causes a working platform or cradle to fall more than five metres.

The responsible person

In the case of a reportable injury or disease:

♦ involving an employee at work – the employer; and

♦ involving a person undergoing training for employment – the person whose undertaking makes the immediate provision of that training.

In any other case, the person for the time being having control of the premises in connection with the carrying on by him of any trade, business or undertaking (whether for profit or not) at which, or in connection with the work at which, the accident, disease or dangerous occurrence happened.

'Work'

This term is defined as meaning work as an employee, as a self-employed person or as a person undergoing training for employment (whether or not under any scheme administered by the Manpower Services Commission).

Regulation 3 – Duty to notify and report fatal and major injuries and dangerous occurrences

Where any person, as a result of an accident arising out of or in connection with work, dies or suffers any of the specific major injuries or conditions, or where there is a dangerous occurrence, the responsible person shall:

♦ forthwith notify the enforcing authority by quickest practicable means; and

♦ within ten days send a report thereof to the enforcing authority on a form approved for this purpose (Form 2508).

Where a person at work is incapacitated for work of a kind that he might reasonably be expected to do, either under his contract of employment or, if there is no such contract, in the normal course of his work, for more than three consecutive days (excluding the day of the

FIG. 7

Report of a case of disease

Filling in this form
This form must be filled in by an employer or other responsible person.

Part A

About you

1 What is your full name?

2 What is your job title?

3 What is your telephone number?

About your organisation

4 What is the name of your organisation?

5 What is its address and postcode?

6 Does the affected person usually work at this address?

Yes ☐ Go to question 7

No ☐ Where do they normally work?

7 What type of work does the organisation do?

Part B

About the affected person

1 What is their full name?

2 What is their date of birth?

/ /

3 What is their job title?

☐ ☐ ☐

4 Are they

☐ male?

☐ female?

5 Is the affected person (tick one box)

☐ one of your employees?

☐ on a training scheme? Give details:

☐ on work experience?

☐ employed by someone else? Give details:

☐ other? Give details:

Part C

The disease you are reporting

1 Please give:

- the name of the disease, and the type of work it is associated with; or
- the name and number of the disease (from Schedule 3 of the Regulations – see the accompanying notes).

2 What is the date of the statement of the doctor who first diagnosed or confirmed the disease?

/ /

3 What is the name and address of the doctor?

Part D

Describing the work that led to the disease

Please describe any work done by the affected person, which might have led to them getting the disease.

If the disease is thought to have been caused by exposure to an agent at work (eg a specific chemical) please say what that agent is.

Give any other information that is relevant.

Give your description here

Continue your description here

Part E

Your signature

Signature

Date

/ /

Where to send the form
Please send it to the enforcing authority for the place where it happened. If you do not know the enforcing authority, send it to the nearest HSE office.

For official use
Client number   Location number   Event number

INV REP ☐ Y ☐ N

accident but including any days that would not have been working days) because of an injury (other than a specified major injury) resulting from an accident at work, the responsible person shall within ten days of the accident send a report thereof to the enforcing authority on the form approved for this purpose (Form 2508).

Regulation 4 – Duty to report the death of an employee

Where an employee, as a result of an accident at work, has suffered a specified major injury or condition that is the cause of his death within one year of the date of the accident, the employer shall inform the enforcing authority in writing of the death as soon as it comes to his knowledge, whether or not the accident has been reported previously.

Regulation 5 – Duty to report a case of disease

Where a person at work suffers from a reportable disease, the responsible person shall forthwith send a report thereof to the enforcing authority on the form approved for this purpose (Form 2508A). This requirement applies only if:

♦ in the case of an employee or a person undergoing training, the responsible person has received a written statement prepared by a registered medical practitioner diagnosing the disease as one of the reportable diseases; or

♦ in the case of a self-employed person, that person has been informed by a registered medical practitioner that he is suffering from the disease so specified.

Regulation 6 – Reporting of gas incidents

Whenever a conveyor of flammable gas through a fixed pipe distribution system, or a filler, importer or supplier (other than by means of retail trade) of a refillable container containing liquefied petroleum gas receives notification of any death or any major injury that has arisen out of or in connection with the gas distributed, filled, imported or supplied, as the case may be, by that person, he/she must forthwith notify the HSE of the incident and within 14 days send a report on the approved form (Form 2508G).

Whenever an employer of self-employed person who is a member of the class of person approved by the HSE for the purposes of paragraph (3) of the **Gas Safety (Installation and Use) Regulations 1994** (i.e. a CORGI registered gas installation business) has in his/her possession sufficient information for it to be reasonable for him/her to decide that a gas fitting or any flue or ventilation used in connection with that fitting, by reason of its design, construction, manner of installation, modification or servicing, is or has been likely to cause death, or any major injury, by reason of:

♦ accidental leakage of gas;

♦ inadequate combustion of gas; and

♦ inadequate removal of the products of combustion of gas

must within 14 days send a report of it to the HSE on the approved form (Form 2508G) unless he/she has previously reported such information.

Regulation 7 – Duty to keep records

The responsible person shall keep a record of:

(a) any event that is required to be reported under Regulation 3, i.e. specified major injury or condition or dangerous occurrence; and

(b) any case of disease required to be reported under Regulation 5.

The records shall be kept at the place where the work to which they relate is carried on or if that is not reasonably practicable, at the usual place of business of the responsible person and an entry in either of such records shall be kept for at least three years from the date on which it is made.

In the case of (a) above, the following particulars shall be kept in records of any event that is reportable under Regulation 3:

1. date and time of the accident or dangerous occurrence;
2. the following particulars of the person affected:
   (a) full name;
   (b) occupation;
   (c) nature of the injury or condition;
3. place where the accident or dangerous occurrence occurred; and
4. a brief description of the circumstances.

In the case of (b) above, the following records shall be kept of instances of the diseases specified in Schedule 2 and reportable under Regulation 5:

1. date of diagnosis of the disease;
2. occupation of the person affected; and
3. name and nature of the disease.

Regulation 11 – Defence in proceedings for an offence contravening the regulations

It shall be a defence in proceedings against any person for an offence under these regulations for that person to prove that he was not aware of the event requiring him to notify or send a report to the enforcing authority and that he had taken all reasonable steps to have all such events brought to his notice.

Retention of forms

As part of the recording requirements, Forms 2508 and 2508A should be maintained by employers for at least 12 months.

ACCIDENT BOOKS

1. Under the Social Security Act 1975, employees must notify their employer of any accident resulting in personal injury in respect of which benefit may be payable. Notification may be given by a third party if the employee is incapacitated.
2. Employees must enter the appropriate particulars of all accidents in an accident book (Form BI 510). This may be done by another person if the employee is incapacitated. Such an entry is deemed to satisfy the requirements in paragraph 1 above.
3. Employers must investigate all accidents of which notice is given by employees. Variations in findings of this investigation and the particulars given in the notification must be recorded.
4. Employers must, on request, furnish the Department for Work and Pensions with such information as may be required relating to accidents in respect of which benefit may be payable, for example, Forms 2508 and 2508A (RIDDOR).
5. Employers must provide and keep readily available an accident book in an approved form in which the appropriate details of all accidents can be recorded. Such books, when completed, should be retained for three years after the date of the last entry.

For the purposes of the above, the appropriate particulars should include:

♦   name and address of injured person;

♦   date and time of the accident;

♦   place where the accident happened;

♦   cause and nature of injury; and

♦   name and address of any third party giving notice.

The accident book must be made freely available to all employees, and employers should monitor entries on a regular basis.

INVESTIGATION PROCEDURES

Investigation by employers of the direct and indirect causes of injury-producing accidents and occupational ill-health is a reactive strategy in safety management. The investigation of incidents, namely accidents that do not result in death or personal injury but may have the potential for same, or incidents that result in property damage or other form of loss, must also be considered.

Effective investigation should identify the causes, both direct and indirect, and the mistakes that may have led to an accident or incident. It should provide information or feedback for incorporation in future health and safety strategies directed at preventing recurrences.

A number of important points may arise as a result of the investigation process:

♦   the accident may have resulted form a breach of statute or regulations by the organisation, the accident victim, the manufacturers and/or suppliers of articles and substances for use at work, or other persons, such as contractors;

♦   the injury or ill-health may be reportable to the enforcing authority under RIDDOR;

♦   the injury or ill-health could form the basis for a civil action based on negligence against the organisation by an employee, member of the public, contractor's employee or other persons;

♦   there may be evidence of damage to plant and equipment, resulting in the need for repair or replacement, with possible delays in replacement;

♦   in most cases, there will be a need for some form of remedial action with a view to preventing a recurrence; and

♦   it is not the purpose of accident investigation to apportion blame, however, this may eventually emerge as a result of investigation.

Practical accident investigation

In any serious accident situation, such as a fatal accident, an accident resulting in major injury, such as fractures, amputations, loss of an eye, or where there has been a scheduled dangerous occurrence, such as the collapse of a crane or scaffold, speed of action is essential. This is particularly the case when it comes to identifying and interviewing witnesses and injured persons. It must be appreciated that information gathered in the period immediately following such an event may well be crucial in any criminal or civil proceedings arising many months after the event.

The following procedure is recommended for the sort of events outlined above:

♦   Establish the facts as quickly and completely as possible with regard to;

♦   the work activity that resulted in the accident;

- environmental factors, such as the level of lighting;
- the particular plant, machinery, work practice or system of work involved; and
- the sequence of events leading to the accident.

- Use an instant camera to take photographs of the scene of the accident prior to any clearing up or remedial action that may follow the accident.
- Draw sketches and take measurements, where necessary, with a view to producing a scale drawing of the events leading up to the accident.
- List the names of all witnesses, namely, those who saw, heard, felt or smelt anything; interview witnesses thoroughly in the presence of a third party, taking care to issue a formal caution prior to any statement being made. Do not prompt or lead any witness.
- Evaluate the facts, and individual witnesses' versions of same, as to accuracy, reliability and relevance.
- Endeavour to arrive at conclusions as to the causes of the accident on the basis of the relevant facts established.
- Examine closely any contradictory evidence. Never dismiss a fact that does not fit in with the rest. Find out more.
- Learn fully about the system of work, working procedure, work activity or work process involved. Consider the people involved in terms of their ages, training, experience and level of supervision, and the nature of the work, for example, routine, sporadic or incidental.
- In certain cases, it may be necessary for items of work equipment, such as lifting appliances, machinery, vehicles and hand tools to be examined by a specialist, for example, a consultant engineer.
- Produce a report for the employer emphasising the causes of the accident and remedies to prevent a recurrence, including any changes necessary to working practices, processes or systems of work.
- In complex accident situations, it may be necessary to establish an investigating committee comprising, for example, a senior manager, technical specialists, health and safety specialist and representatives of the work force, for example, trade union SR.

STATISTICAL DATA

The use of statistics is an important feature of health and safety management, provided the limitations of the data produced are recognised. In particular, largely due to the well-recognised under-reporting of accidents and ill-health, they may not be a true indicator of health and safety performance.

The principal use of statistical data is in the indication of trends in injury and ill-health experience within an organisation.

The following rates are used:

Frequency rate $= \dfrac{\text{Total number of accidents}}{\text{Total number of man-hours worked}} \times 100{,}000$

Incident rate $= \dfrac{\text{Total number of accidents}}{\text{Number of persons employed}} \times 1{,}000$

Severity rate $= \dfrac{\text{Total number of days lost}}{\text{Total number of man-hours worked}} \times 1{,}000$

Mean duration rate	=	Total number of days lost
		Total number of accidents
Duration rate	=	Number of man-hours worked
		Total number of accidents
Sickness absence rate	=	Total man-days lost through sickness x 100
		Total man-days worked

RISK ASSESSMENT

Risk assessment is the cornerstone of much modern protective legislation, for example, health and safety, food hygiene. Under MHSWR and other regulations, such as the COSHH Regulations, the Noise at Work Regulations and the Food Safety (General Food Hygiene) Regulations, employers must undertake risk assessments.

'Risk', 'hazard' and 'danger' – the distinction

In the study and implementation of risk assessment procedures, it is important to have clear definitions of these terms.

'Risk'

This term has been defined in a number of ways:

♦ the chance of loss or injury;
♦ a chance of bad consequences;
♦ exposure to the chance of injury or loss;
♦ the probability of harm, damage or injury; and
♦ the probability of a hazard leading to personal injury and the severity of that injury.

Risk variables

Risk may be encountered at all levels of human existence, both in the work situation and in general life. Risk may be present at:

♦ **personal level**, for example, the risk of contracting dermatitis through unsafe handling of solvents;
♦ **group level**, for example, the risk of a family being killed in a road accident;
♦ **larger group level**, for example, the risk of a town being devastated by an accident at a chemical plant; and
♦ **global level**, for example, the risk of nuclear war.

'Hazard'

A hazard is defined as:

♦ a situation of risk or danger;
♦ a situation that may give rise to personal injury; and
♦ the result of a departure from the normal situation with the potential to cause injury, damage or loss.

'Danger'

This is defined as:

♦ liability or exposure to harm; and
♦ a thing that causes peril.

Individual perception of risk

Human perception is based on the five senses – sight, hearing, touch, taste and smell. No two people, however, perceive risk in the same way, an individual's perception of risk being affected by factors such as attitude to danger, sensory perception, motivation, personality, past experience and the level of arousal, together with individual skill, knowledge and experience. For instance, what may be considered a high-risk situation to one person, such as climbing a ladder or working on a roof, may be considered routine to another.

WHAT IS RISK ASSESSMENT?

References to the risk variable above, show that risk is concerned with factors such as:
♦ the probability or likelihood of an adverse event, such as human injury, arising;
♦ the predicted severity of the outcome, in terms of injury, disease, damage or other form of loss;
♦ the number of people exposed to the risk at any one time; and
♦ the frequency of the risk arising, for example, permanently present, hourly, daily, weekly, every five years, etc.

On this basis, a risk assessment should take into account the above factors. However, risk assessment is not a precise science. Fundamentally, it is a prediction exercise based on the identification of hazards, the measurement and evaluation of the risks arising from these hazards, taking into account current legal requirements (the 'relevant statutory provisions') that relate to the hazards in question. A risk assessment should also incorporate an outcome, or series of outcomes, in terms of the preventive and protective measures necessary to either prevent or control exposure to the identified and evaluated risks.

APPROVED CODE OF PRACTICE TO THE MANAGEMENT OF HEALTH AND SAFETY AT WORK REGULATIONS

Under the MHSWR there is an absolute duty on employers to undertake 'a suitable and sufficient risk assessment'. (See chapter 2) Details on risk assessment procedures are outlined in the HSC ACOP to the regulations, the principal features of which are shown below, and also in **'Five Steps to Risk Assessment** (Health and Safety Executive, 1999).

General principles and purpose of risk assessment

Regulation 3 requires all employers and self-employed people to assess the risks to workers and any others who may be affected by their work or business. This will enable them to identify the measures they need to take to comply with health and safety law. All employers should carry out a systematic general examination of the effects of their undertakings, their work activities and the condition of the premises. Those who employ five or more employees should record the significant findings of that risk assessment.

A risk assessment is carried out to identify the risks to health and safety to any person arising out of, or in connection with, work or the conduct of their undertaking. It should identify how the risks arise and how they impact on those affected. This information is needed to make decisions on how to manage those risks so that the decisions are made in an informed, rational and structured manner, and the action taken is proportionate.

A risk assessment should usually involve identifying the hazards present in any working environment or arising out of commercial and work activities, and evaluating the extent of the risks involved, taking into account existing precautions and their effectiveness.   In this ACOP:

(a)   a **hazard** is something with the potential to cause harm (this can include articles, substances, plant or machines, methods of work, the working environment and other aspects of work organisation);

(b)   a **risk** is the likelihood of potential harm from that hazard being realised. The **extent of the risk** will depend upon:

   ♦   the likelihood of that harm occurring;

   ♦   the potential severity of that harm, i.e. of any resultant injury or adverse health effect; and

   ♦   the population that might be affected by that hazard, i.e. the number of people who might be exposed.

The purpose of the risk assessment is to help the employer to determine what measures should be taken to comply with the employer's duties under the **relevant statutory provisions** and Part II of FPWR.   This covers the general duties under the HSWA, the requirements of Part II of the FPWR and the more specific duties in the various acts and regulations (including these regulations) associated with the HSWA.   Once the measures have been determined in this way, the duty to put them into effect will be defined in the statutory provisions.   For example, a risk assessment on machinery would be undertaken under these regulations, but the PUWER 1998 determine what precautions must be carried out.

Suitable and sufficient

A suitable and sufficient risk assessment should be made.   'Suitable and sufficient' is not defined in the regulations.   In practice, it means the risk assessment should do the following:

(a)   the risk assessment should identify the risks arising from or in connection with work.   The level of detail in a risk assessment should be proportionate to the risk. Once the risks are assessed and taken into account, insignificant risks can usually be ignored, as can risks from routine activities associated with life in general, unless the work activity compounds or significantly alters those risks.   The level of risk arising from the work activity should determine the degree of sophistication of the risk assessment:

   ♦   for small businesses presenting few or simple hazards, a suitable and sufficient risk assessment can be a very straightforward process based on informed judgement and reference to appropriate guidance;

   ♦   in many intermediate cases the risk assessment will need to be more sophisticated;

   ♦   large and hazardous sites will require the most developed and sophisticated risk assessments, particularly where there are complex or novel processes; and

   ♦   risk assessments must also consider all those who might be affected by the undertaking, whether they are workers or others, such as members of the public;

(b)   employers are expected to take reasonable steps to help themselves identify risks, for example, by looking at appropriate sources of information, such as relevant legislation, appropriate guidance, supplier manuals and manufacturers' instructions and reading trade press, or seeking advice from competent sources. The risk assessment should include only what an employer could reasonably be expected to know; they would not be expected to anticipate risks that were not foreseeable; and

(c)   the risk assessment should be appropriate to the nature of the work and should identify the period of time for which it is likely to remain valid. This will enable employers to recognise when short-term measures need to be reviewed and modified, and to put in place medium- and long-term controls where these are necessary.

For activities where the nature of the work may change fairly frequently or the workplace itself changes and develops (such as a construction site), or where workers move from site to site, the risk assessment might have to concentrate more on the broad range of risks that can be foreseen.

Risk assessment in practice

There are no fixed rules about how a risk assessment should be carried out; indeed it will depend upon the nature of the work or business and the types of hazards or risks.

Where employees of different employers work in the same workplace, their respective employers may have to cooperate to produce an overall risk assessment.

In some cases, employers may make a first rough assessment to eliminate from consideration those risks on which no further action is needed. This should also show where a fuller assessment is needed, if appropriate, using more sophisticated techniques. Employers who control a number of similar workplaces may produce a model (generic) risk assessment reflecting the core hazards and risks associated with these activities. Model assessments may be applied by employers or managers at each workplace, but only if they:

(a)   satisfy themselves that the model assessment is appropriate to their type of work; and

(b)   adapt the model to the detail of their own actual work situations, including any extensions necessary to cover hazards and risks not referred to in the model.

A risk assessment should:
 ♦   ensure the significant risks and hazards are addressed;
 ♦   ensure all aspects of the work activity are reviewed, including routine and non-routine activities;
 ♦   take account of the non-routine activities;
 ♦   take account of the management of incidents such as interruptions to the work activity, cleaning arrangements, etc;
 ♦   be systematic in identifying hazards and looking at risks, whether one risk assessment covers the whole activity or the assessment is divided up;
 ♦   take account of the way in which the work is organised, and the effects this can have on health;
 ♦   take account of risks to the public; and
 ♦   take account of the need to cover fire risks.

1. Identifying the hazards

Identify who might be harmed by the hazard, including employees, other workers in the workplace and members of the public. You should identify groups of workers who might particularly be at risk, such as young or inexperienced workers, new and expectant mothers, night workers, homeworkers, those who work alone and disabled staff.

2. Evaluating the risks from the identified hazards

You need to evaluate the risks from the identified hazards. Of course, if there are no hazards, there are no risks. Where risks are already controlled in some way, the effectiveness of those controls needs to be considered when assessing the current extent of risk that remains. You also need to:

♦ **observe the actual practice:** this may differ from the works manual, and the employees concerned or their SRs should be consulted;

♦ **address what actually happens** in the workplace or during the work activity; and

♦ take account of **existing preventive or precautionary measures;** if existing measures are not adequate, ask yourself what more should be done to reduce risk sufficiently.

3. Recording

Employers with five or more employees must record the significant findings of their risk assessment. This record should present an effective statement of the hazards and risks, which then leads management to take the relevant actions to protect health and safety.

This record may be in writing or recorded by other means.

The significant findings should include:

♦ a record of the preventive and protective measures in place to control the risks;

♦ what further action, if any, needs to be taken to reduce risk sufficiently; and

♦ proof that a suitable and sufficient assessment has been made.

4. Review and revision

The regulation requires employers to review and, if necessary, modify their risk assessments, since assessment should not be a once-and-for-all activity.

Assessment under other regulations

Where an employer is assessing a work situation or activity for the first time, an assessment is particularly useful to identify where a more detailed risk assessment is needed to fulfil the requirements of other regulations. An assessment made for the purpose of other regulations will partly cover the obligations to make assessments under these regulations.

PRINCIPLES OF PREVENTION

Regulation 4 of the MHSWR states:

'Where an employer implements any preventive and protective measures he shall do so on the basis of the principles specified in Schedule 1 to these regulations.'

Schedule 1 outlines the General Principles of Prevention, in effect a hierarchy of measures in descending order, namely:

♦ avoiding risks;

♦ evaluating the risks that cannot be avoided;

♦ combating the risks at source;

♦ adapting the workplace to the individual, especially as regards the design of workplaces, the choice of work equipment and the choice of working and production methods, with a view, in particular, to alleviating monotonous work and work at a pre-

determined work rate and to reducing their effects on health;
- ◆ adapting to technical progress;
- ◆ replacing the dangerous by the non-dangerous or the less dangerous;
- ◆ developing a coherent overall prevention policy that covers technology, organisation of work, working conditions, social relationships and the influence of factors relating to the working environment;
- ◆ giving collective protective measures priority over individual protective measures; and;
- ◆ giving appropriate instructions to employees.

A QUANTITATIVE APPROACH TO RISK ASSESSMENT

This approach involves the simple calculation of risk ratings for a range of identified hazards, taking into account factors of probability (or likelihood) and the severity of outcome, in terms of personal injury, damage to plant and facilities and other potential losses.

Each of the factors of probability and severity is estimated on a scale from 1 to 5 or 1 to 10 using specific tables.

TABLE 2: PROBABILITY FACTORS FOR IDENTIFIED HAZARDS

Probability index	Description
10	Inevitable
9	Almost certain
8	Very likely
7	Probable
6	More than even chance
5	Even chance
4	Less than even chance
3	Improbable
2	Very improbable
1	Almost impossible

TABLE 3: SEVERITY OF INJURY

Severity index	Description
10	Death
9	Permanent total incapacity
8	Permanent severe incapacity
7	Permanent slight incapacity
6	Absent from work for more than three weeks with subsequent recurring incapacity
5	Absent from work for more than three weeks but with subsequent complete recovery
4	Absent from work for more than three days but less than three weeks with subsequent complete recovery
3	Absent from work for less than three days with complete recovery
2	Minor injury with no lost time and complete recovery
1	No human injury expected

By use of the tables, a risk rating can be evaluated thus:

Risk rating = Probability X Severity of injury

which produces a risk rating scale from 1 to 100.

The urgency or priority of action in respect of identified risks can be evaluated by use of Table 4.

TABLE 4: PRIORITY OF ACTION SCALE

Risk rating	Priority of action
Below 20	No immediate action but keep under review
21 – 40	Action within one year
41 – 60	Action within one month
61 – 80	Action within one week
81 – 100	Immediate action; possible prohibition situation

The team approach

The evaluation of risk using the above technique is best undertaken on a team basis, the team comprising a senior manager, supervisor, safety adviser and worker representative. It is vital that the senior manager involved has sufficient authority and resources to instigate action, particularly when risk ratings are in excess of 60 in Table 4.

The system should be supported by a reporting and action procedure, which identifies:

♦ the risks;

♦ the assessed risk rating for each risk;

♦ the manager responsible for preventing or controlling exposure to the risk;

♦ the action required;

♦ the time specification for completion of action; and

♦ the procedure for monitoring the implementation of the risk control strategy.

KEY POINTS

♦ Safety monitoring is a proactive exercise directed at identifying hazards and specifying preventive and protective measures.

♦ Safety monitoring can take the form of audits, inspections, surveys, tours and sampling exercises.

♦ The reporting, recording and investigation of accidents and other loss-producing incidents is an important strategy in preventing similar events arising in the future.

♦ Procedures for the reporting of injuries and occupational ill-health are incorporated in RIDDOR.

♦ A clearly identified accident investigation procedure, particularly in the case of fatal and major injury accidents, is an essential feature of health and safety management.

♦ Risk assessment is the cornerstone of most modern protective legislation.

♦ All employers must undertake a suitable and sufficient assessment of the risks, first to which their own employees may be exposed whilst at work and, second, in respect of other people who may be affected by the activities of their undertakings.

♦ Only the significant findings of a risk assessment must be recorded.

♦ Although there is no standard format for a risk assessment, the procedure for risk assessment is outlined in the ACOP to the MHSWR and in '**5 Steps to Risk Assessment'** (Health and Safety Executive, 1999).

5 Human Factors and Safety

The 1990s saw considerable development in the study of human factors as a contributory cause in accidents at work. Under the MHSWR an employer must, when entrusting tasks to his/her employees, take into account their capabilities as regards health and safety. The term 'capability' is, of course, very broad and can be taken to include both physical capability and mental capability and could include the potential for human error when undertaking tasks.

However, human factors is not just about people and the way they perform at work. It examines the role of the organisation and the tasks that people undertake. It is further concerned with the need for organisations to develop and promote the right safety culture, ergonomic considerations, the communication process and the role of training in raising performance.

The subject of stress at work is dealt with later in a separate chapter.

WHAT ARE HUMAN FACTORS?

A system that has relied heavily on the enforcement of legal standards to bring about improvements in the physical conditions of workplaces has not always been successful in reducing accidents and occupational ill-health due to the failure of those concerned to examine the 'human factors' aspects of safety and accident prevention.

To this extent, the MHSWR 1992, for the first time in the history of health and safety legislation, brought in a human factors-related approach to occupational health and safety. Under these regulations, and the subsequent MHSWR 1999, an employer has an absolute duty, when entrusting tasks to his employees, to take into account their capabilities as regards health and safety.

HSE Guidance

Human factors in industrial safety (HSE, 1989) defines the term 'human factors' as 'covering a range of issues including:
- the perceptual, physical and mental capabilities of people and the interaction of individuals with their job and working environments;
- the influence of equipment and system design on human performance; and
- those organisational characteristics that influence safety-related behaviour'.

People at work are directly influenced by a number of factors, namely:
- the organisation;
- the job; and
- personal factors.

These are directly affected by:
- the system for communication within the organisation;
- training systems and procedures in operation;
all of which are directed at preventing human error.

FEATURES OF ORGANISATIONS

Organisations operate on the basis of a hierarchy, a chain of command from the most senior person, for example, chief executive, managing director, downwards to employees at different levels. In most cases, orders and directions pass down the system and information passes back up the system. Conflict in the selection and effectiveness of line managers can arise, foremen and supervisors frequently finding themselves in conflict for a number of reasons, including:

- differing motivations;
- misunderstanding of individual roles;
- differing cultures and objectives; and
- differing priorities and levels of commitment.

Formal organisations commonly demonstrate a number of weaknesses, most commonly communications failures. Moreover, they frequently ignore emotional factors in human behaviour and are frequently perceived as uncaring and lacking in interest or commitment to ensuring appropriate levels of safety, health and welfare for their employees.

Organisational characteristics which influence safety-related behaviour

There are a number of factors, features or characteristics of organisations that influence the way people behave at work, particularly with regard to implementing safe working procedures.

These organisational characteristics that influence safety-related behaviour include:

- the promotion of a positive safety climate in which health and safety is seen by both management and employees as being fundamental to the organisation's day-to-day operations, ie the creation of a positive safety culture;
- the need to ensure that policies and systems that are devised for the control of risk from the organisation's operations take proper account of human capabilities and fallibilities;
- commitment to the achievement of progressively higher standards that are demonstrated at the top of the organisation and cascade through successive levels of same;
- demonstration by senior management of their active involvement, thereby galvanising managers throughout the organisation into action; and
- leadership, where an environment is created that encourages safe behaviour.

THE JOB

Successful management of human factors and the control of risk involves the development of systems designed to take proper account of human capabilities and fallibilities. Tasks should be designed in accordance with ergonomic principles so as to take into account limitations in human performance. Matching the man to the job will ensure that he is not overloaded and that he makes the most effective contribution to the enterprise.

- **Physical match** includes the design of the whole workplace and working environment.
- **Mental match**, on the other hand, involves the individual's information and decision-making requirements, as well as his perception of tasks. Mismatches between job requirements and workers' capabilities provide the potential for human error.

Factors that influence compliance with health and safety practices

These are:

♦ the interaction of individuals with their job and the working environment; and
♦ the influence of equipment and system design on human performance.

The design of the job and working environment should be based on task analysis of the activities required of the operator. This provides the information for evaluating the suitability of tools and equipment, procedures, work patterns and the worker's physical and social surroundings. This should be followed by techniques such as job safety analysis, which forms the basis for the design of safe systems of work.

Major considerations in job design

These include:

♦ identification and comprehensive analysis of the critical tasks expected of individuals and appraisal of likely errors;
♦ evaluation of the required operator decision-making and the optimum balance between human and automatic contributions to safety actions;
♦ application of ergonomic principles to the design of man–machine interfaces, including displays of plant and process information, control devices and panel layouts;
♦ design and presentation of procedures and operating instructions;
♦ organisation and control of the working environment, including the extent of workspaces, access for maintenance work, and the effects of noise, lighting and thermal conditions;
♦ provision of the correct tools and equipment;
♦ scheduling of work patterns, including shift organisation, control of fatigue and stress, and arrangements for emergency operations and situations; and
♦ efficient communications, both immediate and over periods of time.

PERSONAL FACTORS

The study of personal factors is concerned with how behavioural factors such as attitude, motivation and training, together with the mental and physical capabilities of people can interact with health and safety issues. It is also concerned with the potential for human error. The various aspects of human behaviour are considered below.

ATTITUDE

Attitude can be defined in a number of ways:
'a predetermined set of responses built up as a result of experience of similar situations'
'a tendency to behave in a particular way in a particular situation'.

Attitudes held are directly connected with:

♦ a person's self-image;
♦ the influence of groups and the group norms established by groups; and
♦ opinions held, including superstitions, such as that relating to walking under a ladder.

Changing attitudes

One of the important functions of a manager is that of attempting to change attitudes of employees, particularly with regard to their adoption of safe working procedures. Listed below are important factors in attitude change.

The individual

People have their own particular opinions on a wide range of issues that are commonly based on past experience, their upbringing and their level of knowledge and understanding. Most people are resistant to change. These barriers to change may be associated with the individual level of conservatism, along with the degree of intelligence and extent of education. No two people are necessarily motivated in the same way to, for instance, behave safely. Others will blindly follow without question the views and opinions of those they respect. These factors must be considered when endeavouring to change attitudes.

Attitudes currently held

Here there is the problem of cognitive dissonance, the situation where a person holds an opinion that is not compatible with the facts, for instance the view that 'I have been doing this job man and boy and safety is all a matter of common sense'. Regrettably, many accidents are associated with overconfidence in undertaking potentially dangerous tasks.

Other factors affecting attitudes may be the potential for financial gain, which can bring about short-term attitude change, and the skills available to an individual. In the latter case, a person may hold the view that, as a trained operator, he knows what he is doing and is immune from accidents.

Situations

Group norms can have a direct influence on attitudes to the extent that an individual may change his attitude to a particular aspect of safety performance in order to remain accepted as a member of the group.

The influence of change agents, such as HSE inspectors and safety practitioners, and the sanctions that could be imposed, may be significant in bringing about attitude change but this may only be short-lived in some cases.

Again, the climate for change within an organisation may be sufficient to bring about changes in attitude, particularly if the attitude change is necessary to stay in a job.

Management example

Management example is, by far, the strongest of all motivators for bringing about changes in attitude. This may be in the operation of a particular safety procedure or in the use of PPE.

MOTIVATION

A motivator is something that provides the drive to produce certain behaviour or to mould behaviour.

Motivation and safety

Important factors for consideration in motivating people to better levels of safety performance are:

♦ joint consultation in planning the work organisation;

♦ the use of working parties and committees to define objectives, including those for health and safety;

♦ the attitudes currently held by management and employees;

♦ the communications system within the organisation; and

♦ the quality of leadership at all levels – management, trade unions, trade associations, government.

Planned motivation schemes

Planned motivation is a method by which the attitudes, and thereby the performance of people at work, can be improved.

Planned motivation schemes have been described as an 'industrial catalyst', a tool to maximise performance. Such schemes are used in many organisations to improve the performance of, for instance, directors, salesmen, line managers, and maintenance engineers.

Safety incentive schemes are a form of planned motivation. As such, they are designed to provide motivation by:

♦ identifying targets that can be rewarded if achieved; and

♦ making the rewards meaningful and attractive to the people concerned.

Any planned motivation scheme should always be viewed with care, however, in that such schemes may alter behaviour, but not necessarily attitudes held. They are most effective from a health and safety viewpoint where:

♦ people are restricted to one area of work activity, for example, a laboratory, workshop, shop;

♦ measurement of safety performance is relatively simple, perhaps by the use of checklists;

♦ there is regular stimulation or rejuvenation;

♦ support is provided by both management and trade unions; and

♦ the scheme is assisted and promoted through relevant training and the use of safety propaganda.

Important considerations for achieving success in safety incentive schemes are:

♦ linking with some form of safety monitoring, such as safety inspections or safety sampling exercises;

♦ the setting of correct, meaningful and achievable targets and objectives; and

♦ ensuring they are not linked with accident rates as this can discourage the reporting of accidents by employees.

Where these schemes are not regularly monitored, and promoted by management they can be short-lived due to people losing interest. In some cases, they may shift responsibility for health and safety from management to employees if the organisation of same is not carefully controlled.

PERCEPTION

Perception is the process by which people receive information. Visual perception is the most significant form, compared with the other forms of perception, ie hearing, touch, taste and smell.

Perceptual capabilities

How people perceive risk is associated with a number of behavioural factors – attitude, motivation, personality, perception, their ability to process information, memory, the extent of training received, the level of arousal and individual skills available.

No two people perceive risk in the same way. Past experience and the context in which the information or stimulus is presented are important.

HUMAN CAPABILITY

Successful management of human factors and the control of risk involves the development of systems designed to take account of human capabilities and fallibilities. On this basis, tasks should be designed in accordance with ergonomic principles so as to take into account limitations in human performance.

Matching the man to the job will ensure that he is not overloaded and that he makes the most effective contribution to the enterprise. This entails:

♦ **Physical match**

In addition to assessing physical capacity for a variety of tasks, this includes the design of the whole workplace and the working environment to achieve the best performance from people.

♦ **Mental match**

This should take into account the individual's information and decision-making requirements, as well as his perception of tasks.

Human limitations

Everyone has limitations that affect their performance. The following features of human performance can be a contributory factors in accidents.

♦ **Physical limitations**

Reach, lifting ability and capacity, skeletal features, sensory features (visual, aural) and energy level.

♦ **Physiological limitations**

Illness, the effects of drugs and medication, fatigue, the oxygen supply, environmental contaminants, such as fumes, gases, etc, the effect of alcohol, time zone adjustment, ageing and circadian (diurnal) rhythm.

♦ **Psychological limitations**

Ability, aptitude, knowledge, interests, personality, memory and motivation.

♦ **Psycho-social limitations**

Cultural context, group pressures, risk taking and situational influences.

HUMAN ERROR

Mismatches between job requirements and workers' capabilities provide the potential for human error, a contributory factor in accidents. In particular, limitations in human capacity to perceive, attend to, remember, process and act on information are all relevant in the context of human error.

Human factors in industrial safety (HSE, 1989) details a number of factors that can contribute to human error, which, in turn, can be significant causative features of accidents at work. These include the following.

Inadequate information

People do not make errors merely because they are careless or inattentive. Often they have understandable (albeit incorrect) reasons for acting in the way they do. One common reason is ignorance of the production processes in which they are involved and the potential consequences of their actions.

Lack of understanding

This often arises as a result of a failure to communicate accurately and fully the stages of a process that an item has been through. As a result, people make assumptions that certain actions have been taken when this is not the case.

Inadequate design

Designers of plant, processes or systems of work must always take into account human fallibility and never presume that those who operate or maintain plant or systems have a full and continuous appreciation of their essential features. Indeed, a failure to consider such matters is, itself, an aspect of human error.

Where it cannot be eliminated, error must be made evident or difficult. Compliance with safety precautions must be made easy. Adequate information on hazards must be provided. Systems should be 'fail-safe', that is, they should not produce unsafe modes of operation.

Lapses of attention

In some cases, an individual's intentions and objectives are correct and the proper course of action is selected, but a slip occurs in its performance. This may be due to competing demands for attention, which is limited. Paradoxically, highly skilled performers, because they depend upon the finely tuned allocation of their attention, to avoid having to think carefully about every minor detail, may be more likely to make a slip.

Mistaken actions

This is the classic situation of doing the wrong thing under the impression that it is correct. For example, the individual knows what needs to be done, but selects an inappropriate method to achieve it.

Misperceptions

Misperceptions tend to occur when a person's limited capacity to give attention to competing information under stress produces 'tunnel vision', or when a preconceived diagnosis blocks out sources of inconsistent information. There is a strong tendency to assume that an established pattern holds good so long as most of the indications are to that effect, even if there is an unexpected indication to the contrary.

Mistaken priorities

An organisation's objectives, particularly the relative priorities of different goals, may not be clearly conveyed to, or understood by, individuals. A crucial area of potential conflict is between safety and other objectives, such as output or the saving of cost or time. Misperceptions may then be partly intentional as certain events are ignored in the pursuit of competing objectives. When senior management's goals are not clear, individuals at any level in the organisation may superimpose their own.

Wilfulness

Wilfully disregarding safety requirements and rules is rarely a primary cause of accidents. Sometimes, however, there is a fine dividing line between mistaken priorities and wilfulness. Managers may need to be alert to the influences that, in combination, persuade employees and others to take, short cuts through the safety rules and procedures because, mistakenly, the perceived benefits, for example, increased production, outweigh the risks, and the fact that they have got away with in the past.

CLASSIFICATION OF HUMAN ERROR

There are several kinds of human error. They include the following.

Unintentional error

This may arise when an individual may fail to perform a task correctly, for example, operating a control or reading a gauge. These are typical slips or lapses, frequently associated with 'carelessness' or 'lack of attention to the task'.

Mistakes

In this situation, the person shows awareness of a problem but forms a faulty plan for its solution. He will thus carry out, intentionally but erroneously, actions that are incorrect and that may result in hazardous consequences. Typical examples are the operation and maintenance of plant and machinery and in assembly work. Failure to correct individual mistakes through instruction, training and supervision can lead to disaster situations.

Violations

In this case a person deliberately carries out an action that is contrary to a rule that is required organisationally, such as an approved operating procedure. Deliberate sabotage is an extreme example of a violation. Violations involve complex issues concerning conformity, communications, morale and discipline. In piece-work systems, the removal of machinery guards or the defeating of safety mechanisms in order to increase output and, therefore, remuneration, is a common violation.

Skill-based errors

These arise during the execution of a well-learned, fairly routine task. For instance, the probability of a skilled word processor operator striking the wrong key depends upon the nature and complexity of the material being keyed. Skill-based errors commonly occur amongst the more highly skilled members of the organisation, such as machine operators or fork lift truck drivers, who take the view that the skills they possess will automatically protect them from the risk of accidents. Such an attitude to work is accompanied by overconfidence in the task, which can lead to, particularly, machinery-related accidents.

Rule-based errors

These are the types of error that arise when a set of operating instructions or rules is used to guide a sequence of actions. Whilst most people follow the operating instructions for, for instance, a machine, some people may perceive the instructions as unnecessary and, over a period of time, develop their own 'short cuts' for its operation, frequently resulting in incorrect operation and the possibility of accidents.

Knowledge-based errors

These errors are also known as 'errors of general intention' and are the errors that arise when a choice decision has to be made between alternative plans of action. These types of error arise from the detailed knowledge of the system possessed by an individual, but the resulting 'mental model' may be incorrect. This type of error is particularly difficult to predict.

The elimination of human error

For the potential for human error to be eliminated or substantially reduced, all the above factors need consideration in the design and implementation of safe systems of work, processing operations, work routines and activities. Training and supervision routines should take account of these factors, along with the various aspects of human capability.

HUMAN FACTORS AND THE COMMUNICATION PROCESS

Sound levels of communication are an essential feature in the management of an organisation and in accident prevention.

What is communication?

To communicate means 'to impart or transmit' (Oxford Dictionary). Communication is the transfer of information, ideas, feelings, knowledge and emotions between one individual or group of individuals and another. The basic function is to convey meanings.

Objectives of communication

The objectives or goals of communication are:
- to understand others;
- to obtain clear reception and perception of information;
- to obtain understanding;
- to achieve acceptance, ie agreement, and commitment to ideas; and
- to facilitate or obtain effective human behaviour or action.

THE COMMUNICATION PROCESS

Communication involves both a communicator, the originator of the message, and a receiver, the recipient of the message. Communication commonly takes place in four phases or stages, thus:

1. the transmission or sending out of data, both cognitive data and emotional data;
2. receiving or perceiving the data;
3. understanding the data; and
4. acceptance of the data.

Barriers to communication

A number of barriers can arise at the various phases of the process, in particular:
- **Barriers to reception**

Reception of information can be influenced by:
(a) the needs, anxieties and expectations of the receiver/listener;
(b) the attitudes and values of the receiver; and
(c) environmental stimuli, for example, noise.

♦ **Barriers to understanding**

Understanding is a complex process and is affected by:

(a) the use of inappropriate language, for example, technical jargon;

(b) the extent to which the listener can concentrate on receiving the data, ie variations in listening skills;

(c) prejudgements made by the listener;

(d) the ability of the listener to consider factors that may be disturbing or contrary to his ideas or opinions, ie his degree of open mindedness;

(e) the length of the communication; and

(f) the degree of knowledge possessed by the listener.

♦ **Barriers to acceptance**

Acceptance of a communication is affected by:

(a) the attitudes and values of the listener;

(b) individual prejudices held by listeners;

(c) status clashes between the sender and the receiver; and

(d) interpersonal emotional conflicts.

COMMUNICATION WITHIN ORGANISATIONS

Many forms of communication exist within organisations.

Formal and informal communication

Communication that is officially inspired by directors and senior managers is often referred to as 'formal communication'. Communication that is, on the other hand, unofficial, unplanned and spontaneous is classified as 'informal communication'.

One-way and two-way communication

Communication may be one way, for example, safety instructions to employees from a manager, or two way, where, following transmission of a message, the views of certain persons are sought prior to the decision-making process.

Verbal, non-verbal and written communication

These forms of communication are significant. Communication may be by word of mouth (verbal communication), by the use of gestures, eye contact and terminal glances (non-verbal communication) and by the use of memoranda, letters and reports (written communication).

Intentional or unintentional communication

Communication may be intentional, ie consciously transmitted, or unintentional, where information is involuntarily transmitted.

Features of the communication process

Significant features of the communication process are:

♦ the actual lines or channels of communication; and

♦ the relative effectiveness of the different forms of communication.

The direction of communication

One-way communication

One-way communication, such as the giving of an order by a senior manager, may be appropriate in certain circumstances and is certainly faster than two-way communication. However, it does not permit any form of feedback from the receiver of the communication. One-way communication is used principally in the giving of directions, instructions and orders.

Two-way communication

This form of communication is far more effective. It gives people the chance to use their intelligence, to contribute knowledge, to participate in the decision-making process, to fulfil their creative needs and to express agreement or disagreement. It helps both the sender and the receiver to measure their standard of achievement and when both see that they are making progress, their joint commitment to the task will be greater.

Sound levels of two-way communication are essential in the operation of safe systems of work, in particular Permit to Work systems.

VERBAL COMMUNICATION

Verbal communication should not be treated solely in terms of the content of what is being said. It should incorporate all the other things being communicated, such as emotional attitudes, various non-verbal signals, such as eye gaze and body movements, each individual's perception of the other and the social context of the communication.
Fundamentally:

♦ A manager must ensure he tells his employees what they need to know. He should not leave it to them to 'read his mind' or 'pick up the necessary facts', particularly with regard to individual responsibilities for health and safety. He should ensure they are promptly and accurately informed of matters relevant to their work.

♦ Communication should be dispensed in small 'doses' as most people can take in only a limited amount of information at one time. Long and involved communications are seldom read or listened to and, if they are, they are rarely digested. Only a few important points should be communicated at a time.

♦ A manager should phrase his communications in simple direct style. Consideration must be given to the level of education and experience of employees and others. Even well-educated employees, however, are more likely to perceive the intended message correctly if it is phrased in the most straightforward manner.

Barriers to verbal communication

A number of problems can beset effective verbal communication. For instance:
♦ the communicator is unable to think clearly;
♦ there may be difficulties in decoding the message by the receivers;
♦ transmission of the message can be interrupted by noise or distractions;
♦ the receiver may exercise selectivity in reception, interpretation and retention of the information in the message;
♦ the receiver may simply not be listening to the message;
♦ an unsuitable environment, for example, workshop, construction site, may act as an

♦ impediment to good communication;
♦ there may be no perceptible reaction from the receiver of the message; and
♦ rumour fills the gap in the formal communication system, which is normally associated with the operation of the informal 'grape-vine' within the organisation.

NON-VERBAL COMMUNICATION

Non-verbal communication is an important feature of the total communication process. It has several functions.

♦ Non-verbal communication can give support to verbal communication in that:
  ♦ gestures can add to or emphasise words;
  ♦ terminal glances help with speech synchronisation;
  ♦ tone of voice and facial expression indicate the mood in which remarks are intended to be taken; and
  ♦ feedback on how others are responding to what is being said is obtained by non-verbal devices, for example, facial expressions.
♦ It can replace speech where speech is not possible.
♦ It can perform ritualistic functions in everyday life and can communicate complex messages in greeting and farewell ceremonies.
♦ It can express feelings we have about others, for example, like or dislike.
♦ It can express what condition we are in or feelings we have about others – happiness, anger, anxiety – although we may attempt to control them.
♦ It can be used to convey how we would like other people to see us, for example, by the way in which we present ourselves for public scrutiny.

COMMUNICATION ON HEALTH AND SAFETY ISSUES

Communication of the right kind has a vital part to play in health and safety as a participative process. The following aspects of communication are significant.

Safety propaganda

The use of posters, safety signs, exhibitions and other forms of repeating a specific message are important features in the safety communication process. Safety posters should be used to reinforce current health and safety themes, for example, the use of eye protection, correct manual handling techniques, and should be changed on a regular basis. To have the most impact, videos and films should be used as part of scheduled training activities, and not shown in isolation.

Safety incentive schemes

Various forms of planned motivation directed at rewarding good safety behaviour on the basis of formally agreed objectives and criteria have proved successful. Such schemes should not, however, be based on a reduction in accident rates, as this can restrict or reduce accident reporting by employees.

Safety incentive schemes must be accompanied by efficient communication of the results of the scheme and information surrounding the operation of the scheme. To be successful, senior management must have direct involvement and must monitor the progress of the scheme.

The reward element of a safety incentive scheme is important. This can take the form of general recognition within the organisation for best or improved performance in a number of ways. Under no circumstances should financial rewards, such as safety bonuses, feature in a safety incentive scheme.

Health and safety training

The health and safety communication featured in training exercises should incorporate sincerity, authority, confidence, accuracy and humour. There may be a need for the training of trainers in the various aspects of the training programme and in presentation techniques.

Management example

This is, perhaps, the strongest form of non-verbal communication and has a direct effect on attitudes to health and safety held by employees.

WRITTEN COMMUNICATION

This may be of a formal or informal nature, and generally takes the form of business letters, memoranda and internal e-mails and reports.

Business letters

Letters are generally sent to external organisations and individuals, either giving or requesting information. As a formal means of written communication, they must be laid out in a logical and concise manner.

Memoranda and internal e-mails

Generally, these comprise a few paragraphs and are an informal means of communication between members of an organisation. They should be simple and to the point.

Reports

A report is defined as 'a written record of activities based on authoritative sources, written by a qualified person and directed towards a predetermined group'. Reports tend to be of an impersonal nature. They state the facts or findings of the author, for example, following an accident investigation, make recommendations and, in some cases, seek approval for certain actions to be taken or not taken.

Reports provide information, formulate opinions and are directed at assisting people to make decisions. It is imperative, therefore, that a report should follow a logical sequence. It should state the facts unambiguously, be written with clarity and may be accompanied by diagrams, tables and photographs.

THE SIGNIFICANCE OF COMMUNICATION

Communication is the crucial link in successful integrative management. An essential requirement is that channels of communication remain open and are used.

Effective communication is also an important feature of health and safety practice. Lack of communication is a common contributory feature in accidents and other forms of adverse incident, such as a dangerous occurrence. Barriers to effective communication must be overcome if there is to be successful health and safety management in an organisation.

INFORMATION, INSTRUCTION AND TRAINING

The duty on employers to inform, instruct and train employees and others runs as a thread through all modern health and safety legislation. In some cases, as with the HSWA, the duty on employers is qualified by the term 'so far as is reasonably practicable'. In other cases, the duty is absolute or strict, as in the MHSWR.

'Information', 'instruction' and 'training' defined

These terms are not specifically defined in health and safety legislation. However, the giving of information implies the imparting of factual knowledge by one person to another. Under the MHSWR, any information provided by an employer to an employee must be 'comprehensible and relevant'.

'Instruction', on the other hand, involves actually telling people what to do and what not to do. It may incorporate an element of supervision to ensure they are doing it correctly all the time, for example, the use of PPE.

'Training' is defined by the Department of Employment as 'the systematic development of attitude, knowledge and skill patterns required by an individual to perform adequately a given task or job'.

HEALTH AND SAFETY TRAINING

Health and safety training is essential to reduce the number of accidents and incidents of ill-health caused by work. Effective training results in competent employees and contributes to developing a positive health and safety culture. It also ensures compliance with legislation and reduces costs associated with accidents and occupational ill-health, including non-insurable costs such as damaged products, lost production and low morale.

Training involves the provision of knowledge and the implementation of that knowledge. This requires the commitment of managers, the provision of adequate resources and facilities, effective supervision and motivation of employees. It is best delivered through a comprehensive training programme, the steps of which are as follows.

Identification of training needs

A training need is said to exist when the optimum solution to an organisation's problem is through some form of training.

To ensure compliance with duties under the HSWA and MHSWR, training needs should be identified with particular reference to:

♦ induction training for recently recruited employees, including how to work safely, first aid arrangements, fire and evacuation procedures;

♦ orientation training of existing employees on, for instance, promotion, change of job, their exposure to new or increased risks, appointment as a competent person, the introduction of new plant, equipment and technology, and prior to the introduction of safe systems of work; and

♦ refresher training directed at maintaining competence of employees for a range of tasks.

Determine the knowledge and skills required to work in a safe and healthy way. Identify the existing levels and skills of employees. The difference represents the content of the training. Examination of accident records and near misses or cases of ill-health together with training requirements highlighted by risk assessments will be useful. The views of employees or their representatives should be taken into account.

The awareness training needs of directors and managers and the specific training of supervisors will also need to be determined.

Development of training plan and programme

Training programmes must be coordinated with the current human resources needs of the organisation. The first step in the development of any training programme is that of defining the training objectives. These objectives or aims may be related to individual job specifications in the case of new training, or by detailed job analysis and job safety analysis in respect of existing jobs.

As the amount of training required may be considerable it should be prioritised. Legal requirements, induction and awareness training and training in areas where inadequate information would result in serious harm should be given the greatest priority, as should training for employees who change jobs.

Implementation of the training plan and programme

Decisions must be made as to the extent of both active and passive learning systems to be incorporated in the programme. Training must be relevant, interesting, accurate, credible and easy to understand. Examples of active learning systems are coaching or on-the-job training, group discussion, role-play exercises, computer-based/e-learning programmes, and field exercises, such as safety inspections. Active learning methods reinforce what has already been taught on a passive basis. They are the more effective form of training once the basic framework is established. There is more chance of bringing about attitude change on the part of trainees and their level of interest is maintained

Passive learning systems incorporate lectures, and the use of visual material, such as computer-based programmes, videos and slides. With a passive learning system the basic objective is that of imparting knowledge. The principal advantage of these systems is that they provide frameworks and can be used where large numbers of trainees are involved. The best results will be achieved if training is delivered to employees in 'bite-sized chunks'.

Evaluation of results

There are five questions that need to be asked at this stage.

- ♦ Have the training objectives been met? If so, could they have been met more effectively?
- ♦ Are employees competent and working in a safe and healthy manner?
- ♦ Has the number of accidents and near misses reduced?
- ♦ Is there any additional training required?

Operator training in most organisations will need an appraisal of the skills necessary to perform a given task successfully, that is, efficiently and safely. It is normal, therefore, to incorporate the results of this appraisal in the basic training objectives.

One objective of health and safety training is that of bringing about long-term attitude change on the part of trainees, which must be linked with job performance. Any decision as to whether training objectives have been met cannot be taken immediately the trainee recommences work. It may be several months, or even years, before a valid evaluation can be made after continuous assessment of the trainee.

The answer to the second question can only be achieved through feedback from personnel monitoring the performance of trainees, and from the trainees themselves. This feedback can usefully be employed in setting objectives for further training, in the revision of training programmes and in the analysis of training needs for all groups within the organisation.

Training courses

Training is required for many different groups, such as:

- directors and senior managers;
- line managers;
- supervisors;
- appointed safety specialists;
- trade union SRs and representatives of employee safety;
- employees; and
- employees of contractors.

All these groups will need training but the training input and content will vary from group to group. In the case of trade union SRs, for instance, the union may lay down a specific syllabus for this training based on HSE Guidance under the SRSCR 1977. Some organisations also have specific safety training requirements for line managers in order to meet an industry or nationally agreed standard.

Moreover, in recent years, enforcement officers have been seeking evidence of trainees having attended accredited courses, such as those run under the auspices of IOSH, NEBOSH, the Chartered Institute of Environmental Health (CIEH), the Royal Environmental Health Institute of Scotland (REHIS) and the Royal Society for the Promotion of Health (RSPH).

Courses currently offered through these organisations include the following.

IOSH

Working Safely – One-day Course
Managing Safely – Five-day Course
Safety for Senior Executives – One-day
Directing Safely (for small to medium-sized businesses) – One-day

Further information is available from IOSH, The Grange, Highfield Drive, Wigston, Leicestershire LE18 1NN. Tel: 0116 257 3100, Fax: 0116 257 3101. Web site: www.iosh.co.uk Email: saftrain@iosh.co.uk

NEBOSH

National General Certificate in Occupational Safety and Health – minimum 80 hours
National Certificate in Construction Safety and Health – 80 to 100 hours
Specialist Diploma in Environmental Management – 80 to 100 hours
National Diploma in Occupational Safety and Health – Part 1: minimum 172 hours and Part 2: minimum 194 hours

Further information is available from NEBOSH, The Grange, Highfield Drive, Wigston, Leicestershire LE18 1NN. Tel: 0116 257 3100, Fax: 0116 257 3101. Web site: www.nebosh.co.uk Email: info@nebosh.co.uk

CIEH

Foundation Course – One-day
Risk Assessment - Principles and Practice – One-day
Safety for Supervisors – Three days
Intermediate Health and Safety – Three days
Advanced Health and Safety – Five days

Further information is available from Chadwick House Group Limited, Chadwick Court, 15 Hatfields, London SE1 8DJ. Tel: 020 7928 6006 Fax: 020 7827 5865. Web site: www.cieh.org.uk

REHIS

Elementary Health and Safety Course – minimum six hours
Intermediate Health and Safety Course – minimum 16 hours
Certificate in Advanced Health and Safety Course – minimum 36 hours

Further information is available from REHIS, 3 Manor Place, Edinburgh EH3 7DH Scotland. Tel: 0131 225 5444. Web site: www.royal-environmental-health.org.uk

RSPH

Foundation Certificate in Health and Safety in the Workplace – nine guided learning hours
Advanced Diploma in Health and Safety in the Workplace – 36 guided learning hours

Further information is available from RSPH, RSH House, 38A St. George's Drive, London SW1V 4BH. Tel: 020 77630 0121. Web site: www.rsph.org

Fitting the delegate to the course

Many organisations find it difficult to decide on the appropriate health and safety courses for different levels of management, for employees and for specialists, such as safety advisers. Whilst there is little or no guidance on this issue from the authorities, the following recommendations are made.

♦ **Directors and senior managers**
IOSH Safety for Senior Executives or Directing Safely

♦ **Line managers**
IOSH Managing Safely
CIEH Advanced Health and Safety Certificate
CIEH Intermediate Health and Safety Certificate
CIEH Safety for Supervisors
CIEH Risk Assessment: Principles and Practice
REHIS Intermediate Health and Safety Course
REHIS Certificate in Advanced Health and Safety Course
RSPH Advanced Diploma in Health and Safety in the Workplace

♦ **Employees (including employees of contractors)**
IOSH Working Safely
CIEH Foundation Certificate in Health and Safety
REHIS Elementary Health and Safety Course
RSPH Foundation Certificate in Health and Safety in the Workplace

♦   **Safety officers/advisers**

It is always difficult to recommend the level of training necessary for safety specialists. Much will depend upon the type of undertaking or organisation, the number of employees, the number of locations, hazards specific to the operations and ancillary aspects, such as the current claims history and past involvement with enforcement agencies.

Under MHSWR 1999, the safety adviser would generally be classed as the competent person who provides assistance to the employer within the context of Regulation 7 and, on this basis, should have the appropriate skill, knowledge and experience to undertake this task.

The following levels of training are recommended for safety advisers:

♦   large multi-site organisations with a wide variety of risks – NEBOSH National Diploma;

♦   organisations with high-risk premises and processes – NEBOSH National Diploma;

♦   medium-risk workplaces – NEBOSH National General Certificate, IOSH Managing Safely or CIEH/REHIS/RSPH Advanced Health and Safety Certificate; and

♦   low-risk workplaces – IOSH Managing Safely, CIEH/REHIS/RSPH Advanced Health and Safety Certificate or Intermediate/Supervising Health and Safety Certificate.

KEY POINTS

♦   The study of human factors is essential to ensuring sound levels of health and safety management.

♦   Employees are directly influenced by the organisation, the job and personal behavioural factors, such as attitude and motivation.

♦   A range of characteristics of organisations can influence safety-related behaviour;

♦   The careful design of jobs is critical to improving safety performance.

♦   People have a wide range of attitudes to health and safety, some of which may need to be changed in order to ensure safe working.

♦   It may be possible to improve safety performance through planned motivation schemes.

♦   In the design of safe working procedures and systems, the potential for human error must be considered.

♦   All employees must be provided with appropriate information, instruction and training on health and safety-related issues.

6 Ergonomics

Ergonomics is defined as 'the scientific study of work'. It is concerned with the design and specification of working environments in which people, by virtue of the physical and mental limitations, receive maximum consideration. Designing tasks, equipment and workstations to suit the operator can reduce operator error, accidents and ill-health.

This chapter provides an overview of the subject, with particular reference to the design of the 'man-machine interface', the total working system, design ergonomics and anthropometry.

HUMAN FACTORS ENGINEERING

Ergonomics has further been defined as:

(a) the scientific study of the interrelationships between people and their work; and

(b) the study of the relationship between man, the equipment with which he works and the physical environment in which this 'man-machine system' operates.

It is concerned with the design and specification of working environments in which people receive prime consideration. As a scientific discipline, it is very much involved with the process of fitting the task to the individual. On this basis it interacts with several disciplines including physiology, anatomy, environmental factors and various areas of engineering. Furthermore, this 'man-machine interface' is relevant in the design of work layouts, displays and controls on machinery and equipment, safe systems of work and in the setting of work rates.

Under the MHSWR employers must take into account physical and mental capabilities and limitations of people as regards health and safety when allocating tasks. This may entail recourse to ergonomic principles with particular reference to psychological factors, such as learning, individual skills, perception, attitudes, vigilance, information processing and memory. Physical factors, such as strength, stamina and body dimensions may also need to be considered, together with environmental factors and the potential for environmental stress, associated with extremes of temperature, for instance.

Fundamentally, the application of ergonomic principles seeks to maximise human performance and, at the same time, eliminate as far as possible the potential for human error in a wide range of tasks.

Principal considerations

A number of factors must be considered in an ergonomics-based approach to health and safety at work.

The human system

All people are different in terms of their mental and physical capabilities. This is particularly apparent when considering:

(a) the physical elements of body dimensions, strength and stamina; coupled with

(b) the psychological elements of learning, perception, personality, attitude, motivation and reaction to given situations.

Other factors that have a direct effect on performance include the level of knowledge and the degree of training received, personal skills and experience of the work.

Environmental factors

This area examines the effect on the human system of the working environment with regard to, for instance, the layout of the working area and the amount of workspace available and, in particular, the effects on people of environmental stressors, such as extremes of temperature, lighting and humidity, together with exposure to noise and vibration.

The man-machine interface

The man-machine interface involves the passing of information from the machine to the operator through the various display elements associated with the machine, such as a pressure gauge, temperature gauge or revolution counter. Similarly, commands are given to a machine through the use of a range of controls, such as a foot pedal, switch or steering wheel.

The study of displays, control and other design features of machinery, vehicles, automation and communication systems, with a view to reducing operator error and stress on the operator, is a significant feature of ergonomics.

Factors such as:

(a) the location, reliability, ease of operation and distinction of controls; together with;

(b) the identification, ease of reading, sufficiency, meaning and compatibility of displays, are all important in ensuring correct and safe operation of machinery of all types.

TABLE 5 : A COMPARISON BETWEEN MAN AND MACHINES

Advantages	Disadvantages
Man	**Machines**
Adaptable and flexible	Relatively inflexible
Can detect minute stimuli and assess small changes	Can detect if programmed but not assess small changes
Can interpolate and use judgement	Cannot interpolate or use judgement
Can synthesise and learn from experience	Cannot synthesise nor learn from experience
Machines	**Man**
Can operate in hostile environments	Lower capability in hostile environments
Fast response to emergency signals	Slow response to emergency signals
Can apply large forces smoothly	Can apply large forces coarsely
Information storage: short-term memory	Easily distracted; limited short-term memory
Perform routine repetitive tasks reliably	Not reliable to perform repetitive tasks
Compute fast and accurately	Compute slowly and inaccurately
Can operate for long periods without maintenance	Suffer relatively soon from fatigue and monotony

Task characteristics

All tasks, no matter how simple they may appear, incorporate a number of characteristics. These may include:

♦ the frequency of operation of, for instance, a handwheel;
♦ the repetitiveness of the task;
♦ the actual workload;
♦ the criticality of the task in terms of its accurate completion according to a prescribed procedure;
♦ the duration of the task; and
♦ its interaction with other tasks as part of a manufacturing process.

Task demands

The specific characteristics of a task will make a number of physical and mental demands on the operator. Certain tasks may require a high degree of physical strength and stamina, such as manual handling operations. Other tasks, such as inspection tasks, will need a high degree of attention and vigilance in ensuring that products meet specifications and that rejects are removed from the process at a particular stage. Most tasks require some form of memory utilisation.

Instructions and procedures

The quality of both verbal and written instructions to operators and the formal work procedures have a direct relationship with the potential for human error. As such, instructions and written procedures should be clear, comprehensible, relevant, unambiguous, sufficient in detail, easy to use, accurate and produced in an acceptable format. Instructions and procedures should be subject to regular revision, particularly where operators are experiencing difficulties with their interpretation and use.

Task stressors

Many tasks, through a failure by the employer to consider the physical and mental needs of the operator, his level of intelligence, attitude and motivation, can be stressful. The following questions should be asked during the design of tasks and at the task analysis stage.

♦ Does the task isolate the operator, both visually and audibly, from fellow operators?
♦ Does the task put operators under pressure due to the need to complete same within a certain timescale?
♦ Does the task impose a higher level of mental and physical workload on people than normal?
♦ Is the task of a highly repetitive nature?
♦ Do the various tasks create conflict amongst employees?
♦ Do some tasks result in physical pain or discomfort, such as manual handling operations or working at low temperatures?
♦ Is there a risk of distraction in some critical tasks?
♦ Is there sufficient space available to undertake the work safely?
♦ Where a shiftwork system is in operation, does this system take account of the physical and mental limitations of employees?
♦ Where an incentive scheme is in operation, are the incentives offered seen as fair to all concerned?

The socio-technical factors

Socio-technical factors cover a wide range of considerations. They include:
- the social relationship between operators and how they work together as a group;
- group working practices;
- manning levels;
- working hours;
- the provision of meal and rest breaks;
- the formal and informal communication systems; and
- the rewards and benefits available.

Organisational features also come under this heading, such as:
- the actual structure of the organisation and the individual work groups;
- the allocation of responsibilities;
- the identification of authority for certain actions; and
- the interface between different groups.

THE TOTAL WORKING SYSTEM

Taking into account the factors mentioned above, it is quite common for the approach to ergonomics to be summarised under the concept of the 'Total Working System', which is broken down into four major elements as shown in Table below.

TABLE 6 : THE TOTAL WORKING SYSTEM	
Human characteristics	**Environmental factors**
Body dimensions Strength Physical and mental limitations Stamina Learning Perception Reaction	Temperature Humidity Lighting Ventilation Noise Vibration
Man-machine interface	**Total working system**
Displays Controls Communications Automation	Fatigue Work rate Posture Productivity Accidents Safety aspects Occupational ill-health

DESIGN ERGONOMICS

Design ergonomics is an area of ergonomic study concerned with the design and specification of the various features of the man-machine interface, in particular controls and displays.

Controls include various forms of manual controls to machinery and vehicles. Displays provide visual information to the user of the machinery, equipment or vehicle, such as a speedometer, pressure gauge or clock.

Important factors in the design of this man-machine interface are listed below.

Layout

Layout of working areas and operating positions should allow for free movement, safe access and egress, and unhindered visual and oral communication. Congested, badly-planned layouts result in operator fatigue and increase the potential for accidents.

Vision

The operator should be able to set and use controls and read dials with ease. This reduces fatigue and accidents arising from faulty or incorrect perception.

Posture

The more abnormal the working posture, the greater the potential for fatigue and long-term injury. Work processes and systems should be designed to permit a comfortable posture which reduces excessive job movements. This must be considered in the siting of controls and in the organisation of working systems, for example, assembly or inspection tasks.

Comfort

The comfort of the operator, whether driving a vehicle or operating machinery, is essential for his physical and mental well-being. Environmental factors directly affect comfort and should be given priority.

Principles of interface design

Separation

Physical controls should be separated from visual displays. The safest routine is achieved where there is no relationship between them.

Comfort

If separation cannot be achieved, control and display elements should be mixed to produce a system that can be operated with ease.

Order of use

Controls and displays should be set in the order in which they are used, for example, left to right for start up and the reverse direction for close down.

Priority

Where there is no competition for space, the controls most frequently used should be sited in key positions. Controls such as emergency stop buttons should be sited in a position that is most easily seen and reached.

Function

With large consoles, controls can be divided according to functions. Such a division of controls is found in power stations. This layout relies heavily on the operator and his speed of reaction. A well-trained operator, however, benefits from functional division of controls and the potential for human error is greatly reduced.

Fatigue

The siting of controls to suit the convenience of the operator is essential to reducing operator fatigue. In designing a layout for controls, the hand movements and body position of the operator should be observed and studied with a view to reducing or minimising excessive movements.

ANTHROPOMETRY

Anthropometry is a branch of ergonomics dealing with the study and measurement of body dimensions, the orderly treatment of resulting data and the application of this data in the design of workspace layouts and equipment.

This need to match the physical dimensions of people to the equipment they use was aptly demonstrated by the Cranfield Institute of Technology, who created 'Cranfield Man'.

Using a horizontal lathe, researchers examined the positions of controls and compared the locations of these controls with the physical dimensions of the average operator. Table 7 shows the side differences in the two sets of dimensions, which would clearly result in fatigue and an increased potential for error on the part of the operator.

TABLE 7 : PHYSICAL DIMENSIONS OF THE AVERAGE OPERATOR COMPARED WITH THOSE OF 'CRANFIELD MAN'

Average operator dimensions	Dimensions	Operator who would suit these controls
1.75m	Height	1.35m
0.48m	Shoulder width	0.61m
1.83m	Arm span	2.44m
1.07m	Elbow height	0.76m

According to the arrangement of controls to the horizontal lathe, the ideal person to operate same would have been a dwarf with a 2.44m arm span!

Anthropometric techniques have also been successfully employed in the design and location of physical guarding to machinery, with particular reference to the specification of distances at which physical barriers should be erected from identified danger points and the sizing of permissible openings in fixed guards.

ERGONOMICS AND HEALTH AND SAFETY

Ergonomics uses information about human abilities, attributes and limitations to ensure that work equipment, work activities and workplaces are designed to allow for these factors. It is about ensuring a good 'fit' between people and the things that they use.

"CRANFIELD MAN" FIG. 8

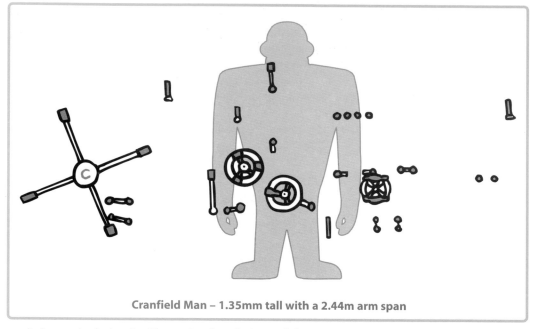

Cranfield Man – 1.35mm tall with a 2.44m arm span

It is particularly significant in the design of, for example, hand tools, control panels, workstation layouts and the chairs used by people operating display screen equipment.

People at work are affected by a range of stressors arising from poor workplace, environmental and equipment design that does not take into account their physical and mental limitations. In some cases, this can lead to accidents involving injury, together with health conditions, such as work-related upper limb disorders caused by repetitive manual activities.

Consideration of ergonomic factors at the design stage of work systems, workstations, machinery and hand tools, together with the regular monitoring of human performance, is an essential element of health and safety management.

KEY POINTS

♦ Ergonomics is the scientific study of work, the process of fitting the individual to the task.

♦ Under the MHSWR, employers must take into account physical and mental capacities and the limitations of employees when allocating tasks.

♦ Poor workplace design can result in stress on operators and an increased potential for human error.

♦ In the design of workstations it is necessary to examine the total working system.

♦ Design ergonomics is concerned with the design and specification of controls and displays with a view to producing the most efficient performance from operators.

♦ The layout of controls to work equipment should take into account the principles of anthropometry.

7 The Workplace

A well-organised workplace is a prerequisite for sound levels of health and safety at work. This chapter deals with the Workplace (Health, Safety and Welfare) Regulations (WHSWR) 1992 and the HSC ACOP with regard to the requirements for maintenance, structure and layout of workplaces, environmental factors and welfare amenity provisions. The requirements for safety signs in the workplace are also covered.

LEGAL REQUIREMENTS FOR WORKPLACES

The law relating to health, safety and welfare in workplaces is covered by general requirements under the HSWA and more specific requirements under the Workplace WHSWR 1992, along with other regulations dealing with, for instance, safety signs.

Health and Safety at Work etc Act 1974

Section 2 of the HSWA places a range of duties on employers with regard to the workplace. Apart from the general duty to ensure, so far as is reasonably practicable, the safety, health and welfare at work of all his employees [section 2(1)], an employer has extended duties thus:

♦ so far as is reasonably practicable as regards any place of work under the employer's control, the maintenance of it in a condition that is safe and without risks to health and the provision and maintenance of means of access to and egress from it that are safe and without such risks [Section 2(2)(d)]; and

♦ the provision and maintenance of a working environment for his employees that is, so far as is reasonably practicable, safe, without risks to health and adequate as regards facilities and arrangements for their welfare at work [Section 2(2)(e)].

It should be recognised that whilst the above duties under the HSWA are qualified by the term 'so far as is reasonably practicable', duties under the WHSWR are largely of an absolute or strict nature.

WORKPLACE (HEALTH, SAFETY AND WELFARE) REGULATIONS 1992

The duties on employers and the self-employed under these regulations are extensive and form the basis for ensuring health, safety and welfare in all workplaces (see definition of 'workplace' next page). Moreover, the duties under the WHSWR do not stand on their own. They must be read in conjunction with the more general duties placed on employers and the self-employed under MHSWR 1999 with particular reference to the undertaking of a suitable and sufficient risk assessment, the implementation of management systems, the appointment of competent persons and the operation of emergency procedures.

Important definitions

Traffic route means a route for pedestrian traffic, vehicles or both and includes any stairs, staircase, fixed ladder, doorway, gateway, loading bay or ramp.

Workplace means any premises or part of premises that are not domestic premises and are made available to any person as a place of work and includes:

(a) any place within the premises to which such a person has access while at work; and

(b) any room, lobby, corridor, staircase, road or other place used as a means of access to or egress from the workplace or where facilities are provided for use in connection with the workplace other than a public road.

The duty to maintain

Maintenance of the workplace is an important requirement. Read in conjunction with the duties under the MHSWR, this implies the need for formally documented planned preventive maintenance systems.

Maintenance of workplace, and of equipment, devices and systems
(Regulation 5 of the Workplace (Health, Safety and Welfare) Regulations)

The workplace and the equipment, devices and systems to which this regulation applies shall be maintained (including cleaned as appropriate) in an efficient state, in efficient working order and in good repair.

The equipment, devices and systems shall be subject to a suitable system of maintenance. This regulation applies to:

(a) equipment and devices, a fault in which is liable to result in a failure to comply with any of these regulations; and

(b) mechanical ventilation systems provided in pursuant of Regulation 6.

Specific duties on employers

The regulations impose specific duties on employers thus:

Environmental factors

♦ Ventilation must be effective and suitable to maintain comfort conditions.

♦ The temperature must be reasonable during working hours.

♦ Lighting must be 'suitable' in terms of the type of lighting and 'sufficient' with regard to the quantity of light provided for different tasks. Emergency lighting must be provided where failure of lighting may create danger.

♦ The workplace must be kept clean and surfaces (floors, walls, etc) must be capable of being kept sufficiently clean. There must be adequate control over refuse.

♦ Sufficient floor area and work space must be provided for employees.

♦ Both indoor and outdoor workstations must be suitable for the work carried out.

♦ Seats provided must be suitable for the person and for the work undertaken.

Structural safety

♦ Floors and traffic routes must be suitable for the purpose, in good repair and free from obstructions.

♦ Measures to prevent risks arising from falls and falling objects must be taken, including the marking of risk areas and the covering of tanks, pits, etc.

♦ Windows and transparent or translucent doors, gates and walls must be of safety material, or protected in certain cases, and be suitably marked where there may be a risk of physical contact.

♦ The design of windows, skylights and ventilators must be such that there is no risk of falling when opening, closing or adjusting, and must be suitably positioned.

- Windows must be capable of being cleaned safely, including the fitting of suitable devices to buildings to permit safe cleaning.
- Traffic routes must be organised in such a way as to ensure safe circulation by pedestrians and vehicles.
- Doors and gates must be suitably designed and constructed and fitted with appropriate safety devices to prevent injury.
- Escalators and moving walkways must function safely. Safety devices and emergency stop controls must be fitted.

Welfare amenity provisions

- Sanitary conveniences must be suitable and sufficient in number, adequately ventilated and lit, kept in a clean and orderly condition with separation of the sexes.
- Washing facilities must be suitable and sufficient in number, located in the vicinity of sanitary conveniences (and changing rooms if required) with hot and cold water supplies, cleaning and drying facilities. They must be ventilated and well lit and kept in a clean and orderly condition with separation of the sexes.
- The drinking water supply must be wholesome, readily accessible, conspicuously marked, with cups or drinking vessels provided unless from a jet supply.
- Accommodation for clothing must be suitable and sufficient, with adequate security for clothing not worn during working hours, and with separate accommodation for working clothes and clothes not worn during working hours in some cases. Facilities for drying clothing must be provided in a suitable location.
- Facilities for changing clothing must be suitable and sufficient, ensure privacy and with separation of the sexes.
- Facilities to rest and eat meals must be suitable and sufficient, including the provision of rest rooms or rest areas. There must be separation of smokers and non smokers, facilities for pregnant women and nursing mothers. Facilities must be provided for taking meals where meals are regularly eaten in the workplace.

THE WORKPLACE AND THE WORKING ENVIRONMENT

The design and control of the workplace and the environment in which people work is an important aspect of health and safety management. Environmental working conditions have a direct effect on safe behaviour at work, the degree of risk of contracting occupational diseases and/or sustaining injury, and on morale, management and employee relations, labour turnover and, ultimately, profitability.

Five aspects must be considered, namely:

- the organisation of the workplace;
- cleanliness of the workplace;
- the prevention or control of environmental stressors;
- welfare arrangements; and
- structural safety.

THE ORGANISATION OF THE WORKPLACE

The following aspects are relevant in the organisation of new workplaces and in the modification or conversion of existing workplaces.

Workplace layout

Factors such as access for employees and transport, together with that of fire, ambulance and police vehicles, the availability of vehicle parking areas and the density of buildings on the site are important. The need for a well-organised traffic system, which does not expose pedestrians to risk of injury, must be considered.

Internal layouts should ensure adequate space is available for employees working in a particular room or area, together with any plant, equipment, machinery, furniture and goods stored. An efficient layout should make a material contribution to preventing overcrowding of working areas.

Cleanliness and waste disposal

It is an offence to operate a dirty workplace. Attention to housekeeping, the establishment and operation of formal cleaning schedules, together with a well-run refuse removal, storage and disposal system, are basic requirements for all workplaces. Not only does this contribute to safe working, but it further reduces the risk of fire, infestation and accidents.

ENVIRONMENTAL STRESSORS

Stress, associated with exposure of employees to extremes of temperature, poor standards of lighting and ventilation, noise and vibration is a contributory factor in occupational ill-health and, in some cases, accidents. Many forms of occupational ill-health, for example, heat stroke and noise-induced hearing loss are directly associated with failure to provide a healthy working environment. The various forms of environmental stressors are dealt with below.

Temperature

Generally, the temperature in a workplace should be 'reasonable'. This implies the need to consider the type of work undertaken, for example, active or sedentary work, the season of the year and heat-producing machinery and equipment located in working areas. Temperatures in work rooms should normally be at least 16°C after the first hour of working unless much of the work involves severe physical effort, in which case the temperature should be at least 13°C.

Ventilation

Two aspects must be considered here, namely:
  ♦ the provision and maintenance of adequate 'comfort' ventilation in terms of a sufficient quantity of fresh or purified air; and
  ♦ means for the removal of airborne contaminants, for example, dusts, gases, vapours and fumes, by the operation and maintenance of local exhaust ventilation (LEV) systems.

Humidity

Excessive amounts of moisture from, for instance, steam-producing equipment can have a direct effect on comfort. Relative humidity should be between 30 and 70%. Where the relative humidity is too low people will experience discomfort due to drying of the throat and nasal passages. High levels of relative humidity, on the other hand, produce a sensation of stuffiness and reduce the rate at which sweat evaporates.

Lighting

Every workplace must have 'suitable and sufficient' lighting, 'suitable' in terms of qualitative factors, such as freedom from glare and the correct distribution of the light, and 'sufficient' with regard to the actual intensity of light, measured in Lux, for both general and specific tasks.

The need for emergency lighting systems must also be considered.

Noise

Exposure to noise above 90 dBA can cause noise-induced hearing loss. Workplace noise can also distract attention and affect concentration, mask audible warning signals from machinery and plant or simply interfere with the safe operation of the work process, thereby being a contributory factor in accidents.

Improving the working environment

High levels of sickness absence are a classic indication of an employer's failure to provide a safe and healthy working environment. Not only do poor environments lead to a range of minor illnesses, such as colds, coughs, visual fatigue and respiratory conditions, with the resulting sickness absence, but they can be a long-term cause of more serious conditions.

Factors mentioned above should be taken into account when undertaking a workplace risk assessment with a view to improving working conditions.

WELFARE AMENITY PROVISIONS

Employers are required to make adequate provision for employee welfare at work. The general requirements for welfare amenity provision are laid down in the WHSWR and ACOP.

Sanitary accommodation

Suitable and sufficient sanitary conveniences must be provided at readily accessible places.

Any room containing a sanitary convenience must be well ventilated, so that offensive odours do not linger. Measures should also be taken to prevent odours entering other rooms. This may best be achieved by providing a ventilated area between the room containing the convenience and the other room. Alternatively, it may be possible to achieve it by mechanical ventilation.

Washing facilities

Suitable and sufficient washing facilities, including showers if required by the nature of the work or for health reasons, must be provided at readily accessible places.

Cleanliness of amenity areas

Arrangements should be made to ensure that rooms containing sanitary conveniences or washing facilities are kept clean. The frequency and thoroughness of cleaning should be adequate for this purpose.

The surfaces of the internal walls and floors of the facilities should normally have a surface that permits wet cleaning, for example, ceramic tiling or a plastic-coated surface. Rooms should be well lit, which will facilitate cleaning to the necessary standard.

Responsibility for cleaning should be clearly established as part of a workplace cleaning schedule, particularly where facilities are shared by more than one workplace.

Drinking water

Where a supply of drinking water is required under Regulation 22, there shall also be provided a sufficient number of suitable cups or other drinking vessels unless the water supply is in a jet from which persons can drink easily.

Accommodation for clothing

This must be suitable and sufficient in that:
- it provides suitable security for clothing not being worn;
- where necessary to avoid risks to health or damage to the clothing, it includes separate accommodation for clothing worn at work and for other clothing;
- so far as is reasonably practicable, it allows or includes facilities for drying clothing; and
- it is in a suitable location.

Provision for drying clothing

Accommodation for work clothing and workers' own personal clothing should enable it to hang in a clean, warm, dry, well-ventilated place where it can dry out during the course of the working day if necessary. If the workroom is unsuitable for this purpose, then accommodation should be provided in another convenient place. The accommodation should consist of, as a minimum, a separate hook or peg for each worker.

Security of clothing

Where facilities to change clothing are required, effective measures should be taken to ensure security of clothing. This may be achieved, for example, by providing a lockable locker for each worker.

Facilities for changing clothing

The ACOP recommends that a changing room should be provided for workers who change into special work clothing and where they remove more than outer clothing. Changing rooms should also be provided where necessary to prevent workers' own clothing being contaminated by harmful substances. Changing facilities should be readily accessible from workrooms and eating facilities, if provided. They should be provided with adequate seating and should contain, or communicate directly with, clothing accommodation and showers or baths if provided. They should be constructed and arranged to ensure privacy of the user.

Facilities to rest and to eat meals

Suitable and sufficient rest facilities must be provided at readily accessible places. Rest rooms and rest areas should include suitable arrangements to protect non-smokers from discomfort caused by tobacco smoke.

Suitable facilities must be provided for any person at work who is a pregnant woman or nursing mother to rest.

Suitable and sufficient facilities must be provided for persons at work to eat meals where meals are regularly eaten in the workplace.

The ACOP makes extensive recommendations on the question of rest facilities and facilities for taking meals in the workplace.

DESIGN AND LAYOUT OF WELFARE AMENITY AREAS

Any arrangement of welfare amenities must take account of minimum legal requirements outlined in the WHSWR and ACOP. The design and layout will also depend upon the number of employees, both male and female, the nature of the business and the personal contamination that may result from processes and operations undertaken. Before finalising arrangements for new or modified amenities, the HSE or local environmental health officer should be consulted.

Bearing in mind the legal principles outlined earlier in this chapter, welfare amenity areas should be designed on the following principles.

♦ In sanitation, handwashing and shower areas the surfaces of floors, walls, ceilings, doors and fittings should be capable of being readily cleansed and maintained. There should be an intervening ventilated space between a sanitation area and a workroom. Lighting and ventilation should be adequate. Walls, doors and fittings should be of vandal-proof design.

♦ Wash basins and showers should have adequate supplies of hot and cold water or of hot water at a suitably controlled temperature. Supplies of soap, clean towels or disposable paper towels, and nail brushes should be provided. Lidded containers should be provided for the storage of soiled paper towels.

♦ In clothing storage and changing areas, suitable seats, preferably of the wall-mounted type, should be provided to permit easy changing of footwear.

♦ There must be effective means for drying clothing.

♦ Drinking fountains, as opposed to the provision of disposable cups and taps, are recommended.

♦ Showers should be provided to enable employees to cleanse themselves after physical work in a dirty and/or hot environment and to enable employees to proceed from work to other activities. A standard of one shower unit per 40 employees is recommended, although there is no legal requirement as to the actual number of showers an employer should provide.

STRUCTURAL SAFETY

Accidents associated with the structural features of workplaces are common, and include slips, trips and falls on the same level, falls down staircases, falls from a height, contact with fixed structural features, doors, gates and vehicles using traffic routes, falls through teagle openings and from elevated work or storage platforms.

Floors and traffic routes

Specific provisions relating to the safety of floors and traffic routes in workplaces are dealt with in Regulation 12 of the WHSWR.

Floors should be of sound construction, free from obstruction and sudden changes in level, and of non-slip finish. Storage areas should be clearly marked by the use of yellow or white lines, and specific 'No Go' areas cross-hatched with yellow lines. All openings in floors and significant differences in floor level should be fenced.

Where a wet process is undertaken, or where frequent floor washing is necessary, the floor should be laid to a fall to a drainage system. Floor channels, incorporating metal gratings or covers, can sometimes be used as an alternative.

Stairs, ladders and catwalks

Suitable and sufficient handrails and, if appropriate, guards must be provided on all traffic routes that are staircases except in circumstances where a handrail cannot be provided

TABLE 8 : AVOIDING SLIPS, TRIPS AND FALLS

Hazard	Control
Spillage (wet or dry)	Clean up spills immediately, ensuring that suitable cleaning materials and chemicals are used in accordance with manufacturers' instructions. Suitable 'wet floor' signage must be displayed and areas may need to be cordoned off.
Trailing wires and cables	Ensure fixed equipment is sited to obviate cables crossing pedestrian routes. Restrict employee/pedestrian access. Avoid, for example, cleaning during times of pedestrian access. Provide appropriate warning signs. Use cable covers and/or securely fix to surfaces.
Accumulation/rubbish	Prevent the build up of accumulations by frequency of emptying containers. Provide adequate sized suitably covered containers.
Carpets/mats	Fix securely, replace when worn or holed and prevent curling edges. Replace by more suitable material eg rubber.
Slippery surfaces	Determine the cause and apply appropriate treatment. Replace surfaces. Provide appropriate warning signs. When caused by moving from a wet area to a dry floor surface suitable footwear should, where possible, be provided. Suitable mats may be provided at point of change.
Inadequate lighting	Provide additional lighting and/or increase levels of illumination. Provide increased natural lighting, eg glass panels or windows.
Changes of level	Highlight changes, for example, by painting, suitable markings or conspicuous tread nosings. Provide better lighting and warning signs.
Sloping floors	Provide better lighting and warning signs. Floor markings and handrails may be required.

Hazard	Control
Steam or smoke resulting in poor visibility	Improve ventilation. Change equipment or process. Provide warning signs.
Unsatisfactory footwear	Provide clear advice/instruction to workers on the type of footwear required. Effective supervision to ensure advice is followed. N.B. If the type of work demands special protective footwear it must be provided by the employer free of charge to comply with legislation.

without obstructing the traffic route. In the case of very wide staircases, further handrails may be necessary in addition to those at the sides. The space between a handrail and treads should be enclosed, or an intermediate rail fitted.

Fixed vertical ladders and catwalks, including bridges to them, should be securely fixed. Back rings should be fitted to vertical ladders from a height of 2m upwards and spaced at 1m intervals. Catwalks and bridges should be adequately fenced by means of 1m high guard rails, 500mm high intermediate rails and toe boards.

External areas, traffic routes and approach roads

External areas of a workplace, including approach roads, should be well lit, with clear demarcation of entry and exit points, traffic routes, storage and parking areas. Traffic routes must be suitable for the people and vehicles using them, sufficient in number, in suitable positions and of sufficient size to allow for vehicle manoeuvring, particularly where lift trucks may be operating. Particular precautions must be taken to prevent vehicles causing danger to people near that route and to ensuring there is efficient separation of vehicle traffic routes from doors, gates and pedestrian routes. Where pedestrians and vehicles use the same traffic routes, there must be sufficient separation between them. All traffic routes must be suitably indicated.

Windows, doors, gates and walls

Every window or other transparent or translucent surface in a wall or partition, or in a door or gate, must, where necessary for reasons of health and safety, be:
- of safety material or protected against breakage; and
- appropriately marked or incorporate features so as, in either case, to make it apparent.

No window, skylight or ventilator:
- that is capable of being opened shall be likely to be opened, closed or adjusted in a manner that exposes any person performing such operation to risk; and
- shall be in a position when open that is likely to expose any person to risk.

All windows and skylights should be of a design or so constructed that they may be cleaned safely.

Doors and gates must be suitably constructed (including being fitted with any necessary safety device). In particular:

♦ any sliding door or gate must have a device to prevent it coming off its track during use;

♦ any upward opening door or gate must have a device to prevent it falling back;

♦ any powered door or gate must incorporate suitable and effective features to prevent it causing injury by trapping any person;

♦ where necessary for reasons of health or safety, any powered door or gate must be capable of being operated manually, unless it opens automatically in the event of power failure; and

♦ any door or gate which is capable of opening by being pushed from either side must be of such construction as to provide, when closed, a clear view of the space close to both sides.

Escalators and moving walkways

Escalators and moving walkways must function safely, be equipped with any necessary safety devices and be fitted with one or more emergency stop controls, which are easily identifiable and readily accessible.

SICK BUILDING SYNDROME

Concern about the reputedly high incidence of sickness amongst people who work in sealed buildings, especially offices, has attracted considerable attention since the 1970s. Various terms have been used to describe the phenomenon - 'building sickness syndrome', 'sick office syndrome', 'tight building syndrome', 'office eye syndrome' and others.

There is still much speculation: its nature, prevalence, causes and even its existence are open to debate.

Definition

The term is ill-defined, one definition used being 'a building in which complaints of ill-health are more common than might reasonably be expected'.

Symptoms and prevalence

Most reports of outbreaks detail a common list of symptoms. These are summarised by the World Health Organisation (WHO) as:

♦ ear, nose and throat irritation;

♦ sensation of dry mucous membranes and skin;

♦ erythema (skin rash);

♦ mental fatigue;

♦ headaches, high frequency of airway infections and coughs;

♦ hoarseness, wheezing, itching and unspecified hypersensitivity; and

♦ nausea, dizziness.

Some investigations have produced more extensive lists of symptoms including, for example, high blood pressure and miscarriages. However, these are not mentioned as occurring amongst staff in 'sick buildings'; they are not specifically attributed to 'sick building syndrome'.

Studies in the UK show a number of patterns:

♦ symptoms are most common in air conditioned buildings but they also occur in buildings that are naturally ventilated;

- clerical staff are more likely than managerial staff to suffer, and complaints are more frequent in the public than the private sector; complaints are more frequent in offices housing many staff;
- people with most symptoms have least perceived control over their environment; and
- symptoms are more frequent in the afternoon than in the morning.

Common features of sick buildings

The WHO identifies a number of features common to sick buildings. They are:
- often forced ventilated;
- often of light construction;
- indoor surfaces that are often covered in light textiles (carpets, furnishing fabrics, etc.);
- energy efficient, kept relatively warm and have a homogeneous thermal environment; and
- airtight, ie windows cannot be opened.

The possible causes

Many causes have been suggested for sick building syndrome, including:
- airborne pollutants:
    - chemical pollutants from the building occupants, fabric and furnishings, office machinery and from outside;
    - airborne dusts and fibres; and
    - microbiological contaminants from carpets, furnishings, building occupants or from the ventilation or air conditioning system;

Note

These may have a directly toxic, pathogenic or irritant effect on occupants or they may have an allergenic effect, ie once the occupants are sensitised, subsequent very small challenges may cause illness.

- odours;
- lack of negatively charged small air ions;
- inadequate ventilation/fresh air supply;
- low relative humidity;
- poor working environment/discomfort due to:
    - high temperatures;
    - inadequate air movement causing stuffiness;
    - poor lighting;
- general dissatisfaction or psychosomatic causes.

Dissatisfaction and psychological causes

Some outbreaks of illness among workers have been attributed to psychological causes.

Conclusion

Whilst the evidence is largely circumstantial, it is useful to summarise the factors that may contribute towards symptoms associated with building sickness. These are:
- ventilation rates;

- temperature and air movement;
- humidity;
- lighting standards;
- airborne pollution;
- airborne organic matter from the air conditioning system; and
- low morale and general dissatisfaction.

SAFETY SIGNS IN THE WORKPLACE

The Safety Signs Regulations 1980 require that safety signs, other than those for fire-fighting, rescue equipment and emergency exits, conform to a standard system with regard to colours and shapes.

Prohibition signs

These are circular with a red band enclosing a crossed out symbol on a white background, for example, 'No smoking'.

Warning signs

These signs are triangular in shape with a yellow background and black borders, symbols and text, for example, 'LPG – Highly flammable'.

Mandatory signs

These are circular in shape incorporating a white mandatory symbol and/or text on a blue background, for example, 'Wear face shield'.

SAFETY SIGNS FIG. 9

Safe condition signs

These are indicated by a green square or rectangle with symbols and lettering in white, for example, 'Emergency stop'.

The Health and Safety (Safety Signs and Signals) Regulations 1996 implemented the Safety Signs Directive. They require employers to use a safety sign wherever there is a risk to health and safety that cannot be avoided or properly controlled by other means. The regulations extended the term 'safety sign' to include hand signals, pipeline markings, acoustic signals and illuminated signs.

Safety signs, including fire exit, fire fighting and fire alarm signs, must convey the message instead of relying solely on text. Fire exit signs must incorporate the 'running man' pictogram. (The display of the sign FIRE EXIT without the pictogram is illegal.)

The regulations also require the marking of pipework containing dangerous substances by fixing labels or signs at sampling and discharge points. Small stores of dangerous substances must also be marked in a similar way.

KEY POINTS

♦ The duties of employers under the WHSWR must be read in conjunction with the more general duties under the MHSWR with particular reference to the requirements for risk assessment, the implementation of management systems and the appointment of competent persons.

♦ Reference must be made to the ACOP when considering implementation of duties under the WHSWR.

♦ Employers must maintain the workplace, equipment, systems and devices in an efficient state, in efficient working order and in good repair.

♦ The implementation of management systems, including planned preventive maintenance and cleaning programmes, is implied under the WHSWR.

♦ Poor levels of environmental control can lead to occupational ill-health.

♦ In considering the workplace, reference must be made to the organisation and layout, cleanliness and housekeeping arrangements, the prevention or control of environmental stressors, welfare arrangements and structural safety.

♦ Poor design and maintenance of structural features of workplaces is a common cause of accidents.

♦ Well-designed and maintained welfare amenity provisions not only reduce the risk of occupational ill-health but promote good employer employee relationships.

♦ Appropriate safety signs, including fire safety signs, must be displayed in workplaces.

8 Fire Safety

This chapter deals with the principles of combustion, methods of heat transfer in buildings, the classification of fire, fire extinction methods and legal requirements relating to fire protection. The subject of fire risk assessment is dealt with later in the chapter.

WHAT IS FIRE?

Every year fire and its effects cause substantial loss of life and extensive damage to property. But what is fire? It can be defined in a number of ways:

◆ a mixture in gaseous form of a combustible substance and oxygen with sufficient energy put into the mixture to cause combustion to take place;

◆ a spectacular example of a fast chemical reaction between a combustible substance and oxygen accompanied by the evolution of heat; and

◆ an unexpected combustion generating sufficient heat or smoke resulting in death, injury and damage to plant, equipment, goods and premises.

PRINCIPLES OF COMBUSTION

In order to appreciate the principles of fire prevention, it is necessary to have a broad understanding of the combustion process. The three requirements for a fire to start and continue are:

◆ the presence of a fuel, ie something that burns, for example, wood, paper, petrol;

◆ an ignition source of sufficient energy to set the fuel alight, for example, a spark, burning ember, lighted match; and

◆ air containing sufficient oxygen to maintain combustion.

These three elements are commonly depicted as the Fire Triangle. If one of these three elements is removed or absent, combustion cannot take place.

Elements of fire

Fuel

Fuels include a large group of organic substances, ie those with carbon in the molecule, such as natural gas (methane), butane, petrol, plastics, natural and artificial fibres, wood, paper, coal and living matter. Inorganic substances are also combustible, such as hydrogen gas, sulphur, phosphorus, magnesium and ammonium nitrate.

Ignition source

This provides the energy that has to be applied to the oxygen/fuel mixture to start a fire. Generally, this energy is in the form of heat, but this is not always the case. The heat can simply be that contained in a combustible substance. This is often the source of ignition energy when hot fuel leaks from a pipe and fires, but it can be generated by friction, such as striking a match against sandpaper or a hot bearing in a machine. Electrical energy in the lightning of a thunderstorm, or when an electrical contact, such as a switch, is made or broken, would also qualify.

Air containing sufficient oxygen

A fire always requires oxygen for it to start or, having started, to continue. The chief source of oxygen is air, which is a mixture of gases comprising nitrogen (78%) and oxygen (21%). The remaining 1% is made up of water vapour, carbon dioxide, argon and other gases.

A number of substances can be a source of oxygen, for example, oxidising agents. These are substances that contain oxygen that is readily available under fire conditions and include sodium chlorate, hydrogen peroxide, nitric acid and organic peroxides. A third source of oxygen is the combustible substance itself, for example, ammonium nitrate.

Spontaneous ignition

Some substances actually burst into flames without apparent means of ignition. Typical examples are haystacks, rags soaked in linseed oil and oil-soaked lagging. This property of substances is known as spontaneous ignition. It is clear from the mechanism of fire that there must be a source of ignition but the source itself is not obvious.

Some organic substances, when exposed to oxygen, undergo slow oxidation, a process similar to fire, releasing little sensible heat. Slow oxidation does not result in the production of carbon dioxide and water but other substances chemically smaller and more easily combustible than the original substance. In effect, the original substance is being made more combustible by oxidation and, in consequence, little heat is generated. When the reduction in combustibility and heat output match, a fire occurs. The source of ignition is the heat of oxidation.

HEAT TRANSMISSION

Heat may be transmitted or transferred by the processes of convection, conduction and radiation.

Convection

When matter is heated the range of vibration of its molecules increases and the matter expands. In a solid this has little significance, but in a fluid, where the particles are free to move through the substance, it gives rise to a convection current in the body of the fluid.

These currents are produced because the unheated particles of a fluid are more dense than the newly heated particles and thus gravitate to the lowest point of the body of the fluid. In doing so, they upwardly displace the hot particles. These hot particles, whether a liquid or a gas, have no specific ability to rise. They rise simply because they are displaced from beneath, and the difference in weight between hot and cold particles is the sole force operating. The greater the difference in temperature between the hottest and coldest particles, the more vigorous will be the convection current produced. If the source of heat is maintained, the cooler particles, already in motion as a result of the greater weight, become heated in turn, whilst the previously heated particles, having been displaced from the heat source, lose some of their heat to the surroundings and become cooler. A convection current is thus continuous and is described as a 'circulation' within the body of the fluid.

Gases act in the same way as fluids. For instance, systems of natural ventilation in buildings operate on the basis of convection currents being established and maintained. Hot air rises and cold air sinks.

Conduction

With solids the increased molecular vibration due to an increase in temperature of one part is imparted by contact with adjoining molecules. Thus, if a length of metal wire is heated at one end it would, by the process of conduction, ultimately reach uniform temperature though its entire length, but for the fact that some heat is lost to the air from its exposed surfaces. This method of transmission is called 'conduction' and is confined largely to solids because of their rigid structure.

Solids are generally classed as good or bad conductors according to their ability or otherwise to conduct heat. Metals are good conductors, whereas wood is a bad conductor.

Conduction also takes place in liquids and gases. In any normal body of liquid or gas the particles are displaced by convection before any appreciable transfer of heat by conduction can take place. Generally, liquids are poor conductors and gases even worse.

Radiation

In convection, heat is transferred from one point to another by the relative movement of particles. In conduction, transference is between adjoining particles that do not move relative to each other. In radiation, however, the molecular heat motion of a body causes to be emitted, or radiated into space, rays or waves travelling in straight lines, in all directions from the source, and at a speed of about 186,400 miles per second.

All hot bodies emit waves, the larger and hotter the body the more and intense the waves. These are waves of energy, which, when directed on to a body, produce sensible heat in the body. Heat radiation travels best through empty space but can also travel through a variety of media.

THE CAUSES OF FIRE

Classic sources of ignition in both industrial and domestic premises are:

♦   **Electrical equipment**
     Arcing, which results in the production of sparks, and hot surfaces created by defective electrical equipment, are a common source of ignition.

♦   **Spontaneous ignition**
     When some liquids are heated or sprayed on to a very hot surface, they may ignite spontaneously without an ignition source actually being present.

♦   **Spontaneous combustion**
     When materials react with oxygen an exothermic reaction takes place, ie one emitting heat. With materials that readily oxidise, there may be some degree of heat accumulation, which eventually causes the material to ignite or burst into flames.

♦   **Smoking**
     In many work situations, smoking by employees and others can be a source of fire, principally from discarded cigarette ends and matches. Smoking in areas where flammable materials are stored, or where flammable vapours may be present, may further be a cause of fire.

♦   **Sparks**
     Sparks, sufficient in energy to act as a source of ignition, can be created by friction between surfaces, for instance, where the moving part of a machine comes into contact with a fixed part, or where two moving surfaces may rub or slide together during routine machine operation.

♦   **Hot work**
     Hot work, such as welding, soldering, hot cutting and brazing, can be a source of

ignition, particularly where flammable vapours may be present. The operation of a Permit to Work system is necessary in most cases involving hot work not undertaken in workshops.

♦ **Static electricity**

In situations where electrostatic charging is produced by induction or friction, the charge, in the form of static electricity, can be carried away from the point of origin and, in the event of accumulation of charge, can be a source of ignition.

♦ **Vehicles**

In vehicle maintenance and parking areas, diesel and petrol-operated engines, vehicle emissions and hot surfaces of, for instance, exhaust systems, can be a source of ignition.

♦ **Open flames**

Many open flame sources are encountered in workplaces, for example, boilers, furnaces, portable heating appliances and pilot lights to same. Misused or badly maintained equipment of this type can be a source of fire.

♦ **Lightning**

In limited cases, lightning can be a source of ignition and this may require the installation of lightning protection by direct earthing.

THE SECONDARY EFFECTS OF FIRE

Whilst the primary effects of fire, in most cases, can cause loss of life and substantial damage, the secondary effects must also be considered in any fire protection strategy. These secondary effects can include:

♦ 'smoke logging' of buildings, which may make them uninhabitable for a period of time;

♦ varying degrees of structural instability of fire-damaged buildings and adjacent buildings;

♦ damage to services, including engineering, electrical and pressure systems, pipework and ancillary systems;

♦ deterioration of wall and ceiling surfaces, which may require subsequent reinstatement and redecoration;

♦ deterioration in the condition of stored final products, which may render these products unsaleable; and

♦ dust explosions in certain types of industrial plant, such as spray drying, milling and grinding plant.

THE CAUSES OF FIRE SPREAD

For ignition to take place, and for the combustion process to become established and continue, three essential elements are necessary, namely: an ignition source; fuel to burn; and air containing sufficient oxygen to maintain combustion. Fire spread in buildings is directly associated with these elements and the process of heat transfer by conduction, convection and radiation.

Fire spread takes place where there is a supply of combustible material and sufficient air to maintain combustion. Typical combustible materials in a workplace include furniture, structural items, such as doors, paper, cardboard, flammable substances, such as paints and thinners, and a wide range of waste materials, some of which may be stored badly in flammable containers, such as polythene sacks and plastic bins. Combined with adequate ventilation, fire will continue to spread as long as flammable materials are present. In many cases, ducts to ventilation systems assist the spread of fire, particularly through sparks and burning embers, which establish secondary fires in adjoining rooms and areas.

Other factors contributing to fire spread include:

♦ flammable wall coatings and floor coverings;
♦ cable ducts that can transfer fire from one part to another due to the flammable nature of the insulation to electric cables contained in ducts;
♦ lift shafts and other vertical shafts, which have not been fireproofed;
♦ holes in floors created for process operations, for example, conveyor openings in floors; and
♦ vehicles parked under and in close proximity to buildings.

Precautions with flammable liquids

♦ All containers should be of the self-closing type. Caps should be replaced after dispensing and liquids should be dispensed over a drip tray.
♦ Containers should be stored in a well-ventilated and fire-protected area.
♦ Fire appliances should be located in a readily accessible position and staff trained in their use.
♦ Flammable liquids should be transported in closed containers of metal construction, although some plastic containers may be acceptable for this purpose.

CLASSIFICATION OF FIRES

Fires are commonly classified into four categories according to the type of fuel and means of extinction.

Class A

Fires involving solid materials, normally of organic nature, in which the combustion occurs with the formation of glowing embers, for example, wood, paper, coal and natural fibres. Water applied as a jet or spray is the most effective extinguishing medium.

Class B

Fires involving:

(i) liquids; and
(ii) liquefiable solids.

Liquids fall into two groups:

♦ miscible with water – methanol, acetone, acetic acid; and
♦ immiscible with water – petrol, benzene, fats and waxes.

Foam, vaporising liquids, carbon dioxide and dry powder can be used on both B(i) and B(ii) type fires. Water spray can be used on type B(i) but not on type B(ii) fires. There may also be restrictions on the type of foam that can be used because some foams break down on contact with alcohols. In all cases, extinction is achieved by smothering. However, water sprayed on to a B(i) fire also acts by cooling and by removal of the fuel, in that the fuel dissolves in the water.

Class C

Fires involving gases or liquid gases, for example, methane, propane and butane. Both foam and dry chemicals can be used on fires involving small quantities of liquefied gas spillages or leakages, particularly when backed up by water to cool the spillage collector or leaking container.

A fire from a gas leak can be extinguished either by isolating the fuel remotely or by injecting an inert gas into the gas stream. Direct flame extinguishment is difficult and may be counterproductive in that, if the leak continues, this may result in reignition, often in the form of an explosion. Extinguishers used on fires involving liquid gas spillages and leaks work by smothering.

Class D

Fires involving electrical equipment must always be tackled by, first, isolating the electrical supply and, second, by the use of carbon dioxide, vaporising liquid or dry powder. The use of these agents minimises damage to electrical equipment.

PRINCIPLES OF FIRE SPREAD CONTROL

Any fire will continue to spread under the right conditions, that is:
♦ the presence of a combustible fuel to burn;
♦ sufficient air with an appropriate oxygen content; and
♦ a continuing source of ignition from the existing fire.

Fire spread control, therefore, is directed at eliminating one or more of the above elements that maintain a fire. The ultimate objective is the extinction of the fire, using one or more of the following techniques.

Starvation

There are three ways that starvation can be achieved:
♦ take the fuel away from the fire;
♦ take the fire away from the fuel; and
♦ reduce the quantity or bulk of the fuel.

The first is achieved every day on a gas hob when the tap is turned off. For industrial installations this means isolating the fuel feed at the remote isolation valve. Examples of taking the fire away from the fuel include breaking down stacks and dragging away the burning debris. Breaking down a fire into smaller manageable units is an example of reducing the quantity or bulk of the fuel.

Smothering

Smothering can be achieved by:
♦ allowing the fire to consume the oxygen while preventing the inward flow of more oxygen; and
♦ adding an inert gas to the burning mixture.

Wrapping a person whose clothing is on fire in a blanket is an example of smothering. Other examples include pouring foam on top of a burning pool of oil or by putting sand on a small fire. A danger inherent in extinguishing fires by smothering occurs when the fire is out but everything is still hot. An inrush of oxygen, caused by disturbing the foam layer, or opening the door to a room, could result in reignition as there may still be sufficient energy present in the form of sensible heat.

If an inert gas is to be used as an extinguishing agent, carbon dioxide or halogenated hydrocarbons, such as BCF, are suitable. Alternatively, nitrogen can be used, and is in fact commonly used in the treatment of petrochemical plant fires. Where a flammable gas pipeline leaks and the escaping gas ignites, nitrogen blanketing can be achieved by injecting nitrogen into the gas downstream of the release.

Smothering is only effective when the source of oxygen is air. It is totally ineffective when the burning substance contains oxygen, such as ammonium nitrate.

Cooling

This is the most common means of fighting a fire, water being the most effective and cheapest medium. For a fire to be sustained, some of the heat output from combustion is returned to the fuel, providing a continuous source of ignition energy. When water is sprayed on to a fire, the heat output serves to heat and vaporise the water, that is, the water provides an alternative heat sink. Ultimately, insufficient heat is added to the fuel and continuous ignition and reignition ceases. In order to assist rapid absorption of heat, water is applied to the fire as a spray rather than a jet, the spray droplets being more efficient in absorbing heat than the stream of water from a jet.

A secondary effect of applying a water spray to a fire is that much of the water is converted to steam, which has a blanketing or smothering effect, thereby reducing the potential for further ignition and reignition.

Another example of heat absorption is provided by dry chemical extinguishers. These are very fine powders that rapidly absorb heat. Dry powders can also be used to produce a smothering effect.

PORTABLE FIRE FIGHTING APPLIANCES

Such appliances are designed to be carried and operated by hand. They contain an extinguishing medium that can be expelled by action of internal pressure and directed on to a fire. This pressure may be stored in the appliance, or obtained by a chemical reaction or by release of gas from a cartridge. The maximum mass of a portable appliance in working order is 23kg.

Portable appliances are of several groups. They must be coloured red and carry a distinguishing coloured band as shown in Table 9.

TABLE 9 : GROUPING AND CODING OF FIRE APPLIANCES

Appliance	Colour code
Water	Red
Foam	Cream
Carbon dioxide	Black
Dry chemical powder	Blue
Vaporising liquid	Green

FIRE ALARM SYSTEMS

A method of giving warning of fire is required in commercial, industrial and public buildings. The purpose of a fire alarm is to give an early warning of fire in a building in order to:

♦ increase the safety of occupants by encouraging them to escape to a place of safety; and

♦ increase the possibility of early extinction of a fire thus reducing the loss of or damage to the premises.

BS 5839 Part 1: 1988 lays down guidelines to be followed for the installation of fire alarm systems. In larger buildings this may take the form of a mains-operated system with break-glass alarm call points, an automatic control unit and electrically operated bells or sirens. In small buildings, it would be reasonable to expect a manually operated, dry battery or compressed air-operated gong, klaxon or bell. To avoid the alarm point being close to the seat of a fire, duplicate facilities are necessary.

FIRE SAFETY LAW

Legal requirements relating to fire protection in workplaces are covered in:

♦ HSWA 1974;

♦ Fire Precautions Act 1971; and

♦ FPWR 1997.

Places of sport, stadia, etc are also covered by the Fire Safety and Safety of Places of Sport Act 1987.

General requirements

In all cases there is a general duty on both employers and occupiers of premises to ensure safety and provide information, instruction and training for employees. There are more specific duties, first, to ensure adequate fire protection and for fire certification. These include the specific training of employees (fire drills), displaying details of the action to be taken in the event of fire and the keeping of records. The nature, scope and frequency of fire drills, and the training to be given to employees in the use of fire appliances, is generally left to the discretion of the fire authority, who act within the guidelines incorporated in the various 'Guides to the Fire Precautions Act 1971', for example, Guide No 2 – Factories.

FIRE PRECAUTIONS ACT 1971

The Act requires the issue by the fire authority of a fire certificate in certain situations.

Fire certificates

A fire certificate shall be issued to a place of work in which:

♦ more than 20 persons are employed to work at any one time; or

♦ more than ten persons are employed other than on the ground, which are in the same building as other places of work and the sum total exceeds 20 or ten respectively; or

♦ in the case of a factory, if 'non-allowable' quantities of explosives or highly flammable materials are stored or used in or under the premises.

A fire certificate must specify clearly and in detail:

♦ the use or uses of the premises;

♦ the means of escape from the relevant building;

♦ the means for ensuring the means of escape can be safely and effectively used;

♦ the means for raising the alarm;

♦ the means for fighting fire for the use of persons on the premises; and

♦ particulars of any explosive and/or highly flammable materials used or stored.

A fire certificate may also require:

♦ maintenance of the means of escape and means of escape into other buildings;

♦ maintenance of other fire precautions, for example, rising mains, fire detection equipment;

♦ details of training and records of such training; and

♦ a limitation on numbers and on fixtures and fittings.

Means of escape in the event of fire

The following general rules apply in the case of means of escape from a building in the event of fire:

1. total travel distance between any point in a building and the nearest final exit or protected stairway should not be more than:

   ♦ 18m if there is only one exit; or

   ♦ 45m if there is more than one exit;

2. two or more exits are necessary:

   ♦ from a room in which more than 60 people work; or

   ♦ if any point in the room is more than 12m from the nearest exit;

3. the minimum width of exit should be 750mm;

4. corridors should be not less than 1m in width and, in the case of offices, where corridors are longer than 45m, they should be divided by fire resisting doors; and

5. stairways should be at least 800mm in width and fire resistant, along with the doors connecting them;

6. a single stairway is sufficient in a building of up to four storeys only;

7. the following are not acceptable as a means of escape:

   ♦ spiral staircases;

   ♦ escalators;

   ♦ lifts;

   ♦ lowering lines; and

   ♦ portable throw-out ladders;

8. fire doors must open outwards only;

9. generally, doors providing means of escape should never be locked. Where they have to be locked for security purposes, they should be fitted with panic bolts or the keys maintained in designated key boxes close to the exit. A notice should indicate that the doors can be opened in case of fire;

10. a final exit notice should be fitted to or above fire exit doors. (See Health and Safety (Safety Signs and Signals) Regulations 1996);

11. appropriate notices should be affixed along fire escape routes, which should be provided with emergency lighting;

- corridors and stairways forming a means of escape should have half-hour fire resistance. The surface finish should be non-combustible;
- fire alarm warnings should be audible throughout the building; and
- normally, no person should have to travel more than 30m to the nearest alarm point.

Fire instructions and training

A fire instruction is a notice informing people of the action they should take on either:
- hearing the alarm; or
- discovering a fire.

In addition to displaying fire instructions:
- people should receive training in evacuation procedures, ie fire drills, at least quarterly;
- the alarm should be sounded weekly; and
- it is advantageous to have key personnel trained in the correct use of fire appliances.

FIRE PRECAUTIONS (WORKPLACE) REGULATIONS 1997

These regulations apply to all workplaces as defined under the WHSWR 1992 other than 'excepted workplaces'.

The regulations do not stand on their own and extend duties on employers under current health and safety and fire safety legislation. As such they must be read in conjunction with a range of duties on employers and controllers of workplaces under the HSWA, Fire Precautions Act 1971, Fire Safety and Safety of Places of Sport Act 1987, WHSWR 1992 and, in particular, MHSWR 1999. The majority of duties under the regulations are of an absolute nature.

Part II (Regulations 3 to 6) deals with the general application of the regulations with regard to fire precautions in the workplace.

Regulation 3 – Application of Part II

Regulation 3 places a general duty on employers to comply with this part of the regulations in respect of any workplace, other than an excepted workplace, which is to any extent under his control, so far as the requirements relate to matters within his control.

Every person who has, to any extent, control of a workplace, other than an excepted workplace, shall ensure that, so far as the requirements relate to matters within his control, the workplace complies with any applicable requirements of this part.

Similar provisions apply in respect of persons who, by virtue of any contract or tenancy, have obligation in respect of the maintenance or repair, or safety, of a workplace.

Any reference to a person having control of any workplace is a reference to a person having control in connection with the carrying on by him of a trade, business or undertaking (whether or not for profit).

Excepted workplaces

Regulation 5 defines an excepted workplace thus:
- any workplace that comprises premises for which a fire certificate is in force or for which an application is pending under the Fire Precautions Act 1971;
- any workplace that comprises premises in respect of which there is a safety certificate under the Safety of Sports Ground Act 1975 or under Part III of the Fire

Safety and Safety of Places of Sport Act 1987, and which are in use for the activities specified;

♦ any workplace that comprises premises to which the Fire Precautions (Sub-surface Railway Stations) Regulations 1989 apply;

♦ any workplace that or is on a construction site to which the Construction (Health, Safety and Welfare) Regulations 1996 apply;

♦ any workplace in or on a ship within the meaning of the Docks Regulations 1988, including any such ship that is in the course of construction or repair;

♦ any workplace that comprises premises to which the Fire Certificates (Special Premises) Regulations 1976 apply;

♦ any workplace that is deemed to form part of a mine for the purposes of the Mines and Quarries Act 1954;

♦ any workplace that is or is in an offshore installation within the meaning of the Offshore Installations and Pipelines Works (Management and Administration) Regulations 1995;

♦ any workplace that is or is in or on an aircraft, locomotive or rolling stock, trailer or semi-trailer used as a means of transport or a vehicle for which a licence is in force under the Vehicle Excise and Registration Act 1994 or a vehicle exempted from duty under that Act; and

♦ any workplace that is in fields, woods or other land forming part of an agricultural or forestry undertaking but that is not inside a building and is situated away from the undertaking's main buildings.

Regulation 4 – Fire fighting and fire detection

Where necessary (due to features of a workplace, activities undertaken, hazards present or other relevant circumstances) in order to safeguard the safety of employees in case of fire, workplaces must be equipped with appropriate fire-fighting equipment and with fire detectors and alarms. Any non-automatic fire-fighting equipment must be easily accessible, simple to use and indicated by signs.

What is 'appropriate' must be determined by the dimensions and use of the building housing the workplace, the equipment it contains, the physical and chemical properties of substances likely to be present and the maximum number of people present at any one time.

An employer must take measures for fire fighting that are adapted to the nature of the activities undertaken and the size of his undertaking and of the workplace concerned, taking into account any persons other than employees who may be present.

He must nominate employees to implement these measures and ensure that the number of such employees, their training and the equipment available to them are adequate, taking into account the size of, and specific hazards involved in, the workplace concerned, and arrange any necessary contacts with external emergency services.

Regulation 5 – Emergency routes and exits

Emergency routes and exits must be kept clear at all times. Where necessary, the following requirements must be complied with:

(a) emergency routes and exits shall lead as directly as possible to a place of safety;

(b) in the event of danger, it must be possible for employees to evacuate the workplace quickly and as safely as possible;

(c) the number, distribution and dimensions of emergency routes and exits shall be adequate having regard to the use, equipment and dimensions of the workplace and the maximum number of persons who may be present there at any one time;

(d) emergency doors shall open in the direction of escape;

(e) sliding and revolving doors shall not be used for exits specifically intended as emergency exits;

(f) emergency doors shall not be so locked or fastened that they cannot be easily and immediately opened by any person who may require to use them in an emergency;

(g) emergency routes and exits must be indicated by signs; and

(h) emergency routes and exits requiring illumination shall be provided with emergency lighting of adequate intensity in the case of failure of the normal lighting.

Regulation 6 – Maintenance

The workplace and any equipment and devices provided under Regulations 4 and 5 shall be subject to a suitable system of maintenance and be maintained in an efficient state, in efficient working order and in good repair.

Amendment of the MHSWR 1992

Part III deals with amendments to the general and specific provisions of the MHSWR.

Regulation 7 states that the general provisions of the MHSWR must be taken into account when interpreting these regulations.

Regulation 8 requires that specific provisions of Part II shall be inserted into the following provisions of the MHSWR, namely:

♦ definition of the 'preventive and protective measures';

♦ risk assessment;

♦ health and safety assistance;

♦ cooperation and coordination (shared workplaces); and

♦ persons working in host employers' undertakings.

Reference to these regulations must be made in Regulation 8 (information for employees) of the MHSWR.

The requirements of Part II of these regulations must be considered in the interpretation of Regulation 9 (cooperation and coordination) of the MHSWR.

Specific provisions

Specific provisions with regard to enforcement, disclosure of information, provisions as to offences, service of notices and civil liability under the HSWA do not apply, and these regulations do not form part of the relevant statutory provisions.

'The workplace fire precautions legislation'

This legislation means:

♦ part II of these regulations;

♦ Regulations 1 to 5, 7 to 12 and 13(2) of the MHSWR as amended by Part III of these regulations in so far as those regulations:

  ♦ impose requirements concerning general fire precautions to be taken or observed by an employer; and

  ♦ have effect in relation to a workplace in Great Britain other than an excepted workplace;

♦ and for this purpose general fire precautions means measures that are to be taken or observed in relation to the risk to the safety of employees in the case of fire in a workplace, other than any special precautions in connection with the carrying on of any manufacturing process.

Part IV – Enforcement and offences

Part IV provides fire authorities and their inspectors with a range of enforcement procedures according to the severity of the situation. This may be by way of:

♦ a written opinion from the authority, stating the breach of the fire precautions legislation and the action that could be taken to remedy it (Regulation 10);

♦ prosecution, where:
  ♦ a person fails to comply with the fire precautions legislation;
  ♦ that failure places employees at serious risk; and
  ♦ that failure is intentional or is due to the person being reckless as to whether he complies (Regulation 11);

♦ service of a prohibition notice (Regulation 12);

♦ (except where an enforcement notice cannot be delayed), following a written notice of intent, service of an enforcement notice where there is a failure to comply with any provisions of the workplace fire precautions legislation and that failure places employees at serious risk in case of fire (Regulations 13); and

♦ application to a court for an enforcement order where a person has failed to comply with any requirement imposed upon him by the workplace fire precautions legislation (Regulation 14).

A person guilty of an offence under Regulation 11 shall be liable:

♦ on summary conviction to a fine not exceeding the statutory maximum; or

♦ on conviction on indictment, to a fine, or to imprisonment for a term not exceeding two years, or both.

Regulation 14 – Enforcement notices: rights of appeal

A person on whom an enforcement notice is served may, within 21 days, from the date of the notice, appeal to the court. Such an appeal may either cancel or affirm the enforcement notice, with or without modification.

Regulation 15 – Enforcement notices: offences

It is an offence for any person to contravene any requirement imposed by an enforcement notice. A person guilty of such an offence shall be liable:

♦ on summary conviction to a fine not exceeding the statutory maximum; or

♦ on conviction on indictment, to a fine, or to imprisonment for a term not exceeding two years, or both.

In any proceedings for an offence under this regulation, it shall be a defence for the person charged to prove that he took all reasonable precautions and exercised all due diligence to avoid the commission of the offence.

FIRE RISK ASSESSMENT

Under the FPWR 1996 and the MHSWR, there is a duty on employers to undertake fire risk assessments of their workplaces. Whilst there is no specific format for undertaking and recording a risk assessment, it is recommended that a workplace fire risk assessment take place in a series of steps or stages.

1. Identifying the fire hazards

This initial stage of a workplace fire risk assessment entails the inspection of a workplace, both inside and outside, with a view to identifying fire hazards.   Inspection should identify sources of ignition and fuels that will burn, thereby creating the ideal environment for fire.

♦ **Sources of ignition**

These include, for example, hot work activities, naked flames, evidence of people smoking, gas and electrical appliances, hot surfaces, etc.

♦ **Fuels**

The average workplace contains a wide range of materials and substances that will burn, such as wood, paper, plastics, furniture, packaging materials, liquid solvents, paint, adhesives and gases, such as acetylene and liquefied petroleum gas (LPG).

2. Identifying persons at risk

Much will depend upon the work activities undertaken, the layout of the workplace, current fire protection measures, structural features, items stored and used and the means of escape. Persons at risk will include not only employees, but members of the public and the employees of contractors working on the premises who may be unfamiliar with the layout of same.

3. Measuring and evaluating the risks

Consideration must be given to current control measures and further controls necessary to reduce risks to an acceptable level, such as segregation of flammable materials, training of employees, development of fire safety management systems and improving the means of fighting fire.

4. Preventing or controlling exposure to risks

A number of strategies are available in this case, such as:

♦ improved control over ignition sources;

♦ segregating high risk processes;

♦ providing extra means of escape in certain cases;

♦ installing smoke and fire detection systems and a better alarm system;

♦ installation of a sprinkler system in high risk areas;

♦ improving the standard of housekeeping and the storage of waste materials;

♦ briefing of visitors and contractors' employees on fire safety procedures; and

♦ incorporating fire safety procedures in the organisation's Contractors Regulations.

5. Recording the findings

Where more than five employees are employed, the significant findings of the fire risk assessment must be recorded, together with information on people who may be particularly at risk.

The record must indicate whether current control measures are adequate and make recommendations, where necessary, for future action to reduce the risk to an acceptable level. This could include, for instance, improved procedures for the maintenance, examination and testing of electrical equipment, particularly portable electrical appliances.

Many fire authorities also require a plan of the workplace to be included with the risk assessment documentation. This plan should indicate fire hazards and precautions taken to prevent or control exposure to these hazards.

6. Reviewing the assessment

A date for review of the assessment, for example, in 12 months' time, should be recorded on the assessment. However, in some cases, it may be necessary to review the assessment earlier in the event of, for instance:

- the introduction of new work processes;
- the introduction of new flammable substances;
- changes in occupation of offices and other areas of a workplace; and
- modifications to layout of the workplace.

TEMPORARY WORKERS

A temporary worker is generally taken to mean a person employed under a fixed term contract of employment or who is employed by an employment business, such as an employment agency.

Temporary workers are classed as 'notional employees' on the basis that they are under the control of the host employer. As such they must be provided with appropriate information, instruction and training on the hazards they are likely to encounter when working in the host employer's undertaking and the precautions they must take to avert these hazards.

FIRE SAFETY INSPECTIONS

The following aspects need inspection and examination as part of a routine fire safety inspection of a workplace.

1. Electrical Appliances

- Inspected, tested and labelled with date of last inspection.
- Heavy load appliances, including space heaters, connected to a permanent outlet.
- Flexes visible at all times.
- Circuit breakers of appropriate capacity installed.
- Prohibition on the use of adaptors.
- Unsafe wiring and connections.

2. Fire Doors and Partitions

- Sound condition.
- Self-closures to doors.
- No obstruction of fire doors.
- Flame retardant partitions.
- Unobstructed smoke detectors and sprinkler heads.

3. Decorations and furnishings
♦ Flame-proofed curtains and other fabrics.
♦ No flammable decorations.

4. Open Flame Devices
♦ No use of candles, gas lamps or other open flame devices.
♦ 'Hot work' activities well controlled.

5. General Storage
♦ Storage areas in a clean and orderly condition.
♦ Flammable refuse stored in metal bins.
♦ No obstruction of electrical panels, fire appliances, fire exits, fire detection devices and sprinkler heads.
♦ No storage of articles on stairways and landings, and in unauthorised areas.

6. Flammable and combustible substances
♦ Adequate ventilation to prevent accumulation of vapours.
♦ Sources of ignition eliminated.
♦ Flammable liquids stored in metal cabinets.

7. Smoking
♦ Restrictions including designated 'No Smoking' areas.
♦ Evidence of unauthorised smoking.

8. Fire Exits
♦ Maintained and capable of opening with ease.
♦ Kept clear at all times.
♦ Suitably marked.
♦ Provision for disabled persons and wheelchair users.

9. Housekeeping and cleaning
♦ Good housekeeping levels.
♦ Storage of flammable refuse.
♦ Safe layout.
♦ Regular cleaning.

10. Fire Appliances
♦ Clearly indicated;
♦ Wall-mounted;
♦ Training in correct use; and
♦ Maintained.

11. Fire Instructions
♦ Clearly displayed.

12. Fire Alarms and Detection Devices
- ♦ Clearly indicated.
- ♦ Employees trained in use of alarm.
- ♦ Maintained.

13. Sprinkler System
- ♦ Inspected and maintained.
- ♦ Sprinkler heads unobstructed.

KEY POINTS

- ♦ Fire is a substantial cause of death and significant losses to organisations.
- ♦ For combustion to take place, there must be an appropriate fuel, a source of ignition and air containing sufficient oxygen to support combustion.
- ♦ Transfer of heat takes place through conduction, convection and radiation.
- ♦ Fire are classified according to the type of fuel and the means of extinction.
- ♦ Extinction of fires may be by smothering, cooling and starvation.
- ♦ A means of warning of fire is required in all workplaces.
- ♦ Specific provisions for fire certification and means of escape in the event of fire are incorporated in the Fire Precautions Act 1971.
- ♦ The FPWR1997 must be read in conjunction with the general duties of employers under the MHSWR 1999, with particular reference to fire risk assessment.

9 Work Equipment

The history of safety at work is very much associated with the appalling injuries arising from the use of machinery suffered by people working in factories, mines, mills, the match factories and dockyards of the 19th century. As such, machinery safety has always featured strongly in legislation, such as the Factories Acts 1937–61, the Mines and Quarries Act 1954 and the Offices, Shops and Railway Premises Act 1963.

This chapter examines the typical hazards associated with work equipment, machinery guards and safety devices and the safety of hand tools and mobile work equipment, together with the requirements of the PUWER 1998.

MACHINERY-RELATED INJURIES

Death and serious injuries associated with machinery and various forms of work equipment are common. Typical injuries include:

♦ amputations of limbs and parts of limbs;

♦ crushing injuries;

♦ entanglement of limbs, clothing and hair in moving parts of machinery;

♦ injuries associated with items being emitted from machinery; and

♦ contact injuries, such as burns, where people may come into contact with hot surfaces of machines.

PRINCIPLES OF MACHINERY SAFETY

As with many areas of occupational health and safety, the risk of machinery-related accidents is associated with two factors:

♦ the objective danger associated with machinery, which is a measure of the severity of injury that could be sustained through contact with the operational parts, such as the head of a power press, a rotating drill or shaft or the in-running nip of a belt drive to a machine; and

♦ the subjective perception of risk on the part of the machinery operator in being able to identify various forms of danger and his ability to avoid that danger.

Any accident prevention strategy must, therefore, be directed to reducing the objective danger from machinery through the provision and use of well-designed machinery guarding systems and various forms of safety device aimed at preventing the operator or other persons coming anywhere near the danger points or areas of a machine. This should be supported by the provision of information, instruction, training and supervision directed at increasing people's perception of the risks.

Features of machines

Machines have:

♦ operational parts, which perform the primary output function of the machine, for instance, the manufacture of a product or a component of a product; and

♦ non-operational or functional parts, which convey power or motion to the operational parts, for instance, drives to motors.

The functional parts comprise a prime mover and transmission machinery, which are defined in the Factories Act 1961 as follows.

Prime mover means any engine, motor or other appliance that provides mechanical energy derived from steam, water, wind, electricity, the combustion of fuel or other source.

Transmission machinery means every shaft, wheel, pulley, system of fast or loose pulleys, coupling, clutch, driving belt or other device by which the motion of a prime mover is transmitted to or received by any machine or appliance.

Any consideration of the relative safety aspects of work equipment should take into account:

♦ the design features of the equipment in terms of the form and distribution of harm that could arise from use;

♦ the actual persons at risk and the general circumstances surrounding the use of work equipment; and

♦ any specific events that could lead to injury during use of the equipment.

These factors are relevant when undertaking a work equipment risk assessment.

MACHINERY HAZARDS

Many machines, including new machines, incorporate hazards in their basic design. These hazards can be classified as follows.

Traps

Traps can take a number of forms:

♦ **Reciprocating trap**

These traps may have an up and down motion, for example, power presses; at the point where the injury occurs, the limb is stationary.

♦ **Shearing trap**

These have a guillotine effect as with, for instance, a simple paper guillotine.

♦ **In-running nips**

This form of trap is to be found between rollers, between a belt and a conveyor and in gear mechanisms.

Entanglement

The risk of entanglement of hair, clothing and limbs is commonly associated with, for instance, revolving shafts, line shafts, chucks and drills.

Ejection

The emission or throwing off of particles from a machine, as with grinding wheels, and the disintegration of swarf produce by a lathe, can result in eye and other forms of injury.

Contact

Contact with a machine at a particular point can cause injury, for example, heat, temperature extremes, sharp projections, as in plastic moulding machines and circular saws.

ACTIVITIES INVOLVING OPERATORS AND OTHER PERSONS

The tasks that people undertake can be a source of danger, such as job loading and removal, tool changing, waste removal, the actual operation of a process, routine and emergency maintenance, gauging, breakdown situations and trying out machines prior to handing over to operators.

MACHINERY HAZARDS FIG. 10

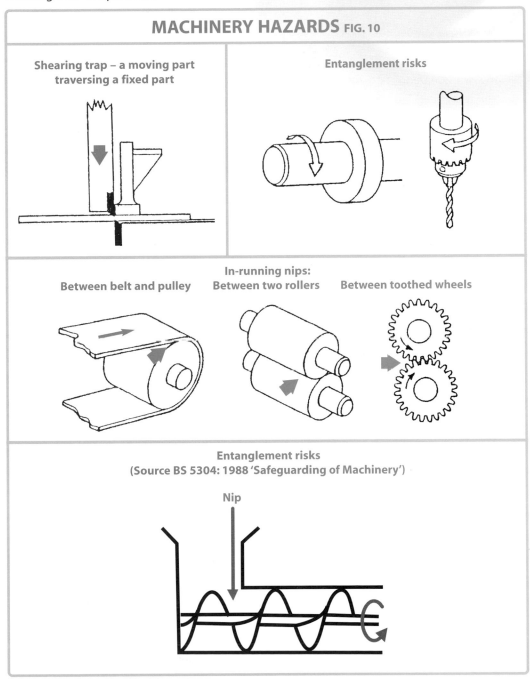

Shearing trap – a moving part traversing a fixed part

Entanglement risks

Between belt and pulley

In-running nips:
Between two rollers

Between toothed wheels

Entanglement risks
(Source BS 5304: 1988 'Safeguarding of Machinery')

Nip

Unauthorised presence and/or use, for instance by contractors' employees, can be another source of danger.

SPECIFIC EVENTS LEADING TO INJURY

The events leading to machinery-related injuries vary considerably. Typical events include:

- unexpected start up or movement;
- reaching into a feeding device;
- uncovenanted stroke by a machine; and
- machine failure.

THE DANGEROUS PARTS OF MACHINERY

The HSE have identified the following parts, or combination of parts, as dangerous should workers operate unsafely or should an unsafe action develop in respect of their motion. Such parts must be securely fenced.

- Revolving shafts, spindles, mandrels and bars.
- In-running nips between pairs of rotating parts.
- In-running nips of the belt and pulley type.
- Projections on revolving parts.
- Revolving beaters, spiked cylinders and revolving drums.
- Revolving mixer arms in casings.
- Revolving worms and spirals in casings.
- Revolving high speed cages in casings.
- Abrasive wheels.
- Revolving cutting tools.
- Reciprocating tools and dies.
- Reciprocating knives and saws.
- Closing nips between platen motions.
- Projecting belt fasteners and fast-running belts.
- Nips between connecting rods or links, and rotating wheels, cranks or discs.
- Traps arising from the traversing carriages of self-acting machines.

MACHINERY GUARDS

There are five specific forms of machinery guard. In many cases, a machinery guard will be linked with a safety device. The guards are described in their relative order of effectiveness.

Fixed guard

This is a guard that has no moving parts associated with it, or dependent on the mechanism of any machinery, and that, when in position, prevents access to a danger point or area. A fixed guard is the most effective form of guard.

This form of guard is designed to prevent all access to the dangerous parts and is principally used to cover non-operational parts. Many fixed guards take the form of solid steel castings, sheet metal, perforated or expanded metal, 'Weldmesh', safety glass panels or polycarbonate panels. Wood as a guard material is not recommended, except where there may be a risk of electric shock.

Interlocking guard

This is a guard that has a movable part so connected with the machinery controls that:

♦ the part(s) of the machinery causing danger cannot be set in motion until the guard is closed;

♦ the power is switched off and the motion braked before the guard can be opened sufficiently to allow access to the dangerous parts; and

♦ access to the danger point or area is denied while the danger exists.

An interlocking guard is also defined as a moving guard, which, in the closed position, prevents all access to the dangerous parts. The control gear for starting up cannot be operated until the guard is fully closed and the guard cannot be opened until the dangerous parts are at rest.

FIG. 11a

Fixed enclosing guard

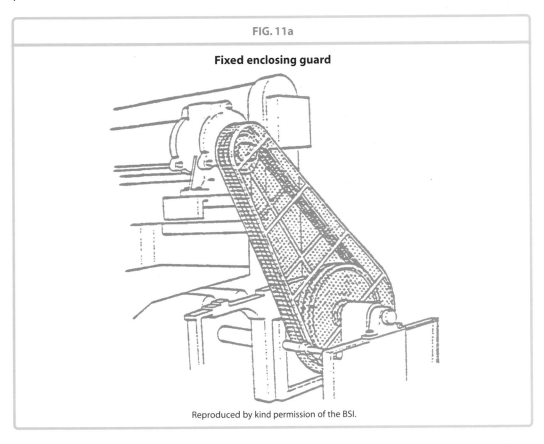

Reproduced by kind permission of the BSI.

For a true interlock system, everything must be at rest before the guard or gate can be opened. Some interlocks control only the power supply, and others, the power supply and movement. In order to achieve the same level of safety as with fixed guards, the reliability and maintenance of interlocking guards are significant.

Methods of interlocking include:

♦ mechanical;
♦ electro-mechanical;
♦ pneumatic (compressed air);
♦ hydraulic (electro) – use of a hydraulic fluid to vary pressure;
♦ key exchange (electrical); and
♦ simple electrical.

FIG. 11b

Perimeter fence guard with fixed panels and interlocking access door

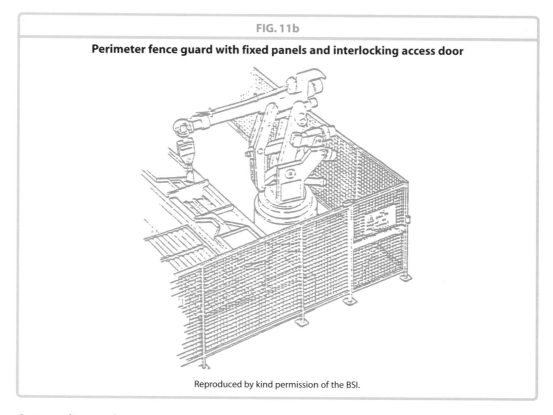

Reproduced by kind permission of the BSI.

Automatic guard

This is a guard which is associated with, and dependent upon, the mechanism of the machinery and operates so as to remove physically from the danger area any part of a person exposed to danger.

These guards incorporate a device so fitted in relation to the dangerous parts that the operator is automatically prevented from contacting same, for example, heavy power presses, press brakes, paper cutting guillotines. The guard is independent of the operator.

The function of an automatic guard is to remove the operator from the dangerous parts of the machine by means of a moving barrier or arm. There is some degree of risk in that the operator can be injured by the moving barrier, and this type of guard is only suitable for large slow-moving barriers, as on presses. These guards operate on a side-to-side, sweep away or push-out motion.

Distance guard

This is a guard that does not completely enclose a danger point or area but places it out of normal reach. It may incorporate a tunnel, fixed grill or rail positioned at sufficient distance so that access to the moving part cannot be gained except by a deliberate unsafe act.

Adjustable guard

This is the least effective and reliable form of guard. It incorporates an adjustable element that, once adjusted by the operator, remains in that position during a particular operation. Adjustable guards feature in woodworking machinery in particular, for example, circular saws and band saws.

SAFETY DEVICES

A safety device is a protective appliance, other than a guard, that eliminates or reduces danger before access to a danger point or area can be achieved. Most safety devices operate on a trip system.

Trip devices

This is a means whereby an approach by a person beyond the safe limit of the working machinery causes the device to actuate and stop the machine, or reverse its motion, thus preventing or minimising injury at the danger point.

MACHINERY GUARD DEVICE FIG. 12

Photoelectric device fitted to a pressbrake

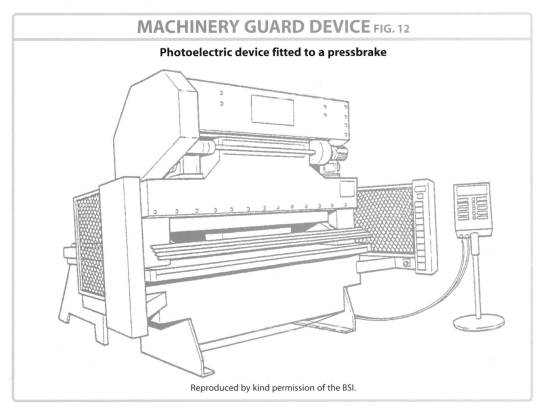

Reproduced by kind permission of the BSI.

There are various forms and types of trip device:

- ◆ mechanical;
- ◆ photo-electric;
- ◆ pressure sensitive mat;
- ◆ ultrasonic device;
- ◆ two-hand control device;
- ◆ overrun device; and
- ◆ mechanical restraint device.

SAFETY MECHANISMS

The detailed design of a mechanism controls the safety of the operator. Any consideration of safety mechanisms should incorporate the following objectives and requirements.

Reliability

Given the conditions a mechanism or component is subjected to over a period of time, it must perform in a reliable way. Warning systems must also be reliable to the extent that they operate for the purposes for which they were designed, and should be reliable when exposed to oil, vibration, shock, water, etc.

Precise operation

The mechanism should operate positively, for example, precise linkage between rams and guards. The transmission angle on linkages must be minimal and control over wear on linkages is essential.

Protection against operator abuse and misuse

Abuse is associated with an operator endeavouring to open a guard before it is due to open, causing damage and wear, and as a result of harsh treatment. Misuse, on the other hand, is a calculated attempt to defeat the safety mechanism. Mechanisms must, therefore, be designed against both abuse and misuse.

Fail-safe

Where the component fails, it must do so in such a way that the machine stops and the guards stay closed, and not vice versa. This cannot always be achieved.

Correct method of assembly

Correct assembly of the safety mechanism is essential.

HAND TOOL SAFETY

Hand tools are designed for a specific purpose. The abuse and misuse of hand tools frequently result in injuries, many of which are of a serious nature, such as amputations of fingers, blinding and severing of arteries as a result of deep cuts. Hand tool-related injuries account for approximately 10% of lost-time injuries.

As with other forms of work equipment, hand tools should be maintained in an efficient state, in efficient working order and in good repair. This implies the frequent inspection of hand tools by management, with the removal from service of defective tools. The correct use of hand tools should be ensured through training and regular supervision of users. Hand tools used by contractors and their employees should also be subject to regular examination.

Hand tool inspections and examinations
A number of points should be considered when examining hand tools.

Chisels
'Mushroomed' chisel heads are a frequent cause of eye injury, including blinding. Mushrooming should be removed through grinding of chisel heads, which should also be kept free from dirt, grease and oil.

Hammers
The shaft should be in sound condition and securely fixed to the hammer head. Where the shaft is split, loose to the head, broken or damaged, it should be replaced. Chipped, distorted and badly worn hammer heads should not be used, and heads should be kept free of oil and grease.

Files
A file should never be used without a handle, and the handle should be in sound condition. Evidence of chips and other signs of damage indicate that a file could be dangerous when used.

Spanners
Open-ended spanners that are splayed or box spanners with splits should be discarded. Adjustable spanners and monkey wrenches should be examined regularly for evidence of free play and splaying of the jaws.

Screwdrivers
Handles and tips should be in good condition and worn-ended screwdrivers should never be used. A screwdriver should never be used as a chisel and, when using a screwdriver, the work should be clamped or secured. Employees should be trained and supervised to use the correct size screwdriver at all times.

SELECTION OF WORK EQUIPMENT

Any form of work equipment must be suitable for the purpose for which it is used or provided and the conditions under which it will be used. This includes mobile work equipment, such as lift trucks, and certain types of commercial vehicles.

In selecting work equipment, consideration should be given to:
♦ its initial integrity as an item of work equipment;
♦ the place where it will be used, including environmental factors, such as the level of lighting, wet or flammable atmospheres;
♦ the purpose for which it will be used;
♦ the form of energy to be used, for example, electrical energy;
♦ ergonomic considerations, in terms of operating positions, working heights, reach distances and the potential for excessive strain by the operator; and
♦ current HSE guidance, where available.

MAINTENANCE REQUIREMENTS FOR WORK EQUIPMENT

Under the PUWER 1998, there is an absolute requirement on employers to maintain work equipment in an efficient state, in efficient working order and in good repair. Moreover, where any machinery has a maintenance log, that log must be kept up to date.

Maintenance requirements should be incorporated in the manufacturer's information for the work equipment, which should be followed implicitly. The duties under the above regulations imply the need for a formally established planned preventive maintenance programme for all work equipment.

Planned preventive maintenance programmes

A planned preventive maintenance programme should incorporate the following elements:

- identification of each item of work equipment (including hand tools and portable electrical appliances), preferably by serial number and description, in a log;
- the procedures for maintenance of each item of work equipment;
- the frequency of maintenance;
- a manager who is responsible for ensuring the specified maintenance is undertaken fully and correctly; and
- any precautions necessary ensure maintenance is undertaken safely, for example, isolation of sources of energy.

PROVISION AND USE OF WORK EQUIPMENT REGULATIONS 1998

These regulations, which are supported by an HSC ACOP and HSE Guidance, cover, firstly, the more general requirements relating to the selection, suitability and maintenance of work equipment, together with procedures for dealing with specific risks and the giving of information, instruction and training. Part III deals with power presses and Part IV, mobile work equipment.

The regulations apply to all forms of work equipment, including second-hand work equipment, and the duties on employers are largely of an absolute nature.

Important definitions

A number of important definitions are incorporated in Regulation 2.

Work equipment means any machinery, appliance, apparatus or tool or installation for use at work (whether exclusively or not).

Use in relation to work equipment means any activity involving work equipment and includes starting, stopping, programming, setting, transporting, repairing, modifying, maintaining, servicing and cleaning.

Inspection in relation to an inspection under paragraph 1 or 2 of Regulation 6:
- (a) means such visual or more rigorous inspection by a competent person as is appropriate for the purpose described in that paragraph; and
- (b) where it is appropriate to carry out testing for the purpose, includes testing the nature and extent of which are appropriate for the purposes.

Part II of PUWER deals with the more general aspects of work equipment safety, which are dealt with below.

Regulation 4 – Suitability of work equipment

Every employer shall ensure that work equipment is so constructed or adapted as to be suitable for the purpose for which it is used or provided.

In selecting work equipment, every employer shall have regard to the working conditions and to the risks to the health and safety of persons that exist in the premises or undertaking in which that work equipment is to be used and any additional risk posed by the use of that work equipment.

Every employer shall ensure that work equipment is used only for operations for which, and under conditions for which, it is suitable.

In this regulation, 'suitable' means suitable in any respect, which it is reasonably foreseeable, will affect the health or safety of any person.

Regulation 5 – Maintenance

Every employer shall ensure that work equipment is maintained in an efficient state, in efficient working order and in good repair.

Every employer shall ensure that where any machinery has a maintenance log, the log is kept up to date.

Regulation 6 – Inspection

Every employer shall ensure that, where the safety of work equipment depends upon the installation condition, it is inspected:
  (a) after installation and before being put into service for the first time; or
  (b) after assembly at a new site or in a new location,

to ensure that it has been installed correctly and is safe to operate.

Every employer shall ensure that work equipment exposed to conditions causing deterioration, which is liable to result in dangerous situations, is inspected:
  (a) at suitable intervals; and
  (b) each time the exceptional circumstances that are liable to jeopardise the safety of the work equipment have occurred,

to ensure that health and safety conditions are maintained and that any deterioration can be detected and remedied in good time.

Every employer shall ensure that the results of an inspection made under this regulation are recorded and kept until the next inspection under this regulation is recorded.

Every employer shall ensure that no work equipment:
  (a) leaves his undertaking; or
  (b) is obtained from the undertaking of another person, is used in his undertaking, unless it is accompanied by physical evidence that the last inspection required to be made under this regulation has been carried out.

Regulation 7 – Specific risks

Where the use of work equipment is likely to involve a specific risk to health or safety, every employer shall ensure that:

(a) the use of that work equipment is restricted to those persons given the task of using it; and

(b) repairs, modifications, maintenance or servicing of that work equipment is restricted to those persons who have been specifically designated to perform operations of that description (whether or not also authorised to perform other operations).

The employer shall ensure that persons designated for the above purposes have received adequate training relating to any operations to which they have been so designated.

Regulation 8 – Information and instructions

Every employer shall ensure that all persons who use work equipment have available to them adequate health and safety information and, where appropriate, written instructions pertaining to the use of that work equipment.

Every employer shall ensure that any of his employees who supervises or manages the use of work equipment has available to him adequate health and safety information and, where appropriate, written instructions pertaining to the use of that work equipment.

The information and instructions required by either of the above paragraphs shall include information and, where appropriate, written instructions on:

(a) the conditions in which and the methods by which the work equipment may be used;

(b) foreseeable abnormal situations and the action to be taken if such a situation were to occur; and

(c) any conclusions to be drawn from experience in using the work equipment.

Information and instruction required by this regulation shall be readily comprehensible to those concerned.

Regulation 9 – Training

Every employer shall ensure that all persons who use work equipment have received adequate training for the purposes of health and safety, including training in the methods that may be adopted when using the work equipment, any risks that such use may entail and the precautions to be taken.

Every employer shall ensure that any of his employees who supervises or manages the use of work equipment has received adequate training for the purposes of health and safety, including training in the methods that may be adopted when using the work equipment, any risks that such use may entail and the precautions to be taken.

Regulation 11 – Dangerous parts of machinery

Every employer shall ensure that measures are taken in accordance with the next paragraph, which are effective:

(a) to prevent access to any dangerous part of machinery or to any rotating stock-bar; or

(b) to stop the movements of any dangerous part of machinery or rotating stock-bar before any part of a person enters a danger zone.

The measures required by the above paragraph shall consist of:

(a) the provision of fixed guards enclosing every dangerous part or rotating stock-bar where and to the extent that it is practicable to do so, but where or to the extent that it is not, then;

(b) the provision of other guards or protection devices where and to the extent that it is practicable to do so, but where or to the extent that it is not, then;

(c) the provision of jigs, holders, push-sticks or similar protection appliances used in conjunction with the machinery where and to the extent that is practicable to do so, but where or to the extent that it is not, then;

(d) the provision of information, instruction, training and supervision.

All guards and protection devices provided under sub-paragraphs (a) and (b) above shall:

(a) be suitable for the purpose for which they are provided;

(b) be of good construction, sound material and adequate strength;

(c) be maintained in an efficient state, in efficient working order and in good repair;

(d) not give rise to any increased risk to health or safety;

(e) not be easily bypassed or disabled;

(f) be situated at sufficient distance from the danger zone;

(g) not unduly restrict the operating cycle of the machinery, where such a view is necessary; and

(h) be so constructed or adapted that they allow operations necessary to fit or replace parts and for maintenance work, restricting access so that it is allowed only to the area where the work is to be carried out and, if possible, without having to dismantle the guard or protection device.

In this regulation **danger zone** means any zone in or around machinery in which a person is exposed to a risk to their health or safety from contact with a dangerous part of machinery or rotating stock-bar.

Regulation 12 – Protection against specified hazards

Every employer shall take measures to ensure that the exposure of a person using work equipment to any risk to his health or safety from any hazard specified in the third paragraph below is either prevented or, where this is not reasonably practicable, adequately controlled.

The measures required by paragraph one above shall:

(a) be measures other than the provision of PPE or of information, instruction, training and supervision, so far as is reasonably practicable; and

(b) include, where appropriate, measures to minimise the effects of the hazard as well as to reduce the likelihood of the hazard occurring.

The hazards referred to in paragraph one above are:

(a) any article or substance falling or being ejected from work equipment;

(b) rupture or disintegration of parts of work equipment;

(c) work equipment catching fire or overheating;

(d) the unintended or premature discharge of any article or of any gas, dust, liquid, vapour or other substance, which, in each case, is produced, used or stored in the work equipment; and

(e) the unintended or premature explosion of the work equipment or any article or substance produced, used or stored in it.

Regulation 13 – High or very low temperature

Every employer shall ensure that work equipment, parts of work equipment and any article or substance produced, used or stored in work equipment, which, in each case, is at a very high or low temperature, shall have protection where appropriate so as to prevent injury to any person by burn, scald or sear.

Regulations 14 to 18 – Controls and control systems

These regulations cover specific requirements in respect of:

♦ controls for starting or making a significant change in operating conditions;
♦ stop controls;
♦ emergency stop controls;
♦ controls; and
♦ control systems.

They are particularly relevant to those involved in the selection, examination, testing and maintenance of machinery.

Regulation 19 – Isolation from sources of energy

Every employer shall ensure that where appropriate work equipment is provided with suitable means to isolate it from all sources of energy.

The means mentioned above shall not be considered suitable unless they are clearly identifiable and readily accessible.

Every employer shall take appropriate measures to ensure that reconnection of any energy source to work equipment does not expose any person using the work equipment to any risk to his health or safety.

Regulation 20 - Stability

Every employer shall ensure that work equipment or any part of work equipment is stabilised by clamping or otherwise for purposes of health or safety.

Regulation 21 – Lighting

Every employer shall ensure that suitable and sufficient lighting, which takes account of the operations to be carried out, is provided at any place where a person uses work equipment.

Regulation 22 – Maintenance operations

Every employer shall take appropriate measures to ensure that work equipment is so constructed or adapted that, so far as is reasonably practicable, maintenance operations that involve a risk to health or safety can be carried out while the work equipment is shut down or, in other cases:

(a) maintenance operations can be carried out without exposing the person carrying them out to a risk to his health or safety; or
(b) appropriate measures can be taken for the protection of any person carrying out maintenance operations that involve a risk to his health or safety.

Regulation 23 – Markings

Every employer shall ensure that work equipment is marked in a clearly visible manner with any marking appropriate for reasons of health and safety.

Regulation 24 – Warnings

Every employer shall ensure that work equipment incorporates any warnings or warning devices that are appropriate for reasons of health and safety.

Warnings given by warning devices on work equipment shall not be appropriate unless they are unambiguous, easily perceived and easily understood.

Note: Part III of PUWER covers mobile work equipment and Part IV, power presses.

MANAGEMENT SYSTEMS

The duties of employers under PUWER must be read in conjunction with the general duties of employers under the MHSWR. The following factors must be incorporated in management systems involving work equipment of all types:

- the assessment of risks at the selection stage of new equipment in terms of:
    - the actual construction of the equipment;
    - the intended use of the equipment;
    - its suitability for use in the workplace; and
    - the conditions under which it will be used;
- taking into account the requirements and prohibitions imposed under the relevant statutory provisions, principally PUWER;
- on-going safety assessment of existing work equipment;
- the implementation of formally documented planned preventive maintenance systems;
- designation of certain trained persons to undertake identified high-risk activities, such as maintenance or fault-finding without guards in position;
- the provision of information, instruction and training for employees using any form of work equipment; and
- the development, documentation and implementation of management procedures aimed at ensuring safe use of work equipment in all work situations, including requirements for the inspection and examination of work equipment.

Second hand, hired and leased work equipment
Second hand equipment

In situations where existing work equipment is sold by one organisation to another and brought into use by the second organisation, under PUWER it becomes 'new equipment' and must meet the requirements for such equipment, even though it is second hand. This means that the purchasing organisation will need to ascertain that the equipment meets the specific hardware provisions of Regulations 11 to 24 before being put into use.

Hired and leased equipment

This equipment is treated in the same way as second hand equipment, namely, that it is classed as 'new equipment' at the hire/lease stage. On this basis, organisations hiring or leasing any item of work equipment will need to ensure that it meets the requirements of Regulations 11 to 24 before being put into use.

PRESSURE VESSELS AND PRESSURE SYSTEMS

Traditionally, pressure vessels have been associated with death and serious injuries caused by explosions. The hazards arising from the storage and use of steam, gases and liquids under pressure in pressure vessels, such as steam boilers, are principally associated with overheating in boilers and boiler corrosion.

Overheating in pressure vessels may arise as a result of:

♦ lack of testing and maintenance of controls and alarms, leading to malfunction; and
♦ in some cases, inadequate standards of control.

The long-term effects of boiler corrosion can be both explosions and boiler failure.

Pressure systems incorporate one or more pressure vessels, pipework and a range of protective devices fitted to pressure vessels, such as a high- and low-water alarm, water gauges, safety valves, pressure gauge, stop valve and anti-priming pipe, all of which are installed to ensure maximum safety of operation.

LEGAL REQUIREMENTS FOR PRESSURE SYSTEMS

Pressure Systems Safety Regulations 2000

Under these regulations a **pressure system** is defined as meaning:

♦ a system comprising one or more pressure vessels of rigid construction, any associated pipework and protective devices;
♦ the pipework with its protective devices to which a transportable pressure receptacle is, or is intended to be, connected; or
♦ a pipeline and its protective devices,

which contains a relevant fluid, but does not include a transportable pressure receptacle.

A **relevant fluid** means:

♦ steam;
♦ any fluid or mixture of fluids that is at a pressure greater than 0.5 bar above atmospheric pressure, and that is:
    ♦ a gas, or
    ♦ a liquid that would have a vapour pressure greater than 0.5 bar above atmospheric pressure when in equilibrium with its vapour at either the actual temperature of the liquid or 17.5°C; or
♦ a gas dissolved under pressure in a solvent contained in a porous substance at ambient temperature and that could be released from the solvent without the application of heat.

The main requirements of the regulations are outlined below.

Any person who designs, manufactures, imports or supplies any pressure system or any article that is intended to be a component part of any pressure system shall ensure that:

♦ the pressure system or article is properly designed and constructed from suitable material, so as to prevent danger;
♦ the pressure system or article is so designed and constructed that all necessary examinations for preventing danger can be carried out;

♦ where the pressure system has any means of access to its interior, it is so designed and constructed as to ensure, so far as is practicable, that access can be gained without danger; and

♦ the pressure system is provided with such protective devices as may be necessary for preventing danger, and any device designed to release contents shall do so safely, so far as is practicable [Regulation 4].

Anyone who designs, supplies, modifies or repairs any pressure system must provide sufficient written information to enable the requirements of the regulations to be complied with.

Any person who manufactures a pressure vessel shall ensure that it is correctly marked [Regulation 5].

The employer of a person who installs a pressure system shall ensure that nothing about the way in which it is installed gives rise to danger or otherwise impairs the operation of any protective device or inspection facility [Regulation 6].

The user of an installed pressure system and owner of a mobile system shall not operate the system or allow it to be operated unless he has established the safe operating limits of that system [Regulation 7].

The user of an installed system and owner of a mobile system shall not operate the system or allow it to be operated unless he has a **written scheme for the periodic examination**, by a competent person, of the following parts of the system;

♦ all protective devices;

♦ every pressure vessel and every pipeline in which (in either case) a defect may give rise to danger; and

♦ those parts of the pipe work in which a defect may give rise to danger,

and such parts of the system shall be identified in the scheme [Regulation 8].

The competent person must prepare a written report of the examination to a format prescribed in the regulations, including details of any repairs, modifications and changes in the safe operating limits of the system deemed necessary to prevent danger or ensure the safe operation of the system [Regulation 9].

Where a competent person carrying out an examination of a pressure system is of the opinion that it will give rise to imminent danger unless certain repairs or modifications are carried out, or unless suitable changes to the operating conditions have been made, he shall forthwith make a written report to the user, and within 14 days of the completion of the examination send a written report containing the same particulars to the enforcing authority [Regulation 10].

The user of a pressure system shall provide for any person operating the system adequate and suitable instructions for:

♦ the safe operation of the system; and

♦ the action to be taken in the event of emergency.

The user shall ensure that the system is not operated except in accordance with the instructions provided [Regulation 11].

The user shall ensure that the system is properly maintained in good repair, so as to prevent danger [Regulation 12].

The employer of a person who modifies or repairs a pressure system shall ensure that nothing about the way it is modified or repaired gives rise to danger or otherwise impairs the operation of any protective device or inspection facility [Regulation 13].

The user of an installed system and owner of a mobile system must keep a record of the report of the last examination by a competent person, information from suppliers and any agreement relating to postponement of examination by a competent person [Regulation 14].

Where a person is charged with an offence under the regulations, it shall be a defence for the person charged to prove:

♦ that the commission of the offence was due to the act or default of another person not being one of his employees; and

♦ that he took all reasonable precautions and exercised all due diligence to avoid the commission of the offence [Regulation 16].

KEY POINTS

♦ Machines have operational and non-operational parts.

♦ Hazards arising from machinery are associated with traps, the risk of entanglement, ejection of items from machines and contact with surfaces of machinery.

♦ A range of guards and safety devices is available to prevent injuries arising from the use of machinery.

♦ Abuse and misuse of hand tools is a common cause of injury.

♦ Work equipment must be maintained in an efficient state, in efficient working order and in good repair.

♦ Management systems must take account of the above requirement through the operation of planned preventive maintenance systems.

♦ The PUWER 1998 lays down a hierarchy of protection measures with regard to work equipment.

♦ Second hand, hired and leased work equipment is subject to the requirements of PUWER.

10 Electrical Safety

Approximately 30 people at work die every year as a result of electrocution. Most of these fatalities arise from contact with overhead and underground cables. Other people may suffer shock, which can cause permanent and severe injury as a result of, for instance, falling from a ladder following a shock, and burns.

This chapter examines the hazards associated with the use of electricity, including the risk of fire, the principal precautions and the requirements of the Electricity at Work Regulations 1989.

THE PRINCIPAL HAZARDS

Hazards arising from the use of electricity can broadly be divided into two categories, namely: the risk of death and serious injury arising from contact with live parts; and the risk of fire and explosion where electrical discharge could be the source of ignition.

Human injury is associated with shock, burns, various physical injuries caused by explosions, the use of microwaves, accumulators and, batteries, and eye injuries inflicted during electric arc welding.

Electric shock

This is the effect on the body and, in particular, the central nervous system, produced by the passage of electric current. The effect on the human body varies according to the strength of the current which, in turn, varies with the voltage and the electrical resistance of the body. The resistance of the body varies according to the points of entry and exit of the current and other factors, such as body weight and/or the presence of moisture on the surface of the body.

In any consideration of electrical safety, Ohm's Law is significant.

Ohm's Law

$$R \text{ (Resistance)} = \frac{E \text{ (Pressure in volts)}}{I \text{ (Current in amps)}}$$

TABLE 10 : TYPICAL RESPONSES TO CURRENT/VOLTAGE

Voltage	Response	Current
15 volts	Threshold of feeling	0.002–0.005 amps
20 – 25 volts	Threshold of pain	–
30 volts	Muscular spasm (non-release)	0.015 amps
70 volts	Minimum for death	0.1 amps
120 volts	Maximum for 'safety'	0.002 amps
200 – 240 volts	Most serious/fatal accident	0.2 amps

Common cause of death is ventricular fibrillation (spasm) of the heart muscle, which occurs at 0.05 amps. The vascular system ceases to function and the victim dies of suffocation. It is important to remember the old maxim – 'It's the current that kills!'

First aid for a victim of electric shock must be cardiac massage together with mouth-to-mouth resuscitation until normal breathing and the heart action return. A victim who is 'locked on' to a live electrical appliance must not be approached until the appliance is electrically dead.

Burns

A current passing through a conductor produces heat. Burns can be caused by contact with hot conductors or by the passage of electric current through the body. Electric arcing from short circuits may also cause burns. **(See 'The Risk of Fire')**

Explosions

Electrical short circuit or sparking from the electrical contacts in switches or other equipment is a common cause of explosions and subsequent human injury or death. This presupposes the presence of a flammable atmosphere, for example, vapour, dust or gas.

Eye injuries

These can result from exposure to ultraviolet rays from accidental arcing in a process such as welding.

Microwave apparatus

Microwaves can damage the soft tissues of the body.

Accumulators and batteries

Hydrogen gas may be produced as a by-product of battery charging, which can result in explosive atmospheres with the subsequent risk of burns.

THE RISK OF FIRE

Electrical energy is a common source of ignition of major fires. Some insulating materials and materials used for electrical connections may be flammable and can give rise to small fires in switchgear, distribution boxes or electricity sub-stations. The risk of losses from fire increases when local fires go undetected.

Sources of electrical ignition include:

♦ **sparks** – between conductors or a conductor and earth;

♦ **arcs** – which are a larger and brighter discharge of electrical energy and are more likely to cause a fire;

♦ **short circuits** – which arise when a current finds a path from live to return other than through electrical apparatus, resulting in high current flow, heating of conductors to white heat and arcing;

♦ **overloading** – where too much current flow causes heating of conductors; and

♦ **old and defective/damaged wiring** – through breakdown of the insulation resulting in short circuit, or the use of progressively more equipment on an old circuit resulting in overloading.

PRINCIPLES OF ELECTRICAL SAFETY

The prime objective of safety measures is to protect people from the risk of electric shock, together with fire and burns, arising from contact with electricity. There are two basic preventative measures against electric shock, namely:

♦ protection against direct contact, for example, by providing suitable and adequate insulation for parts of equipment liable to be charged with electricity; and

♦ protection against indirect contact, for example, by providing effective earthing for metallic enclosures, which are liable to be charged with electricity if the basic insulation fails for any reason.

Where it is not possible to provide adequate insulation as protection against direct contact, a range of measures is available, including protection by the use of physical barriers or enclosures, and protection by position, that is, placing live parts out of reach.

PROTECTION MEASURES

Earthing

This implies connection to the general mass of earth in such a manner as will ensure at all times an immediate discharge of electrical energy without danger. Earthing, to provide protection against indirect contact with electricity, can be achieved in a number of ways, including the connection of extraneous conductive parts of premises (radiators, taps, water pipes) to the main earthing terminal of the electrical installation. This creates an equipotential zone and eliminates the risk of shock that could occur if a person touched two different parts of the metalwork liable to be charged, under earth fault conditions, at different voltages.

Where an earth fault exists, such as when a live part touches an enclosed conductive part, for example, metalwork, it is vital to ensure that the electrical supply is automatically disconnected. This protection is provided by the use of overcurrent devices, ie correctly rated fuses or circuit breakers, or by correctly rated and placed residual current devices. The maintenance of earth continuity is vital.

Fuses

A fuse is basically a strip of metal of such size as would melt at a predetermined value of current flow. It is placed in the electrical circuit and, on melting, cuts off the current to the circuit and the electrical appliance. A fuse should be of a type and rating appropriate to the circuit and the appliance it protects.

Circuit breakers

These devices incorporate a mechanism that trips a switch from the ON to OFF position if an excess of current flows in the circuit. A circuit breaker should be of the type and rating of the circuit and appliance it protects.

Earth leakage circuit breakers (residual current devices)

Fuses and circuit breakers do not necessarily provide total protection against electric shock. Earth leakage circuit breakers provide protection against earth leakage faults, particularly at those locations where effective earthing cannot necessarily be achieved.

Residual current devices for protecting people have a rated tripping current (sensitivity) of not more than 30 millamps.

Reduced voltage

Reduced voltage systems are another form of protection against electric shock, the most commonly used system being the 110 volt centre point earthed system. In this system the secondary winding of the transformer providing the 110 volt supply is centre tapped to earth, thereby ensuring that at no part of the 110 volt circuit can the voltage to earth exceed 55 volts.

Safe systems of work

Where work is to be undertaken on electrical apparatus or part of a circuit, a formally operated safe system of work is essential. This commonly takes the form of a Permit to Work system, which ensures the following procedures and precautions:

- ◆ switching out and locking off the electricity supply, ie isolation;
- ◆ checking by the use of an appropriate voltage detection instrument that the circuit, that part of same to be worked on, is dead before work commences;
- ◆ high levels of supervision and control to ensure that work is undertaken correctly and that Permit to Work procedures are followed;
- ◆ particular attention must be given to the precautions where electrical installation or maintenance work is to be undertaken in wet surroundings, in external areas and in confined spaces;
- ◆ appliances should be examined by a competent person on a regular basis, including the leads, and any extension leads used that may have become damaged;
- ◆ physical precautions, such as the erection of barriers and signs restricting access to the area, are implemented; and
- ◆ formal cancellation of the Permit to Work once the work is completed satisfactorily and return to service of the appliance, plant or system in question.

New electrical installations should be installed in accordance with recommended standards, such as BS 7671 **Requirements for electrical installations**.

Planned preventive maintenance

All electrical equipment, appliances and installations should be maintained to prevent danger. Planned preventive maintenance programmes should incorporate a system of regular visual examination and inspection and, where necessary, testing by a competent person.

ELECTRICAL EQUIPMENT AND APPLIANCES

The regular examination and testing of electrical equipment and appliances is a prerequisite of sound electrical safety procedures. As part of an on-going system, the following points should be considered:

- ◆ electrical systems should be designed, installed and maintained by competent persons in accordance with the Electricity at Work Regulations 1989, HSE Memorandum of Guidance and the Institute of Electrical Engineers (IEE) ('Wiring') Regulations;
- ◆ competent persons should be truly competent for the particular tasks they undertake. Blanket competence for all tasks is not recommended;
- ◆ electrical equipment and appliances should meet the requirements of current UK and EU standards;
- ◆ portable electrical appliances should be maintained and tested at appropriate frequencies by a competent person;
- ◆ there must be a formal procedure where suspect electrical equipment and appliances are taken out of service until inspected and tested by a competent person;

♦ visual inspections of electrical equipment and appliances, flexible cables, plugs and sockets should be undertaken on a regular basis;

♦ electrical equipment and appliances should be used safely by trained employees; and

♦ particular attention must be paid to double insulated appliances, ie those appliances marked with a 'double square' symbol. As such appliances do not incorporate an earth lead, they must be correctly connected if the plug is not one of the moulded-on type.

Visual inspection of electrical appliances

In addition to the testing of appliances by a competent person, employers are recommended to ensure the following visual inspections are made on a regular basis.

Plugs

The plug should be inspected to ensure it is safely connected to the cable, ie there are no frayed ends or loose wires, and there is no evidence of damage to the plug casing.

Cables

Flexible cable should be inspected for evidence of damage. Typical causes of damage are being run over, being dragged over sharp surfaces, making contact with moving parts of equipment and machinery, making contact with hot surfaces or chemicals, being constantly flexed or stretched near the point of termination to either the plug or appliance that the cable supplies.

Joints in cables

Poor joints in a cable should be avoided, and a complete run of cable used, unless a correct joint is made using a specific cable coupler. The danger may not be obvious but the earth path may be broken and, therefore, no protection provided should a further fault make the casing of the equipment live. Maintenance procedures should ensure the earth path is checked regularly.

Sockets

Sockets should be examined for evidence of physical damage. They should not be overloaded, for example, by supplying too many appliances. Fused blocks should be used where a socket is supplying more than one appliance.

PORTABLE ELECTRICAL APPLIANCES

Approximately 25% of incidents involving electricity are associated with portable electrical appliances. To ensure compliance with the general provisions of the **Electricity at Work Regulations 1989**, there is an implied duty on employers, in particular, to undertake some form of testing of electrical equipment. Further guidance and information on portable appliance testing is incorporated in the **Memorandum of Guidance,** which accompanies the Regulations and **HSE (1990): Guidance Note PM32: The safe use of portable electrical apparatus (Electrical safety).**

Electrical equipment is very broadly defined in the regulations as including anything used, intended to be used or installed for use, to generate, provide, transmit, transform, rectify, convert, conduct, distribute, control, store, measure or use electrical energy.

Portable appliances include such items as electric drills, kettles, floor polishers and lamps, in fact any item that will connect into a 13 amp socket. 110 volt industrial portable electrical equipment should also be considered as portable appliances.

SAFETY OF APPLIANCES

The operator or user of an electrical appliance is protected from the risk of electric shock by insulation and earthing of the appliance, which prevent the individual from coming into contact with a live electrical part. For insulation to be effective it must offer a high resistance at high voltages. In the case of earthing, it must offer a low impedance to any potentially high fault current that may arise.

A principle of electrical safety is that there should be two levels of protection for the operator or user and this results in two classes of appliance.

Class 1 appliances incorporate both earthing and insulation (earthed appliances), whereas **Class 2** appliances are doubly insulated. The testing procedures for Class 1 and Class 2 appliances differ according to the type of protection provided.

APPLIANCE TESTING PROGRAMMES

Testing should be undertaken on a regular basis and should incorporate the following:
(a) inspection for any visible signs of damage to or deterioration of the casing, plug terminals and cable sheath;
(b) an earth continuity test with a substantial current capable of revealing a partially severed conductor; and
(c) high voltage insulation tests.

The test results should be recorded, thus enabling future comparisons to determine any deterioration or degradation of the appliance.

Control system

The control system should include:
(a) clear identification of the specific responsibility for appliance testing;
(b) maintenance of a log listing portable appliances, date of test and a record of test results; and
(c) a procedure for labelling appliances when tested with the date for the next inspection and test.

Any appliance that fails the above tests should be removed from use.

FREQUENCY TESTING

An estimation of the frequency of testing must take into account the type of equipment, its usage in terms of frequency of use and risk of damage, and any recommendations made by the manufacturer/supplier.

THE USE OF PORTABLE APPLIANCE TESTING EQUIPMENT

Electrical tests of appliances should confirm the integrity or otherwise of earthing and insulation. To simplify this task a competent person may use a proprietary portable appliance testing (PAT) device. In this case, the unit under test is plugged into the socket of the testing device. Some tests are carried out through the plug, others through both the plug and an auxiliary probe to the casing of the appliance.

THE TESTS

Two basic tests are offered by PAT devices, namely:

1. Earth bond test

This applies a substantial test current, typically around 25 amps, down the earth pin of the plug to an earth test probe, which should be connected by the user to any exposed metalwork on the casing of the unit under test. From this the resistance of the earth bond is determined by the PAT device.

2. Insulation test

This applies a test voltage, typically 500 volts DC, between the live and neutral terminals bonded together and earth, from which the insulation resistance is calculated by the PAT device.

Other tests

1. Flash test

This tests the insulation at a higher voltage, typically 1.5kV for Class 1 appliances and 3kV for Class 2 appliances. From this test the PAT device derives a leakage current indication. This is a more stringent test of the insulation that can provide an early warning of insulation defects developing in the appliance.

It is recommended that this test should be undertaken at a greater frequency than every three months to avoid overstressing the insulation.

2. Load test

This test measures the load resistance between live and neutral terminals to ensure that it is not too low for safe operation.

3. Operation test

This is a further level of safety testing that proves the above tests were valid.

4. Earth leakage test

This is undertaken during the operation test as a further test of the insulation under its true working conditions. It should also ensure that appliances are not responsible for nuisance tripping of residual current devices.

5. Fuse test

This will indicate the integrity of the fuse and that the appliance is switched on before the other tests.

Earthed Class 1 appliances

The following tests are undertaken:

(a) earth bond test;

(b) insulation test; and

(c) in certain cases, flash test.

Double-insulated Class 2 appliances

The following tests are undertaken:

(a)   insulation test; and

(b)   flash test.

ELECTRICITY AT WORK REGULATIONS 1989

These regulations apply to all work associated with electricity and state general principles of electrical safety rather than detailed requirements. Further detailed information is available in the HSE (1989) Memorandum of Guidance on the Electricity at Work Regulations 1989, Guidance on Regulations.

The regulations impose duties on 'duty holders', namely, employers, employees and managers of mines and quarries.

The term 'electrical equipment' is defined as including anything used or installed for use to generate, provide, transmit, transform rectify, convert, conduct, distribute, control, store, measure or use electrical energy.

Employers' duties

The general requirements of these regulations include the following:

♦   so far as is reasonably practicable, all systems to be constructed and maintained as to prevent danger;

♦   work activities must be carried out in such a manner as to prevent danger;

♦   protective equipment must be suitable for its purpose, suitably maintained and properly used;

♦   no equipment must be put into use where its strength and capability may be exceeded as to give rise to danger;

♦   equipment must not be exposed to adverse or hazardous environments;

♦   earthing or other suitable precautions must be provided where a system may become electrically charged;

♦   conductors must be insulated or be safe by position;

♦   suitable precautions must be taken to maintain the integrity of referenced conductors;

♦   joints and connections must be mechanically and electrically suitable;

♦   efficient means must be provided for protection against excess current;

♦   suitable means must be provided for cutting off the supply of electrical energy and the isolation of any circuit;

♦   adequate precautions must be taken on equipment made dead;

♦   adequate precautions must be taken on work on or near live conductors;

♦   adequate working space, means of access and lighting to be provided where necessary; and

♦   competent persons must be appointed where technical knowledge or experience is necessary to prevent danger.

Defence under the regulations

Where charged with an offence under the regulations, a person may plead that he took all reasonable precautions and exercised all due diligence to prevent the commission of the offence.

KEY POINTS

♦ Electrocution is one of the principal causes of death at work and in the home.

♦ Only a very small amount of current is needed to cause death through ventricular fibrillation (heart spasm).

♦ Other injuries can be caused as result of burns, explosion and exposure to ultraviolet rays in the case of the eyes during welding.

♦ Electrical discharge can be a significant cause of fire.

♦ The three principles of electrical safety are insulation, isolation and earthing.

♦ Electrical protection involves the use of fuses, circuit breakers, earth leakage circuit breakers and reduced voltage systems, together with the operation of safe systems of work.

♦ A formal system for the inspection and testing of equipment and appliances should be operated by all employers.

♦ The Electricity at Work Regulations 1989 lay down requirements for the safe use of electricity at work.

♦ Electrical installation and maintenance should be undertaken by, or under the supervision of, competent persons.

11 *Occupational Health & Hygiene*

This chapter is concerned with the classification of health risks and an outline of some of the more common occupational diseases and conditions. The various areas of occupational health and hygiene practice, largely directed at protecting the health of workers, along with health surveillance techniques are also considered, together with occupational health initiatives covering, for instance, smoking at work.

OCCUPATIONAL HEALTH RISKS

What is occupational health?

Occupational health is concerned with the health of people at work and is defined as a branch of preventive medicine that examines:

(a)   the relationship of work to health; and

(b)   the effects of work on the worker.

Whilst there is a general duty on employers to ensure, so far as is reasonably practicable, the health of employees and others under the HSWA, more specific legislation, such as the Noise at Work Regulations, COSHH and Control of Asbestos at Work Regulations greatly reinforce and extend this general duty. In many cases it has entailed the employment of occupational health practitioners, such as occupational health nurses and occupational physicians in organisations with identified health risks.

What is occupational hygiene?

Occupational hygiene is a branch of science concerned with the identification, measurement, evaluation and control of airborne contaminants, and physical phenomena, such as noise, which could have otherwise adverse effects on the health of people at work.

OCCUPATIONAL DISEASES AND CONDITIONS

Occupational health risks are associated with diseases and conditions arising from work activities, such as lead poisoning and repetitive strain injury (RSI). Many of these diseases and conditions such as lead poisoning have been known since Roman times, and much of the earlier British legislation on this subject goes back to the days of the Industrial Revolution. They are associated with work as the causative factor and, in the majority of cases, must be reported to the enforcement authority when diagnosed by a medical practitioner.

As such, occupational diseases and conditions may be 'reportable' under the RIDDOR 1995 to the enforcement authority and 'prescribed' under social security legislation for the purposes of industrial injuries benefit.

Classification of the causes

People at work may contract diseases and conditions through a wide range of physical, chemical, biological and work-related causes. For instance, people handling chemicals might contract non-infective dermatitis, those exposed to excessive noise may contract occupational deafness and people working in close proximity to animals could become infected by anthrax or brucellosis. Similarly, those engaged in manual tasks of a repetitive nature run the risk of contracting a work-related upper limb disorder.

Examples of diseases and conditions coming within these classifications include the following.

Physical causes

    Temperature – heat stroke, heat stress, heat cataract, hypothermia.

    Noise – noise-induced hearing loss (occupational deafness).

    Vibration – vibration-induced white finger.

    Pressure – decompression sickness.

    Radiation – radiation sickness.

    Dust – coal worker's pneumoconiosis.

Chemical causes

    Organic compounds – occupational cancers.

    Acids and alkalis – non-infective dermatitis.

    Metals – lead and mercury poisoning.

    Non-metals – arsenic and mercury poisoning.

Biological causes

    Animal-borne (zoonoses) – brucellosis, anthrax, psittacosis.

    Human-borne – viral hepatitis.

    Vegetable-borne – farmer's lung (aspergillosis).

Work-related (ergonomic) causes

    Job movements – cramp in relation to handwriting and typing, tennis elbow, work-related upper limb disorders.

    Friction and pressure – bursitis, cellulites, 'beat' conditions, such as beat wrist and beat knee, and tenosynovitis (traumatic inflammation of the tendons or associated tendon sheaths of the hand or forearm).

THE MORE COMMON OCCUPATIONAL DISEASES AND CONDITIONS

Dermatitis

This is the most common occupational disease, manifested by scaling, cracking, reddening, blistering and crusting of the skin. Many agents used in workplaces cause dermatitis, and these can broadly be classified into two groups.

1. Primary irritants cause dermatitis at the site of contact with the skin if permitted to remain in contact with the skin for a sufficient period of time and in a particular concentration. Primary irritants include strong acids and alkalis, solvents and mineral oils.

2. Secondary cutaneous sensitisers include substances such as rubber, nickel, many chemical compounds and certain plants, such as those of the primula family. Where there is continuing exposure to these substances, the skin may become sensitised with the result that even the slightest exposure may produce a skin response. Sensitisation is very much a matter for clinical investigation to identify the sensitising agent.

Heat stroke

This condition may be encountered in workers in high-temperature environments, such as foundries and steel works. In some cases, the person falls unconscious and shows an extremely high body temperature. Heat stroke is caused by a failure of the body's thermoregulatory system, which is the system that enables the individual to adjust to very high or very low temperatures.

Emergency treatment should be directed at reducing the patient's body temperature as quickly as possible.

Pneumoconiosis

The pneumoconioses are a group of diseases associated with the inhalation of dust in its various forms. Table 11 indicates the particular form of pneumoconiosis and the causative agent.

TABLE 11 : THE VARIOUS FORMS OF PNEUMOCONIOSIS

Disease	Causative agent
Anthracosis	Coal (anthracite) dust
Silicosis	Free silica particles
Siderosis	Iron particles
Asbestosis	Asbestos fibres
Byssinosis	Cotton dust
Coal worker's pneumoconiosis	Coal dust

Inhalation of these dusts results in fibrosis, ie damage to lung tissue, distortion of the lung structure, loss of elasticity of the lung and varying degrees of interference with the respiratory function.

Asbestosis

This is a fibrotic condition of the lung arising from the inhalation of asbestos fibres. It results in thickening and scarring of the lung tissue. People suffering from the disease show breathlessness, may have an unproductive cough, a bluish tinge to the skin and, in some cases, clubbing of the fingers.

A substantial number of cases develop mesothelioma, lung cancer or cancer of the bronchus.

Occupational cancers

Many chemical substances, such as aromatic amines, benzene, chromates, vinyl chloride monomer (VCM) and the combustion products of coal, are associated with malignant cancers of the bladder, scrotum, skin, liver and bronchus.

Exposure to radiation and radon may also cause cancer.

Lead poisoning

This may be contracted through exposure to both organic and inorganic lead compounds, generally having an effect on the central nervous system. The effects of acute exposure include restlessness, excitement and muscular twitchings. In the case of chronic exposure to lead, the condition is manifested by headache, pallor, a blue line around the gums, anaemia, palsy and encephalopathy, a form of mental disorder.

Viral hepatitis

Infection with viral hepatitis (inflammation of the liver) takes two forms. Hepatitis A is a form of epidemic jaundice spread through human contact or through contaminated food and water.

Serum hepatitis or hepatitis B, on the other hand, may arise in those who handle blood or blood products, for example, medical practitioners, laboratory technicians. The symptoms include muscle pain, malaise, headache, nausea, vomiting, anorexia, abdominal pain and pruritis.

Work-related upper limb disorders

These are a group of conditions arising from RSI. They commonly affect groups such as keyboard operators, assembly workers and people involved in tasks of a repetitive nature involving forceful, frequent twisting and repetitive movements.

This group includes tenosynovitis, tennis elbow, carpal tunnel syndrome, tendonitis and peritendinitis. The clinical signs and symptoms include local aching pain, swelling, tenderness and crepitus (a grating sensation in the joint), which are aggravated by movement or pressure.

(See further chapter 13 **Display screen equipment**.

Noise-induced hearing loss (occupational deafness)

Exposure to noise at work can result in hearing loss, which may be mild or severe.

The mild form is characterised by occasional difficulty in conversation with people, people's speech may be indistinct and there is difficulty in hearing the normal domestic sounds, such as a clock ticking.

With a severe degree of deafness, there is greater difficulty in conversation, even when face to face with people. In addition to the symptoms shown by a mild degree of deafness, with severe cases there is a sensation of whistling or ringing in the ears, the condition known as tinnitus.

Vibration-induced white finger

This condition is associated with the use of vibratory hand tools operating at specific frequencies, such as pneumatic tools, chain saws and electrically operated power tools.

Initial symptoms include mild tingling and numbness of the fingers. Subsequently, the tips of the fingers become blanched, particularly early in the morning or during cold weather. On further exposure the affected area increases, sometimes to the base of the fingers, sensitivity during attacks is reduced and the characteristic reddening of the areas marks the end of an attack causing severe pain. Prolonged and further exposure may cause further advancement of the condition with the fingers sometimes taking on a blue-black appearance. In severe cases, gangrene and necrosis (death of tissue) have been known.

Legionnaires' disease

This disease is caused by the inhalation of aerosols containing the bacterium, *Legionella pneumophila*. Legionella bacteria occur in at least ten different forms and are widely distributed in the environment. They are commonly encountered in water cooling systems, recirculating and hot water systems, air conditioning systems, humidifiers, water storage tanks, calorifiers and associated pipework to these systems. They are also commonly found in rivers, streams, ponds and in the soil.

Initial symptoms include high fever, chills, headache and muscle pain. After a short period a dry cough develops and most patients have difficulty in breathing. Some patients may develop diarrhoea or vomiting and may eventually become confused or delirious. The disease may be fatal in some cases.

HEALTH SURVEILLANCE

Health surveillance is an area of occupational health practice that entails the regular review of the health of employees exposed to different forms of health risk, for instance, to hazardous substances, work-related upper limb disorders, noise and radiation.

The duty on employers to provide health surveillance for employees can be found in regulations, including the COSHH Regulations and the MHSWR.

COSHH

Under these regulations there is a broad duty on an employer to ensure the provision of suitable health surveillance where appropriate. This may arise as a result of a health risk assessment in respect of a defined substance hazardous to health.

More specifically, health surveillance is necessary where an employee is exposed to a listed substance or process, such as VCM, potassium or sodium chromate or dichromate. Health surveillance must also be provided:

(a) where there is an identifiable disease or adverse health effect that may be related to the exposure;

(b) where there is a reasonable likelihood that this may occur under the particular work conditions; and

(c) where there are valid techniques for detecting indication of it.

In this latter case, a typical identifiable disease is non-infective dermatitis, commonly encountered through exposure to detergents, detergent sanitisers, solvents and oils.

MHSWR

These regulations place an absolute duty on every employer to ensure that his employees are provided with such health surveillance as is appropriate, having regard to their health and safety issues, as identified by the (risk) assessment.

Much will depend upon the outcome of the risk assessment undertaken. In most cases, however, many employees may be exposed to some form of health risk of a physical, chemical, biological or psychological nature at some point during their employment.

HEALTH AND SAFETY EXECUTIVE GUIDANCE ON HEALTH SURVEILLANCE

HSE guidance accompanying the MHSWR outlines the objectives of health surveillance thus:

'The primary benefit, and therefore the objective, of health surveillance should be to detect adverse health effects at an early stage, thereby enabling further harm to be prevented.

In addition the results of health surveillance can provide a means of:

(a) checking the effectiveness of control measures;

(b) providing feedback on the accuracy of risk assessment; and

(c) identifying and protecting individuals at increased risk because of the nature of their work.'

Once it is decided that health surveillance is appropriate, it should be maintained during the employee's employment unless the risk to which the worker is exposed and associated health effects are short term. The minimum requirement for health surveillance is the keeping of an individual health record.

The guidance goes on to state:

'Where appropriate, health surveillance may involve one or more health surveillance procedures depending upon suitability in the circumstances. Such procedures can include:

(a) inspection of readily detectable conditions by a responsible person acting within the limits of their training and experience;

(b) enquiries about symptoms, inspection and examination by a qualified person such as an occupational health nurse;

(c) medical surveillance, which may include clinical examination and measurements of physiological and psychological effects by an appropriately qualified person;

(d) biological effect monitoring, ie the measurement and assessment of early biological effects such as diminished lung function in exposed workers;

(e) biological monitoring, ie the measurement and assessment of workplace agents or their metabolites either in tissues, secreta, excreta, expired air or any combination of these in exposed workers.'

The purpose of health surveillance

Objectives

Wherever employees may be exposed to substances hazardous to health in the course of their work, the objectives of a health surveillance strategy are:

(a) the protection of the health of individuals by detecting adverse changes, attributed to exposure to substances hazardous to health, at the earliest possible stage;

(b) assistance in assessing the effectiveness of physical control measures;

(c) the collection, maintenance and use of data for the detection and evaluation of hazards to health; and

(d) assessment of immunological status of employees doing specific work with microorganisms hazardous to health.

The outcome of health surveillance

The results of any health surveillance procedure should lead to some form of action, which will be to the benefit of employees.

HEALTH SURVEILLANCE TECHNIQUES AND PROCEDURES

An appropriate strategy to protect people at work from risks to their health should incorporate one or more of the following elements.

Pre-employment health screening

This form of health surveillance, frequently undertaken by occupational health nurses, can include not only an assessment of general fitness for the job but also specific aspects of that job, such as vision screening of drivers and DSE users, initial audiometry for people who may subsequently be exposed to noise and the assessment of individual disability levels where manual handling operations are involved. This form of screening may also seek information as to previous illnesses through the use of a personal health questionnaire completed by the job applicant.

Primary and secondary monitoring

Primary monitoring is concerned largely with the clinical observation of sick people who may seek treatment or advice on their conditions. This form of observation may identify new risks that were not previously considered.

Secondary monitoring, on the other hand, is directed at controlling the hazards to health that have already been recognised. Audiometry is a classic form of secondary monitoring whereby the hearing levels of employees are checked on, for example, a six-monthly or annual basis to assess whether there has been any further deterioration in hearing due to exposure to noise. The annual health screening of food handlers by an occupational health nurse is an important form of secondary monitoring.

Health supervision of vulnerable groups

Certain groups, such as young persons, the aged, the disabled and pregnant workers, may be more vulnerable to health risks than others. Special attention must be given to these groups in terms of health counselling, assistance with rehabilitation and reorganisation of their jobs to remove harmful factors.

Assessment of health risks

This form of assessment can involve, for instance, examination of current work layouts and arrangements, taking into account ergonomic aspects of jobs and the potential for stress and fatigue. The effects of shift working, long periods of work and the physical and mental effects of repetitive tasks may also be taken into account. Shift workers and those working long shifts could well benefit from health surveillance.

Health records

Apart from the duty to maintain health records under the COSHH Regulations, there is clearly a case for maintaining a health record for every employee. Not only is it possible for the occupational health practitioner to obtain useful information on unidentified health risks from accumulated records, but an individual's health record could well be important evidence where an employee may be taking a civil action for negligence against the organisation many years later, or where enforcement action may be taken under current health and safety legislation.

The following records on individual employees are recommended:

♦ pre-employment and subsequent health questionnaires submitted by employees;

♦ details of pre-employment and subsequent health examinations and screening undertaken by an occupational health nurse;

♦ relevant medical and occupational history, smoking habits, disabilities and handicaps;

♦ injuries resulting from occupational and non-occupational accidents;

♦ illnesses occurring at work or on the way to or from work;

♦ history of sickness absence;

♦ details of occupational diseases and conditions diagnosed;

♦ care and treatment provided;

♦ advice given, recommendations and work limits imposed;

♦ referrals made to other medical specialists or agencies;

♦ correspondence relating to the health of individual employees;

♦ dispersal of cases following emergencies and treatment; and

♦ details of communication between occupational health practitioners and others, including written reports.

OCCUPATIONAL HYGIENE

As stated earlier in this chapter, occupational hygiene is an area of health protection concerned with the identification, measurement, evaluation and control of contaminants and other phenomena, such as noise, which can have adverse effects on health. As such it entails monitoring of the working environment on a continuous or intermittent basis using a range of techniques.

ENVIRONMENTAL MONITORING

Environmental monitoring implies the continuous or intermittent sampling of workplace atmospheres with a view to detecting the presence of contaminants. These contaminants may take the form of gases, fumes, dusts and mists. It also entails other activities, such as radiation and noise monitoring, which are covered in separate chapters.

Environmental monitoring can be undertaken on a short-term and long-term basis.

Short-term sampling

Generally known as 'grab sampling' or 'snap sampling', this implies taking an immediate sample of air from the workplace and, in most cases, passing it through a particular chemical reagent, which responds to the contaminant being monitored. Glass stain detector tubes, specific to the contaminant being sampled, are commonly used, which give a quick indication as to whether there is an unhealthy environment that needs further sampling on a long-term basis.

Long-term sampling

Long-term sampling techniques incorporate the use of instruments which are, broadly, of two types:

♦ **Personal samplers**

These devices are attached to the individual to measure total exposure during, for example, a working shift. They may take a number of forms, for example, gas monitoring badges, filtration devices and impingers (see next page).

♦ **Static sampling systems**

These are sampling systems stationed in the working area that sample continuously over a period of time, for example, a working shift, or over longer periods where necessary. They operate using mains- or battery-operated pumps that draw in a constant flow of air for sampling during operation. Long-term stain detector tubes are also used for this purpose.

PERSONAL SAMPLING INSTRUMENTS

These take a number of forms depending upon the contaminant being monitored, and include the following.

Gas monitoring badges

This type of device, worn by the operator, incorporates a solid sorbent or impregnated carrier in the form of a badge. Contact is by diffusion, and the level of exposure is indicated by a change in colour or through analytical determination.

Filtration devices

These devices incorporate a low flow constant sample pump, usually located on a waist belt, linked to a sampling head. The sampling head is located close to the operator's breathing zone and incorporates a filter. Airborne contamination is subsequently arrested in the filter.

Determination of the results is by gravimetric analysis, solvent extraction, gas chromatography or atomic absorption techniques.

Impingers

With this type of personal sampler, air is bubbled through an impinger , a glass cyclone or bubble tube, located in the operator's breathing zone, which contains an appropriate absorbing medium. Impingers work in conjunction with a constant flow sampling pump.

Analysis is by gas chromatography or spectrophotometry.

Sorbent tubes

These incorporate a tube filled with two layers of solid adsorbent capable of completely removing chemicals from the air. The tube has breakable end tips and is inserted into a tube holder located in the operator's breathing zone. They operate in conjunction with a constant flow sample pump.

STATIC SAMPLING EQUIPMENT

This form of equipment is located in the working area and samples continuously in most cases. Various devices are available.

Constant flow pump devices

This type of sampling device incorporates a pump that takes in a measured quantity of air on a continuing basis. For sampling dusts, selective filters are used, whereas in the case of volatile substances, a range of absorbing media is used.

Long-term stain detector tubes

These are linked to a constant flow pump and tube holder, sampling over an eight hour period in most cases.

Direct monitoring devices

These include multi-gas detection and monitoring devices that are capable of monitoring the concentration in air of a number of, particularly, gases at any one time.

They incorporate a digital display and give an instant read out of individual concentrations at any time. In some cases, they can be linked to an alarm that operates in the event of a predetermined concentration of an airborne contaminant being exceeded.

OCCUPATIONAL HEALTH INITIATIVES

The maintenance of a fit and healthy workforce is seen by many organisations as an important ingredient for success. These initiatives can include:

- well-women screening programmes, particularly directed at detecting early signs of cervical and breast cancer;
- identification of hearing and eyesight deficiencies through regular audiometry and vision screening respectively for employees;
- providing assistance for employees to cease smoking through the provision of counselling, hypnosis and nicotine patches;
- special programmes covering alcohol and drug addiction amongst employees; and
- provision of fitness facilities on site.

SMOKING, DRUGS, ALCOHOL AND LIFESTYLE

Smoking at work

The relationship of cigarette smoking in particular to various forms of cancer is well established. It has a direct effect on people in terms of reduced lung function and an increased potential for lung conditions, such as bronchitis. With the increasing attention that has been given to the risks associated with passive smoking, organisations should consider the development of a policy on smoking at work.

The problem has been identified mainly in poorly ventilated open-plan offices and amongst employees who may suffer some form of respiratory complaint, for example, asthma or bronchitis. Other people may complain of soreness of the eyes, headaches and stuffiness.

In 1988 the HSE's booklet Passive Smoking at Work drew the attention of readers to the concept of passive smoking, where non-smokers inhale environmental tobacco smoke from burning cigarettes, cigars and pipes exhaled by smokers. Work carried out by the Independent Scientific Committee on Smoking and Health identified a small but measurable increase in risk from lung cancer for passive smokers of between 10 and 30%. The booklet also suggests that passive smoking could be the cause of one to three extra cases of lung cancer every year for each 100,000 non-smokers who are exposed throughout life to other people's smoke.

A policy on smoking at work should state the intention of the organisation to eliminate smoking in the workplace by a specific date, the legal requirements on the employer to provide a healthy working environment, and that smoking is bad for the health of smokers and non-smokers alike. The 'organisation and arrangements' for implementing the policy should state the individual responsibilities of managers in supporting and implementing the various stages of the operation, and of the staff to comply with policy.

Drugs in the workplace

Many people see drug taking as the panacea for stress, relying on tranquilisers to reduce anxiety and amphetamines (pep pills) to counter fatigue. This form of drug taking represents a major risk to health, particularly if the individual consumes alcohol.

The possession of a range of drugs is a criminal offence. Evidence of drug taking or 'pushing' in the workplace should be reported to a senior manager. Where appropriate, the advice of the police should be obtained.

A programme to assist identified drug users to break the habit may need to be considered and put into operation. A range of national agencies is available to assist in such situations.

Alcohol at work

The consumption of alcohol at work may be one of the outcomes of stress in certain cases. Alcoholism is a true addiction, and the alcoholic must be encouraged to obtain medical help and advice.

The repeated consumption of strong spirits, especially on an empty stomach, can lead to chronic gastritis and possible inflammation of the intestines, which interferes with the absorption of food substances, notably those in the vitamin B group. This, in turn, damages the nerve cells causing alcoholic neuritis, injury to the brain cells leading to certain forms of insanity and, in some cases, cirrhosis of the liver.

A healthy lifestyle

Regular exercise, such as swimming, walking and cycling, taking sufficient rest and paying attention to the food one eats are all features of a healthy lifestyle. Many organisations provide health education on these aspects with a view to ensuring a healthy workforce, together with health surveillance, where appropriate, in order to encourage employees towards a healthier lifestyle.

KEY POINTS

- There is a general duty on employers under the HSWA to ensure, so far as is reasonably practicable, the health of employees.
- Since the 1980s considerable emphasis has been given to the health protection of people at work.
- Occupational health is concerned with protecting the health of people at work from physical, chemical, biological and work-related diseases and conditions.
- Occupational hygiene deals with the identification, measurement, evaluation and control of environmental contaminants, such as dusts and gases, along with physical phenomena, such as noise and vibration.
- Occupational health practice should commence at the pre-employment stage and continue through the working life of the employee.
- Health surveillance of employees may be required as a result of risk assessments undertaken by employers.
- Health surveillance is an area of occupational health practice entailing the regular review of the health of employees who may be exposed to health risks.
- Increasingly, employers need to maintain health records of employees and former employees.
- Environmental monitoring entails the use of personal dosemeters and static sampling equipment.
- The need for employees to maintain a healthy lifestyle can be demonstrated through a range of occupational health initiatives.

12 Manual Handling Operations

A substantial part of many people's jobs involves manual handling of loads, such as parcels, sacked items, components and even people. Manual handling injuries account for over 50% of all lost time injuries. In most cases these injuries arise through incorrect or poor handling techniques.

This chapter examines the injuries that can be sustained from manual handling operations, the requirements of the Manual Handling Operations Regulations, manual handling risk assessment and safe manual handling procedures.

MANUAL HANDLING INJURIES

Manual handling injuries, such as ligament strains, prolapsed intervertebral discs and hernias, account for more than 50% of lost time injuries at work throughout the European Union. In addition, more than a third of all work-related injuries result from manual handling activities.

Statistics from the last 60 years indicate that in almost every year the number of people injured in this way has increased. The vast majority of reported manual handling accidents result in over three day injury, most commonly a sprain or strain, often of the back. Not only manual workers contribute to these statistics, however. Those in sedentary occupations are similarly at risk, for example, office workers, library staff, hospital administration workers and checkout operators in shops or supermarkets.

TYPES AND SITES OF BODILY INJURY

HSE Guidance accompanying the Manual Handling Operations Regulations classifies the types and sites of bodily injury as shown in Table 12 below.

What comes out of the statistical information on manual handling injuries is the fact that four out of five people will suffer some form of back condition at some times in their lives, the majority of these conditions being associated with work conditions.

TABLE 12 : TYPES AND SITES OF BODILY INJURY ARISING FROM MANUAL HANDLING OPERATIONS

Types of bodily injury	%	Sites of injury	%
Sprains and strains	65	Backs	45
Superficial injuries	9	Fingers and thumbs	16
Contusions	7	Arms	13
Lacerations	7	Lower limbs	9
Fractures	5	Rest of torso	8
Other forms of injury	5	Hands	6
		Other sites	3

Injuries and conditions associated with manual handling can be of both an internal and external nature. External injuries include cuts, bruises, crush injuries and lacerations to fingers, forearms, ankles and feet. Generally, such injuries are not as serious as the internal forms of injury, which include muscle and ligament tears, hernias (ruptures), prolapsed intervertebral (slipped) discs and damage to knee, shoulder and elbow joints.

Muscle and ligament strain

When muscles are utilised for manual handling purposes, they are subjected to varying degrees of stress. Carrying a load generally imposes a pronounced static strain on many groups of muscles, especially those of the arms and trunk. As a result, fatigue very soon sets in, with pains in the back muscles, which perform static work only, occurring sooner than in the arm muscles, which perform essentially dynamic work.

Ligaments are fibrous bans occurring between two bones at a joint. They are flexible but inelastic, come into play only at the extremes of movement and cannot be stretched when they are taut. Ligaments set the limits beyond which no movement is possible in a joint.

A joint can be forced beyond its normal range only by tearing a ligament resulting in a sprain of that joint. There are many causes of a torn ligament, in particular, jerky handling movements that place stress on a joint due, perhaps, to failing to assess the load prior to lifting, and uncoordinated team lifting and dropping a load half-way through a lift, which may be due to not having a defined drill for two-man or team-lifting operations.

Hernia (Rupture)

A hernia is a protrusion of an organ from one compartment of the body into another, for example, a loop of intestine into the groin, or through the frontal abdominal wall. Both these forms of hernia can result from incorrect handling techniques and particularly from the adoption of bent back stances, which produce compression of the abdomen and lower intestines.

The most common form of hernia or 'rupture' associated with manual handling is the inguinal hernia. The weak point is the small gap in the abdominal muscles where the testis descends to the scrotum. Its vessels pass through the gap, which therefore cannot be sealed. Excessive straining, and even coughing, may cause a bulge at the gap and a loop of intestine or other abdominal structure easily slips into it. An inguinal hernia sometimes causes little trouble but it can, without warning, become strangulated, whereby the loop of intestine is pinched at the entrance to the hernia. Its contents are obstructed and no fresh blood reaches the area.

Prompt attention is needed to preserve the patient's health, and even his life may be at risk if the condition does not receive swift attention. The defect, in most cases, will need to be repaired surgically.

Prolapsed or 'slipped' disc

The spine consists of a series of small interlocking bones or vertebrae. The human spine incorporates:

♦ seven neck or cervical vertebrae;
♦ twelve thoracic vertebrae;
♦ five lumbar vertebrae; and
♦ four caudal vertebrae (see FIG. 13).

The sacral vertebrae are united, as are the caudal vertebrae, the others being capable of

THE HUMAN SPINE FIG. 13

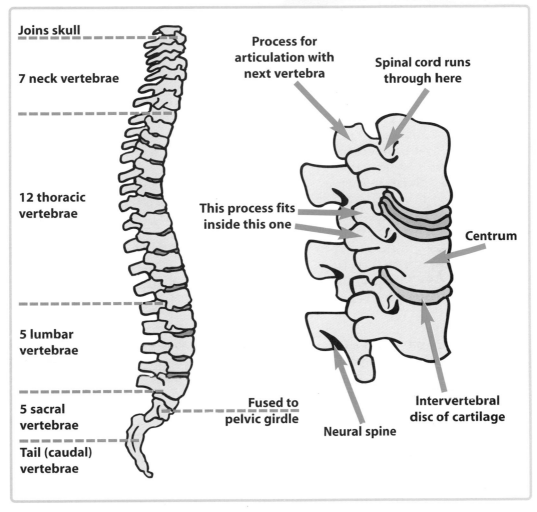

Joins skull

7 neck vertebrae

12 thoracic
vertebrae

5 lumbar
vertebrae

5 sacral
vertebrae

Tail (caudal)
vertebrae

Process for
articulation with
next vertebra

Spinal cord runs
through here

This process fits
inside this one

Centrum

Fused to
pelvic girdle

Neural spine

Intervertebral
disc of cartilage

independent, but coordinated articulating movement. Each vertebra is separated from the next by a pad of gristle-like material or intervertebral disc. These discs act as a form of shock absorber to protect the spine.

A prolapsed or slipped disc occurs when one of these intervertebral discs is displaced from its normal position and is no longer performing its function properly. In other cases, there may be squashing or compression of a disc. This results in a painful condition, sometimes leading to partial paralysis, which is caused when the back is bent while lifting, as a result of falling awkwardly, getting up out of a low chair or putting the spine under similar stress.

Rheumatic disorders

These are painful disorders of joints or muscles not directly due to infection or injury. This group includes rheumatic fever, rheumatoid arthritis, osteoarthritis, gout and 'fibrosisitis', itself an ill-defined group of disorders in which muscular and/or joint pain are common factors.

Evidence supports the fact that stress on the spine, muscles, joints and ligaments during manual handling activities in early working life results in rheumatic disorders as people get older. The need for training of young people in safe manual handling procedures is, therefore, of great importance.

MANUAL HANDLING TECHNIQUES

It is vital that all people engaged in manual handling operations be aware of the basic principles of safe manual handling. These principles should always be followed during manual handling and in the training of employees in manual handling techniques.

MANUAL HANDLING FIG. 14

Stop and think.
Plan the lift. Where is the load going to be placed? Use appropriate handling aids if possible. Do you need help with the load? Remove obstructions such as discarded wrapping materials. For a long lift, such as floor to shoulder height, consider resting the load mid-way on a table or bench in order to change grip.

Position the feet.
Feet apart, giving a balanced and stable base for lifting (tight skirts and unsuitable footwear make this difficult). Leading leg as far forward as is comfortable.

Adopt a good posture.
Bend the knees so that the hands when grasping the load are as nearly level with the waist as possible. But do not kneel or overflex the knees. Keep the back straight (tucking in the chin helps). Lean forward a little over the load if necessary to get a good grip. Keep shoulders level and facing in the same direction as the hips.

Get a firm grip.
Try to keep arms within the boundary formed by the legs. The optimum position and nature of the grip depends on the circumstances and individual preference, but it must be secure. A hook grip is less fatiguing than keeping the fingers straight. If it is necessary to vary the grip as the lift proceeds, do this as smoothly as possible.

Keep close to the load.
Keep the load as close to the trunk for as long as possible. Keep the heaviest side of the load next to the trunk. If a close approach to the load is not possible try sliding it towards you before attempting to lift it.

Put down, then adjust.
If precise positioning of the load is necessary, put it down first, then slide it into the desired position.

Don't jerk.
Carry out the lifting movement smoothly, keeping control of the load.

Move the feet.
Don't twist the trunk when turning to the side.

Feet positions

Place feet hip breadth apart to give a large base. Put one foot forward and to the side of the object to be lifted. This gives better balance.

Correct grip

Ensure that the grip is by the roots of the fingers and palm of the hand. This keeps the load under control and permits the load to be distributed better over the body.

Arms close to the body

This reduces muscle fatigue in the arms and shoulders and the effort required by the arms. It ensures that the load, in effect, becomes part of the body and moves with the body.

Flat back

This does not mean in a vertical position but at an angle of approximately 15 degrees. This prevents pressure on the abdomen and ensures an even pressure on the vertebral discs. The back will take the weight but the legs do the work.

Chin in

It is just as easy to damage the spine at the top as it is at the bottom. To keep the spine straight at the top, elongate the neck and pull the chin in. Do not tuck the chin on to the chest as this bends the neck.

Use of body weight

Use the body weight to move the load into the lifting position and to control movement of the load.

PLANNING THE LIFT

When considering the movement of a load, the operator should ensure his/her route is unobstructed and that there are no slipping or tripping hazards. The area where the load is to be deposited should be clear. Any PPE, such as safety helmet or hearing protection, should be put on before commencing the lift.

ASSESSING AND TESTING THE LOAD

The majority of injuries occur when actually lifting a load. Operators should be instructed to consider the following questions before lifting.

- ◆ Are there any rotating or moving parts?
  - ◆ If so, do not use them to lift with.
- ◆ Is the load too big to handle?
  - ◆ If so, get help.
- ◆ Is the load too heavy?
  - ◆ Rock the load. This will give a rough idea of its weight.
  - ◆ If too heavy, get help.

PERSONAL PROTECTIVE CLOTHING

The provision and use of the correct PPE is an essential feature of safe manual handling. The following instructions should be incorporated in manual handling training and activities.

Hand protection

Any load should be examined for evidence of sharp edges, protruding wires, splinters or anything that could injure the hands. The correct type of gloves should be worn to prevent hand injury.

Feet protection

Footwear that is suitable for the job should be worn, ie:
- with steel toe caps to protect the feet against falling objects or situations where feet could be trapped under a load;
- with steel insoles to protect against protruding nails; and
- with soles that will resist heat, oil and acid.

TWO PERSON OR TEAM LIFTING

All the principles involved in a one person lift should be used, with one variation. The leading foot should point in the direction of travel.

One person should give the order to lift, ensuring that his partner or partners understand the order prior to commencing. It is vital there be unison in the movement of both people and the load.

MANUAL HANDLING OPERATIONS REGULATIONS 1992

These regulations implemented the European 'Heavy Loads' Directive. They supplement the general duties placed on employers and others under the HSWA and the MHSWR, and are supported by HSE Guidance.

Important definitions

Injury does not include injury caused by any toxic or corrosive substance that:
- (a) has leaked or spilled from a load;
- (b) is present on the surface of a load but has not leaked or spilled from it; or
- (c) is a constituent part of a load.

Load includes any person and any animal.

Manual handling operations means any transporting or supporting of a load (including the lifting, putting down, pushing, pulling, carrying or moving thereof) by hand or bodily force.

Regulation 4 – Duties of employers

1. Each employer shall:
- (a) so far as is reasonably practicable, avoid the need for his/her employees to undertake any manual handling operations at work that involve a risk of their being injured;
- (b) where it is not reasonably practicable to avoid the need for his/her employees to undertake any manual handling operations at work that involve the risk of their being injured shall;
  - (i) make a suitable and sufficient assessment of all such manual handling operations to be undertaken by them, having regard to the factors that are specified in the Schedule;

(ii) take appropriate steps to reduce the risk of injury to those employees arising out of their undertaking any such manual handling operations to the lowest level reasonably practicable;

(iii) take appropriate steps to provide any of those employees who are undertaking such manual handling operations with general indications and, where reasonably practicable to do so, precise information on:

    (aa) the weight of each load; and

    (bb) the heaviest side of any load, of which the centre of gravity is not positioned centrally;

2. Any assessment such as referred to in paragraph 1(b)(i) of this regulation shall be reviewed by the employer who made it if:

(a)   there is reason to suspect it is no longer valid; or

(b)   there has been a significant change in the manual handling operations to which it relates;

and where as a result of any such review changes to the assessment are required, the relevant employer shall make them.

Regulation 4 – Duties of employees

Each employee shall while at work make full and proper use of any system of work provided for his use by his employer in compliance with Regulation 4(1)(b)(ii) of the regulations.

The Schedule

Factors to which the employer must have regard and questions he must consider when making an assessment of manual handling operations (Regulation 4(1)(b)(i)).

Column 1	Column 2
FACTORS	**QUESTIONS**

1. The tasks	**Do they involve:**
	holding or manipulating loads at distance from trunk?
	unsatisfactory bodily movement or posture, especially:
	    twisting the trunk?
	    stooping?
	    reaching upwards?
	excessive movement of loads, especially:
	    excessive lifting or lowering distances?
	    excessive carrying distances?
	    excessive pushing or pulling of loads?
	    risk of sudden movement of loads?
	    frequent or prolonged physical effort?
	    insufficient rest or recovery periods?
	    a rate of work imposed by a process?

Column 1	Column 2
FACTORS	**QUESTIONS**
2. The loads	**Are they:** heavy? bulky or unwieldy? unstable, or with contents likely to shift? sharp, hot or otherwise potentially damaging?
3. The working environment	**Are there:** space constraints preventing good posture? uneven, slippery or unstable floors? variations in levels of floors or work surfaces? extremes of temperature or humidity? conditions causing ventilation problems or gusts of wind? poor lighting conditions?
4. Individual capability	**Does the job:** require unusual strength, height, etc? create a hazard to those who might reasonably be considered to be pregnant or have a health problem? require special information or training for its safe performance?
5. Other factors	Is movement or posture hindered by personal protective clothing or equipment?

KEY POINTS

- Most people are involved in manual handling operations during their working life time.
- Manual handling injuries account for more than 50% of lost time injuries at work.
- Manual handling injuries include prolapsed intervertebral discs, hernias, ligament strains and superficial injuries, such as cuts and abrasions.
- Rheumatic disorders frequently arise in later life as a result of manual handling injuries incurred earlier.
- All employees should be supervised and trained in correct manual handling techniques.
- The Manual Handling Operations Regulations require employers to undertake a manual handling risk assessment where manual handling cannot be avoided, ie a load cannot be handled by mechanical means.
- Factors such as the task, the load, the working environment and individual capability must be considered in a manual handling risk assessment.

13 Display Screen Equipment

The health risks associated with the use of DSE are essentially those of visual fatigue, postural fatigue and RSI.

Under the Health and Safety (Display Screen Equipment) Regulations 1992 employers have specified duties towards defined 'users' of DSE, including the requirement to undertake a workstation risk analysis to consider the daily work routine of users, provide eye and eyesight tests where appropriate, and to provide information and training.

WHAT IS DISPLAY SCREEN EQUIPMENT?

This term is very broadly defined in the Health and Safety (Display Screen Equipment) Regulations 1992 as meaning any alphanumeric or graphic display screen, regardless of the display process involved.

According to the HSE Guidance accompanying the regulations, the definition of DSE covers both conventional (cathode ray tube) display screens and other display processes, such as liquid crystal displays, and other emerging technologies. Display screens mainly used to display line drawings, graphs, charts or computer-generated graphics are included, but screens where the main use is to show television or film pictures are not. Judgements about mixed media workstations will need to establish the main use of the screen; if this is to display text, numbers and/or graphics, it is within the scope of the regulations. The definition is not limited to typical office visual display terminals but covers, for example, non-electronic display systems such as microfiche.

DISPLAY SCREEN EQUIPMENT – THE RISKS

Considerable attention has been paid by the HSE and employers since the 1990s to the risks to people associated with the use of DSE. Allegations of the risk of contracting epilepsy and facial dermatitis, exposure to electromagnetic radiation and adverse effects on pregnant workers have, in the main, proved unfounded.

The recognised risks are as follows.

Visual fatigue

Excessive amounts of time working at a screen without a break can result in visual fatigue. The need, therefore, to take screen breaks must be stressed to employees. In many cases, visual fatigue may identify the need for vision screening followed by the provision and use of prescription spectacles for this type of work. The use of a document holder, which reduces the need for excessive focusing and refocusing of the eyes, should greatly assist in reducing visual fatigue.

Postural fatigue

Neck, back and shoulder pains arising from the adoption of constrained postures at a keyboard are associated with postural fatigue. Through improved workstation design and layout, postural fatigue can be considerably reduced. In particular, any chair provided for DSE users should be comfortable, should support the back and provide sufficient leg-room. The provision of foot rests is recommended.

Other forms of operational stress

Noise from the unit and ancillary equipment, excessive heat and inadequate lighting and ventilation may cause varying degrees of stress. In the first case, it may be possible to relocate particularly noisy printers or replace them with less noisy ones. Environmental control of temperature, lighting and ventilation is essential. Desk lamps should be provided for use in conjunction with document holders.

Many people also complain of excessive background noise in open-plan offices, which they find stressful and which affects their ability to concentrate on complex tasks using DSE. The provision of 'quiet rooms' for this sort of work is recommended.

Work-related upper limb disorders

Whilst these disorders have been referred to in chapter 11, the potential for DSE users to contract these disorders, along with visual fatigue and postural fatigue, may need to be taken into account in a workstation risk analysis. (See later in this chapter.)

These disorders affect the fingers, hands, wrists, elbows, shoulders and neck and are caused by repetitive strain. They take a number of forms:

♦ **Epicondylitis** – inflammation of the area where a muscle joins a bone;

♦ **Peritendenitis** – inflammation of the area where a tendon joins a muscle;

♦ **Carpal tunnel syndrome** – a painful condition in the area where nerves and tendons pass through the carpal bone in the hand;

♦ **Tenosynovitis** – inflammation of the synovial lining of the tendon sheath;

♦ **Tendenitis** – inflammation of the tendons, particularly in the fingers;

♦ **Dupuytren's Contracture** – a condition affecting the palm of the hand, where it is impossible to straighten the hand and fingers; and

♦ **Writer's cramp** – cramps in the hands, forearms and fingers.

Measures to prevent RSI include:

♦ improving the design of workstations and working areas, with particular reference to the positioning of keyboards and screens, and the heights of chairs;

♦ adjustment of work loads, which permit rest periods away from the screen;

♦ provision of wrist supports/bars;

♦ health surveillance by an occupational health nurse to detect early stages of the disorder; and

♦ improved training and supervision.

HEALTH AND SAFETY (DISPLAY SCREEN EQUIPMENT) REGULATIONS 1992

Important definitions

Display screen equipment means any alphanumeric or graphic display screen, regardless of the display process involved.

Operator means a self-employed person who habitually uses DSE as a significant part of his normal work.

User means an employee who habitually uses DSE as a significant part of his normal work.

Workstation means an assembly comprising:

(a) DSE (whether provided with software determining the interface between the equipment and its operator or user, a keyboard or any other input device);
(b) any optional accessories to the DSE;
(c) any disk drive, telephone, modem, printer, document holder, work chair, work desk, work surface or other item peripheral to the DSE; and
(d) the immediate environment around the DSE.

Note: The definitions of 'operator' and 'user' are particularly significant in the interpretation of the regulations.

Exemptions from the regulations

The regulations do not apply to:
(a) drivers' cabs or control cabs for vehicles or machinery;
(b) DSE on board a means of transport;
(c) DSE mainly intended for public operation;
(d) portable systems not in prolonged use;
(e) calculators, cash registers or any equipment having a small data or measurement display required for direct use of the equipment; or
(f) window typewriters.

Regulation 2 – Workstation risk analyses

There is an absolute duty on employers to perform a suitable and sufficient analysis of those workstations that:
(a) (regardless of who has provided them) are used for the purposes of his undertaking by **users**; or
(b) have been provided by him and are used for the purposes of his undertaking by **operators**,
for the purposes of assessing the health and safety risks to which those persons are exposed in consequence of that use.

Any assessment made by an employer shall be reviewed by him if:
(a) there is reason to suspect that it is no longer valid; or
(b) there has been a significant change in the matters to which it relates;
and where as a result of any such review changes in the assessment are required, the employer concerned shall make them.

The employer shall reduce the risks identified in consequence of the above assessment to the lowest extent reasonably practicable.

Regulation 4 – Daily work routine

Every employer must so plan the activities of users at work in his undertaking that their daily work on DSE is periodically interrupted by breaks or changes of activity as to reduce their workload at that equipment.

Regulation 5 – Eyes and eyesight

Where a person:
(a) is a user; or
(b) is to become a user,

of DSE his employer shall ensure that he is provided at his request with an appropriate eye and eyesight test, any such test to be carried out by a competent person.

An eye and eyesight test carried out shall:
(a) in the case of a user, be carried out as soon as practicable after being requested by the user concerned; and
(b) in the case of a person who is to become a user, before the employee concerned becomes a user.

At regular intervals after an employee has been provided with an eye and eyesight test, his employer shall ensure he is provided with a further eye and eyesight test of an appropriate nature, any such test to be carried out by a competent person.

Where a user experiences visual difficulties that may reasonably be considered to be caused by work on DSE, his employer shall ensure that he is provided at his request with an appropriate eye and eyesight test, any such test to be carried out by a competent person as soon as practicable after being requested.

Every employer shall ensure that each user employed by him is provided with special corrective appliances appropriate for the work being done by the user concerned where:
(a) normal corrective appliances cannot be used; and
(b) the result of an eye and eyesight test that the user has been given shows such provision to be necessary.

Nothing shall require an employer to provide an employee with an eye and eyesight test against the employee's will.

Regulation 6 – Provision of training

Employers must ensure users are provided with adequate health and safety training in the use of any workstation upon which they may be required to work and where a workstation has been substantially modified.

Regulation 7 – Provision of information

Employers must ensure that operators and users are provided with adequate information about all aspects of health and safety relating to their workstations, and on the measures taken by the employer to comply with the regulations.

WORKSTATION RISK ANALYSIS

The Schedule to the regulations sets out the minimum requirements for workstations which must be taken into account in any workstation risk analysis.

1. Extent to which employers must ensure that workstations meet the requirements laid down in this Schedule

An employer shall ensure that a workstation meets the requirements laid down in this Schedule to the extent that:
(a) those requirements relate to a component that is present in the workstation concerned;

(b)   those requirements have effect with a view to securing the health, safety and welfare of persons at work; and

(c)   the inherent characteristics of a given task do not make compliance with those requirements inappropriate in respect of the workstation concerned.

2. Equipment
General

The use as such of the equipment must not be a source of risk for operators and users.

Display screen

The characters on the screen shall be well defined and clearly formed, of adequate size and with adequate spacing between the characters and lines.

The image on the screen should be stable, with no flickering or other forms of instability.

The brightness and the contrast between the characters and the background shall be easily adjustable by the user, and also easily adjustable to ambient conditions.

The screen must swivel and tilt easily and freely to suit the needs of the operator or user.

It shall be possible to use a separate base for the screen or an adjustable table.

The screen shall be free of reflective glare and reflections liable to cause discomfort to the user.

Keyboard

The keyboard shall tilt and separate from the screen so as to allow the operator or user to find a comfortable working position avoiding fatigue in the hands and arms.

The space in front of the keyboard shall be sufficient as to facilitate use of the keyboard.

The keyboard shall have a matt surface to avoid reflective glare.

The arrangement of the keyboard and characteristics of the keys shall be such as to facilitate the use of the keyboard.

The symbols on the keys shall be adequately contrasted and legible from the design working position.

Work desk or work surface

The work desk or work surface shall have a sufficiently large, low reflectance surface and allow a flexible arrangement of the screen, keyboard, documents and related equipment.

The document holder shall be stable and adjustable and shall be positioned so as to minimise the need for uncomfortable head and eye movements.

There shall be adequate space for operators and users to find a comfortable position.

Work chair

The work chair shall be stable and allow the user easy freedom of movement and a comfortable position.

The seat shall be adjustable in height.

The seat back shall be adjustable in both height and tilt.

A foot rest shall be made available to any user who wishes one.

3. Environment
Space requirements

The workstation shall be dimensioned and designed so as to provide sufficient space for the user to change position and vary movements.

DISPLAY SCREEN EQUIPMENT WORKSTATION DESIGN AND LAYOUT FIG. 15

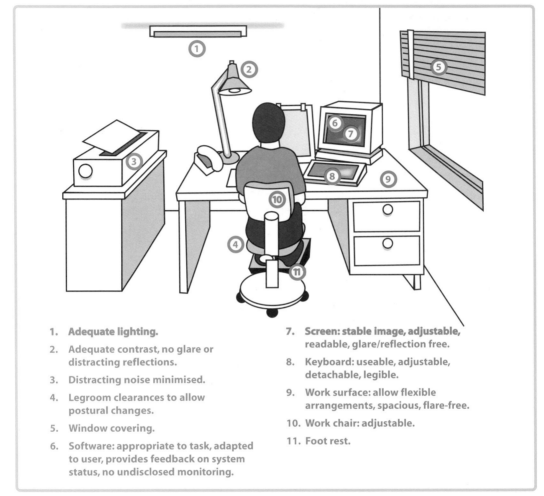

1. **Adequate lighting.**
2. **Adequate contrast, no glare or distracting reflections.**
3. **Distracting noise minimised.**
4. **Legroom clearances to allow postural changes.**
5. **Window covering.**
6. **Software: appropriate to task, adapted to user, provides feedback on system status, no undisclosed monitoring.**
7. **Screen: stable image, adjustable, readable, glare/reflection free.**
8. **Keyboard: useable, adjustable, detachable, legible.**
9. **Work surface: allow flexible arrangements, spacious, flare-free.**
10. **Work chair: adjustable.**
11. **Foot rest.**

Lighting

Any room lighting or task lighting provided shall ensure satisfactory lighting conditions and an appropriate contrast between the screen and the background environment, taking into account the type of work and the vision requirements of the operator or user.

Possible disturbing glare and reflections on the screen or other equipment shall be prevented by coordinating workplace and workstation layout with the positioning and technical characteristics of the artificial light sources.

Reflections and glare

Workstations shall be so designed that sources of light, such as windows and other openings, transparent and translucid walls, and brightly coloured fixtures or walls cause no direct glare and no distracting reflections on the screen.

Windows shall be fitted with a suitable system of adjustable covering to attenuate the daylight that falls on the workstation.

SEATING AND POSTURE FOR TYPICAL OFFICE TASKS FIG. 16

1. Seat back adjustability.
2. Good lumbar support.
3. Seat height adjustability.
4. No excess pressure on underside of thighs and back of knees.
5. Foot supported if needed.
6. Space for postural change, no obstacles under desk.
7. Forearms approximately horizontal.
8. Minimal extension, flexion or deviation of wrists.
9. Screen height and angle should allow comfortable head position.
10. Space in front of keyboard to support hands/wrists during pauses in keying.

Noise

Noise emitted by equipment belonging to any workstation shall be taken into account when a workstation is being equipped, with a view in particular to ensuring that attention is not distracted and speech is not disturbed.

Heat

Equipment belonging to any workstation shall not produce excess heat that could cause discomfort to operators or users.

Radiation

All radiation with the exception of the visible part of the electromagnetic spectrum shall be reduced to negligible levels from the point of view of the protection of operators' or users' health and safety.

Humidity

An adequate level of humidity shall be established and maintained.

4. Interface between computer and operator/user

In designing, selecting, commissioning and modifying software, and in designing tasks using DSE, the employer shall take into account the following principles:

(a) software must be suitable for the task;

(b) software must be easy to use and, where appropriate, adaptable to the user's level or knowledge or experience. No quantitative or qualitative checking facility may be used without the knowledge of operators or users;

(c) systems must provide feed to operators or users on the performance of those systems;

(d) systems must display information in a format and at a pace that are adapted to operators or users; and

(e) the principles of software ergonomics must be applied, in particular, to human data processing.

(See **FIGS. 15 and 16** Workstation layout recommendations)

KEY POINTS

♦ The principal hazards associated with DSE are visual fatigue, postural fatigue and RSI.

♦ The use of a document holder greatly assists in the prevention of visual fatigue.

♦ Chairs should be adjustable in height and back to reduce the potential for postural fatigue.

♦ Employers must undertake a workstation risk analysis in the case of defined users of DSE, taking into account the factors outlined in the Schedule to the regulations.

♦ Users of DSE are entitled to eye and eyesight tests on request, which must be paid for by the employer.

14 Hazardous Substances

Many people use, or come into contact with, some form of hazardous substance at work, for example, acids, alkalis, solvents, flammable, toxic and harmful substances. The legislation on this subject is extensive being incorporated, principally, in the COSHH Regulations and the Chemicals (Hazard Information and Packaging for Supply) (CHIP) Regulations. There are also many HSE Guidance Notes dealing with the general and specific aspects of hazardous substances, together with safety data provided by suppliers.

Apart from examining current legislation, this chapter deals with the principles of toxicology, the form taken by substances, which is significant in their potential for harm, prevention and control strategies and occupational exposure limits.

PRINCIPLES OF TOXICOLOGY

Toxicology is the study of the body's responses to toxic substances. Toxic substances are widely used in industry. Some indications of the most common hazards associated with them are listed in the Social Security (Industrial Injuries)(Prescribed Diseases) Regulations 1985.

EFFECTS OF EXPOSURE

Exposure to toxic substances can have different types of effect.

Acute effect
A rapidly produced effect following a single exposure to an offending agent.

Chronic effect
An effect produced as a result of prolonged exposure or repeated exposures of a long duration to an offending agent.

Local effect
An effect usually confined to the initial point of contact. The site may be the skin, mucous membranes of the eyes, nose or throat, the liver, bladder, etc.

Systemic effect
Such effects occur in parts of the body other than at the initial point of contact and are associated with an effect on a body system, such as the central nervous system.

ROUTES OF ENTRY OF TOXIC SUBSTANCES

Toxic substances enter the body in a number of ways.

Inhalation
Inhalation of such substances, in the form of a dust, gas, mist, fog, fume or vapour, accounts for approximately 90% of all ill-health associated with exposure to toxic substances. The results may be acute, as in the case of gassing accidents, for example, chlorine, carbon monoxide, or chronic, as with exposure to chlorinated hydrocarbons, lead compounds,

benzene, numerous dusts producing pneumoconiosis, mists and fogs, such as that from paint spray, oil mist, and fume, as encountered with welding and flame cutting operations.

Pervasion

The skin, if intact, is proof against most, but not all, inputs. There are certain substances and microorganisms that are capable of passing straight through the intact skin into underlying tissue, or even into the bloodstream, without apparently causing any changes to the skin. The resistance of the skin to external irritants varies with age, sex, race, colour and, to a certain extent, diet.

Pervasion, as a route of entry, is normally associated with occupational dermatitis, the cause of which may broadly be divided into two groups:

♦ **primary irritants** – namely, substances that will cause dermatitis at the site of contact if permitted to act for a sufficient length of time and in sufficient concentrations, for example, strong acids, alkalis and solvents; and

♦ **secondary cutaneous sensitisers** – substances that do not necessarily cause skin changes on first contact, but produce a specific sensitisation of the skin. If further contact occurs, for example, after a period of seven days or more, dermatitis will develop at the site of the second contact. Typical skin sensitisers are certain plants, rubber, nickel and many chemicals.

It should be noted that, for certain people, dermatitis may be a manifestation of psychological stress, having no relationship with exposure to toxic substances.

Ingestion

Certain substances are carried into the intestine, from which some will pass into the body by absorption. Similar to the lung, the intestine acts as a selective filter that keeps out many but not all harmful agents presented to it.

Injection

A forceful breach of the skin, sometimes as a cause of injury, can carry substances through the skin barrier.

TARGET ORGANS AND TARGET SYSTEMS

Certain substances have a direct or indirect effect on specific body organs (target organs) and body systems (target systems).

Target organs include the liver, lungs, brain, skin and bladder. Target systems include the central nervous system, reproductive system and circulatory system.

THE FORM TAKEN BY A HAZARDOUS SUBSTANCE

In the assessment and evaluation of risks associated with exposure to hazardous substances, and in any environmental monitoring of aerosols (airborne concentrations of substances) under consideration, it is necessary to consider the actual physical form taken by that substance. A comparison based on particulate size is shown in Table 13.

Forms of aerosol

Features of the various forms of aerosol are outlined below.

Dusts

Dust is an aerosol composed of solid inanimate particles. (ILO) Dusts are solid airborne particles, often created by operations such as grinding, crushing, milling, sanding and demolition. Two of the principal dusts encountered in industry are silica and cement dust.

Dusts may be:
- **fibrogenic**, that is, they cause fibrosis of the lung, a form of lung damage, for example, silica, cement dust, coal dust and certain metal dusts; and
- **toxic**, that is, they eventually poison the body systems, for example, arsenic, mercury, beryllium, phosphorus and lead.

Mists

A mist, comprising airborne liquid droplets, is a finely dispersed liquid suspended in air. Mists are mainly created by spraying, foaming, pickling and electroplating. Health risks arise most frequently from acid mist produced in industrial treatment processes, as in the case of oil mist and chromic acid mist.

Fumes

These are fine solid particulates formed from the gaseous state usually by the vaporisation or oxidation of metals, for example, lead fume. Fumes generally form an oxide in contact with air. They are created by industrial processes that involve the heating and melting of metals, such as welding, smelting and arc air gouging. A common fume risk is lead poisoning associated with the inhalation of lead fumes.

Gases

These are formless fluids usually produced by chemical processes involving combustion or by the interaction of chemical substances. A gas will normally seek to completely fill the space into which it is liberated. Carbon monoxide is classic gas encountered in industry, sometimes as a result of process faults. Certain gases, such as acetylene, hydrogen and methane are particularly flammable.

Vapours

Vapours are the gaseous form of a material normally encountered in a solid or liquid state at normal room temperature and pressure. Typical examples are solvents, such as trichloroethylene, which releases vapours when the container is opened. Other liquids produce a vapour on heating, the amount of vapour being directly related to the boiling point of that particular liquid.

A vapour contains very minute droplets of the liquid. In the case of a fog, however, the droplets are much larger.

Smoke

Smoke is a product of incomplete combustion, mainly of organic materials. It may contain fine particles of carbon in the form of ash, soot and grit that are visibly suspended in air.

TABLE 13: COMPARISON OF TYPES OF AIRBORNE CONTAMINANT

Contaminant	Particle size range (microns)	Characteristics
Dust	0.1 – 75.0	Generated by natural fragmentation or mechanical cutting or crushing of solids, for example, wood, rock, coal, metals, etc. **Grit** particles, usually taken to be above 75 microns, are unlikely to remain airborne.
Fume	0.001 – 1.0	Small solid particles of condensed vapour, especially metals, as in welding or melting processes. Often agglomerate into larger particles as the smaller particles collide.
Smoke	0.01 – 1.0	Aerosol formed by incomplete combustion of organic matter; does not include ash, for example, fly ash.
Mist	0.01 – 10.0	Aerosol of droplets formed by condensation from the gaseous state or as dispersion of a liquid state, for example, with hot open-surface tanks, electroplating.
Vapour	0.005	Gaseous state of materials that are liquid or solid at normal room temperature and pressure, for example, solvent vapours.
Gas	0.0005	Materials that do not normally exist as liquids or solids at normal room temperature and pressure.

CLASSIFICATION OF HAZARDOUS SUBSTANCES

Classification of hazardous substances is dealt with the Chemicals CHIP Regulations. Classification is based on the characteristic properties of substances and their effects on man and the environment. These classifications must be taken into account when undertaking a health risk assessment under the COSHH Regulations.

The following classifications or 'categories of danger' are used:

HEALTH EFFECTS

Very toxic

A substance that, if inhaled or ingested, or if it penetrates the skin, may involve extremely serious, acute or chronic health risks and even death.

Toxic

A substance that, if inhaled or ingested, or if it penetrates the skin, may involve serious, acute or chronic health risks or even death.

Harmful

A substance that, if inhaled or ingested, or if it penetrates the skin, may involve limited health risks.

Corrosive

A substance that may, on contact with living tissues, destroy them.

Irritant

A non-corrosive substance that, through immediate, prolonged or repeated contact with the skin or mucous membranes, causes dermatitis or localised inflammation.

PHYSICO-CHEMICAL EFFECTS

Explosive

A substance that may explode under the effect of a flame or that is more sensitive to shocks than dinitrobenzene.

Oxidising

A substance that gives rise to a highly exothermic reaction when in contact with other substances, particularly flammable substances.

Extremely flammable

Liquids having a flash point of less than 0ºC and a boiling point of less than or equal to 35ºC, and when such a liquid forms more than 45% by weight or more than 250g of the contents of an aerosol dispenser, the contents of that dispenser.

Highly flammable

A substance that:
(a) may become hot and finally catch fire in contact with air at ambient temperature without any application of energy;
(b) may readily catch fire after brief contact with a source of ignition and which continues to burn or to be consumed after removal of the source of ignition, for example, methanol;
(c) is gaseous and flammable in air at normal pressure, for example, butane;
(d) in contact with water or damp air evolves highly flammable gases in dangerous quantities, for example, calcium carbide produces acetylene; or
(e) is a liquid having a flash point below 21ºC and when such a liquid forms more than 45% by weight or more than 250g of the contents of an aerosol dispenser, the contents of that dispenser.

Flammable

A substance that:
(a) is a liquid having a flash point equal to or greater than 21ºC and less than or equal to 55ºC and that when tested by an approved technique does not support combustion; and

(b) forms the contents of an aerosol dispenser when they include more than 45% by weight or 250g of a liquid that has a flash point equal to or greater than 21ºC and less than or equal to 100ºC.

Radioactive

A substance that emits ionising radiations, for example, isotopes of chemical elements such as Cobalt60 and Strontium90. Emissions may take the forms of alpha particles, beta rays, gamma rays or neutrons.

Narcotic

Chemical substances, for example, alcohol, that affect the brain and central nervous system, causing a depressant effect on their functions.

Carcinogenic

Substances that cause cancer. They may be in solid or liquid form and of a chemical or physical nature.

Cryogenic

Substances that, because of their low temperature, present a special danger, for example, liquid nitrogen and liquid oxygen.

Mutagenic

Substances capable of causing damage to the individual cell, resulting in uncontrolled cell division and possibly cancer. Substances that cause inherited changes.

Teratagenic

Substances which cause harm to the unborn.

SUBSTANCES DANGEROUS FOR THE ENVIRONMENT

These are substances that may have short-term, medium-term or long-term environmental effects on ground, air and water.

SAFETY DATA

Appendix 1 of the ACOP **Safety data sheets for substances and preparations dangerous supply**, (HSC, 1994) in conjunction with the CHIP Regulations lists the following headings that must be incorporated in a Safety Data Sheet provided by a supplier thus:

1. identification of the substance/preparation and company;
2. composition/information on ingredients;
3. hazards identification;
4. first aid measures;
5. fire fighting measures;
6. accidental release measures;
7. handling and storage;
8. exposure controls/personal protection;
9. physical and chemical properties;
10. stability and reactivity;

11. toxicological information;
12. ecological information;
13. disposal considerations;
14. transport information;
15. regulatory information; and
16. other information.

It is incumbent on the person responsible for supplying the substance or preparation to supply information specified under the above headings.

A safety data sheet should be dated with the date of publication or revision, as appropriate. In the latter case, the safety data sheet should be marked clearly with the work 'revision'.

OCCUPATIONAL EXPOSURE LIMITS

HSE Guidance Note EH40 **Occupational exposure limits** gives details of occupational exposure limits (OELs) that should be used for determining the adequacy of control of exposure by inhalation to substances hazardous to health. These limits form part of the requirements of the COSHH Regulations 1999.

The advice given in Guidance Note EH40 should be taken in the context of the requirements of the COSHH Regulations, especially:

♦ Regulation 6 (health risk assessments);
♦ Regulation 7 (control of exposure);
♦ Regulations 8 and 9 (use and maintenance of control measures); and
♦ Regulation 10 (monitoring of exposure).

Additional guidance may be found in the COSHH General ACOP.

Units of measurement

The list of OELs given in the Guidance Note, unless otherwise stated, relate to personal exposure to substances hazardous to health in the air of the workplace.

Concentrations of gases and vapours in air are usually expressed as parts per million (ppm), a measure of concentration by volume, as well as in milligrams per cubic metre (mg/m^3) of air, a measure of concentration by mass.

Concentrations of airborne particles (fume, dust, etc) are usually expressed in mg/m^3, with the exception of mineral fibres, which are expressed as fibres per millilitre of air.

MAXIMUM EXPOSURE LIMITS AND OCCUPATIONAL EXPOSURE STANDARDS

Maximum exposure limits (MELs)

A MEL is the maximum concentration of an airborne substance, averaged over a reference period, to which employees may be exposed by inhalation under any circumstances and is specified together with the appropriate reference period in Schedule 1 of the COSHH Regulations.

Regulation 7(4) of COSHH, when read in conjunction with Regulation 16, imposes a duty on the employer to take all reasonable precautions and to exercise all due diligence to achieve these requirements.

In the case of substances with an eight-hour long-term reference period, unless the assessment carried out in accordance with regulation 6 shows that the level of exposure is most unlikely ever to exceed the MEL, to comply with this duty the employer should undertake a programme of monitoring in accordance with Regulation 10 so that he can show, if it is the case, that the MEL is not normally exceeded, that is, that an occasional result above the MEL is without real significance and is not indicative of a failure to maintain adequate control.

Some substances listed in Schedule 1 of the COSHH Regulations have been assigned short-term MELs, ie a 15 minute reference period. These substances give rise to acute effects and the purpose of limits of this kind is to render insignificant the risks to health resulting from brief exposure to the substance. For this reason short-term exposure limits should never be exceeded.

Occupational exposure standards (OESs)

An OES is the concentration of an airborne substance, averaged over a reference period, at which, according to current knowledge, there is no evidence that it is likely to be injurious to employees if they are exposed by inhalation day after day to that concentration and which is specified in a list approved by the HSC.

OESs are approved by the HSC following a consideration of the often limited available scientific data by the Working Group on the Assessment of Toxic Chemicals (WATCH).

For a substance that has been assigned an OES, exposure by inhalation should be reduced to that standard. If exposure by inhalation exceeds the OES, then control will still be deemed to be adequate provided that the employer has identified why the OES has been exceeded, and is taking appropriate steps to comply with the OES as soon as is reasonably practicable. In such a case, the employer's objective must be to reduce exposure to the OES, but the final achievement of this objective may take some time.

Factors that need to be considered in determining the urgency of the necessary action include the extent and cost of the required measures in relation to the nature and degree of the exposure involved.

LONG-TERM AND SHORT-TERM EXPOSURE LIMITS

Substances hazardous to health may cause adverse effects, for example, irritation of the skin, eyes and lungs, narcosis or even death after short-term exposure, or via long-term exposure through accumulation of substances in the body or through the gradual development of increased risk of disease with each contact.

It is important to control exposure so as to avoid short-term and long-term effects. Two types of exposure limit are therefore listed in Guidance Note EH40.

The long-term exposure limit (LTEL) is concerned with the total intake over long periods and is therefore appropriate for protecting against the effects of long-term exposure.

The short-term exposure limit (STEL) is aimed primarily at avoiding acute effects, or at least reducing the risk of occurrence. Specific STELs are listed for those substances for which there is evidence of a risk of acute effects occurring as a result of a brief exposure.

For those substances for which no STEL is listed, it is recommended that a figure of three times the LTEL averaged over a 15 minute reference period be used as a guideline for controlling exposure to short-term excursions.

Both LTELs and STELs are expressed as airborne concentrations averaged over a specific reference period. The period for the LTEL is normally eight hours. When a different period is used, this is stated. The averaging period for a STEL is normally 15 minutes, such a limit applying to any 15 minute period throughout the working shift.

Guidance Note EH40 and the COSHH Regulations

Guidance Note EH40 is an important document in the interpretation and implementation of duties under the COSHH Regulations. Along with the various ACOPs and other documentation issued with the regulations, reference should be made to the Guidance Note in activities directed at securing compliance with the regulations.

CONTROL OF SUBSTANCES HAZARDOUS TO HEALTH REGULATIONS 1999

The COSHH Regulations apply to every form of workplace and to every type of work activity involving the use of substances that may be hazardous to health to people at work.

The regulations are accompanied by a number of ACOPs, including:

♦ **Control of substances hazardous to health**;

♦ **Control of carcinogenic substances**; and

♦ **Control of biological agents**

together with a series of schedules that must be read in conjunction with specific requirements under the regulations.

The COSHH Regulations and the various ACOPs set out a strategy for safety with substances hazardous to health covering more than 40,000 chemicals and materials, together with hazardous substances generated by industrial processes.

Because of the significance of these regulations, the principal areas are dealt with below.

Regulation 2 – Definitions

Approved Supply List has the meaning assigned to it in Regulation 4 of the CHIP Regulations 1994.

Biological agent means any microorganism, cell, culture or human endoparasite, including any that have been genetically modified, which may cause any infection, allergy, toxicity or otherwise create a hazard to human health.

Carcinogen means:

(a) any substance or preparation that is classified in accordance with the classification provided by Regulation 5 of the CHIP Regulations 1994 would be in the category of danger, carcinogenic (1) or carcinogenic (2) whether or not the substance or preparation would be required to be classified under these Regulations; or

(b) any substance or preparation that is
(i) listed in Schedule 1; and
(ii) any substance or preparation arising from a process specified in Schedule 1 that is a substance hazardous to health.

Fumigation means any operation in which a substance is released into the atmosphere so as to form a gas to control or kill pests or other undesirable organisms. **Fumigate** and **fumigant** shall be construed accordingly.

Maximum exposure limit for a substance hazardous to health means the MEL approved by the HSC for the substance in relation to the specified reference period when calculated by a method approved by the HSC.

Microorganism includes any microbiological entity, cellular or non-cellular, which is capable of replication or of transferring genetic material.

Occupational exposure standard for a substance hazardous to health means the standard approved by the HSC for that substance in relation to the specified reference period when calculated by a method approved by the HSC.

Preparation means a mixture or solution of two or more substances.

Respirable dust means airborne material that is capable of penetrating to the gas exchange region of the lung.

Substance means any natural or artificial substance whether in solid or liquid form or in the form of a gas or vapour (including microorganisms).

Substance hazardous to health means any substance (including any preparation) that is:
(a)   a substance that is listed in Part 1 of the approved supply list as dangerous for supply within the meaning of the CHIP Regulations 1994 and for which an indication of danger specified for the substance in Part V of that list is very toxic, toxic, harmful, corrosive or irritant;
(b)   a substance for which the HSC has approved a MEL or OES;
(c)   a biological agent;
(d)   dust of any kind, except dust that is a substance within paragraph (a) or (b) above, when present at a concentration in air equal to or greater than:
 (i) 10 mg/m^3, as a time-weighted average over an eight hour period of total inhalable dust; or
 (ii) 4 mg/m^3, as a time-weighted average over an eight hour period of respirable dust;
(e)   a substance, not being a substance mentioned in sub-paragraphs (a) to (d) above, which creates a hazard to the health of any person that is comparable with the hazards created by substances mentioned in those sub-paragraphs.

Total inhalable dust means airborne material that is capable of entering the nose and mouth during breathing and is thereby available for deposition in the respiratory tract.

Regulation 6 – Assessment of health risks created by work involving substances hazardous to health
An employer shall not carry on any work that is liable to expose any employees to any substances hazardous to health unless he has made a suitable and sufficient assessment of the risks created by that work to the health of those employees and the steps that need to be taken to meet the requirements of the regulations.
The assessment shall be reviewed forthwith if:
(a)   there is reason to suspect that the assessment is no longer valid; or

(b)   there has been a significant change in the work to which the assessment relates;
and where, as a result of the review, changes in the assessment are required, those changes shall be made.

A 'suitable and sufficient assessment'

The General ACOP indicates that a suitable and sufficient assessment should include:

(a)   an assessment of the risks to health;

(b)   the steps that need to be taken to achieve adequate control of exposure, in accordance with Regulation 7; and

(c)   identification of other action necessary to comply with Regulations 8 to 12.

An assessment of the risks created by any work should involve:

(a)   a consideration of:
    (i)   which substances or types of substances (including microorganisms) employees are liable to be exposed to (taking into account consequences of possible failure of any control measures provided to meet the requirements of Regulation 7);
    (ii)   what effects these substances can have on the body;
    (iii)   where the substances are likely to be present and in what form;
    (iv)   the ways in which and the extent to which any groups of employees or other persons could potentially be exposed, taking into account the nature of the work and process and any reasonably foreseeable deterioration in, or failure of, any control measure provided for the purpose of Regulation 7;

(b)   an estimate of exposure, taking into account engineering measures and systems of work currently employed for controlling potential exposure; and

(c)   where valid standards exist, representing adequate control, comparison of the estimate with those standards.

Detailed guidance on health risk assessment is provided in the HSE publication **A step-by-step guide to COSHH assessment** (HMSO).

Regulation 7 – Prevention or control of exposure to substances hazardous to health

Every employer shall ensure that the exposure of his employees to substances hazardous to health is either prevented or, where this is not reasonably practicable, adequately controlled.

So far as is reasonably practicable, the prevention or adequate control of exposure of employees to substances hazardous to health, except to a carcinogen or biological agent, shall be secured by measures **other than** the provision of PPE.

Without prejudice to the generality of paragraph 1, where the assessment made under Regulation 6 shows that it is not reasonably practicable to prevent exposure to a carcinogen by using an alternative substance or process, the employer shall employ **all** of the following measures:

(a)   the total enclosure of the process and handling systems unless this is not reasonably practicable;

(b)   the use of plant, processes and systems of work that minimise the generation of, or suppress and contain, spills, leaks, dusts, fumes and vapours of carcinogens;

(c)   the limitation of the quantities of a carcinogen at the place of work;

(d)   the keeping to a minimum of the number of persons exposed;

(e)   the prohibition of eating, drinking and smoking in areas that may be contaminated by carcinogens;

(f)   the provision of hygiene measures including adequate washing facilities and regular cleaning of walls and surfaces;

(g)   the designation of those areas and installations that may be contaminated by carcinogens, and the use of suitable and sufficient warning signs; and

(h)   the safe handling, storage and disposal of carcinogens and the use of closed and clearly labelled containers.

Where the above measures do not prevent or provide adequate control of exposure to carcinogens then, in addition to taking those measures, the employer shall provide those employees with suitable PPE as will adequately control their exposure to those substances.

Any **PPE** shall comply with current health and safety design or manufacture requirements including those of the Personal Protective Equipment at Work Regulations 1992.

Where there is exposure to a substance for which a MEL has been approved, the control of exposure shall, so far as the inhalation of that substance is concerned, be treated as adequate, only if the level of exposure is reduced so far as is reasonably practicable and in any case below the MEL.

Without prejudice to the generality of paragraph 1, where there is exposure to a substance for which an OES has been approved, the control of exposure shall, so far as inhalation of the substance is concerned, be treated as adequate, only if:

(a)   the OES is not exceeded; or

(b)   where the OES is exceeded, the employer identifies the reasons for the standard being exceeded and takes appropriate action to remedy the situation as soon as is reasonably practicable.

Where **respiratory protective equipment (RPE)** is provided in pursuance of this regulation, then it shall:

(a)   be suitable for the purpose; and

(b)   comply with the requirements to PPE above or, where no equipment is imposed by virtue of that paragraph, be of a type approved or shall conform to a standard approved, in either case by the HSE.

In the event of a failure of a control measure that might result in the escape of carcinogens into the workplace, the employer shall ensure that:

(a)   only those persons who are responsible for the carrying out of repairs and other necessary work are permitted in the affected area and they are provided with suitable RPE and protective clothing; and

(b)   employees and other persons who might be affected are informed of the failure forthwith.

Schedule 3 of these regulations shall have effect in relation to **biological agents**.

In this regulation **adequate** means adequate having regard only to the nature of the substance and the degree of exposure to substances hazardous to health. **Adequately** shall be construed accordingly.

Regulation 8 – Use of control measures etc.

Every employer who provides any control measure, PPE or other item or facility pursuant to these regulations shall take all reasonable steps to ensure that it is properly used or applied as the case may be.

Every employee shall make full and proper use of any control measure, PPE or other item or facility provided pursuant to these regulations and shall take all reasonable steps to ensure it is returned after use to any accommodation provided for it and, if he discovers any defect therein, he shall report it forthwith to his employer.

Regulation 9 – Maintenance, examination and test of control measures, etc

Any employer who provides any **control** measure to meet the requirements of Regulation 7 shall ensure that it is maintained in efficient state, in efficient working order and in good repair and, in the case of **PPE**, in a clean condition.

Where **engineering controls** are provided to meet the requirements of Regulation 7, the employer shall ensure that thorough examination and tests of those engineering controls are carried out:

(a) in the case of LEV plant, at least once every 14 months, or for LEV plant used in conjunction with a process specified in column 1 of Schedule 4, at no more than the interval specified in the corresponding entry in column 2 of that Schedule; and

(b) in any other case, at suitable intervals.

Where RPE (other than disposable RPE) is provided to meet the requirements of Regulation 7, the employer shall ensure that at suitable intervals thorough examination and, where appropriate, tests of that equipment are carried out.

Every employer shall keep a suitable record of examination and tests carried out in accordance with paragraphs 2 and 3 above of this regulation, and of any repairs carried out as a result of those examinations and tests, and that record or a suitable summary thereof, shall be kept available for at least five years from the date on which it was made.

Regulation 10 – Monitoring exposure at the workplace

In any case in which:

(a) it is a requisite for ensuring the maintenance of adequate control of the exposure of employees to substances hazardous to health; or

(b) it is otherwise requisite for protecting the health of employees

the employer shall ensure that the exposure of employees to substances hazardous to health is monitored in accordance with a suitable procedure.

Where a substance or process is specified in column 1 of Schedule 4, monitoring shall be carried out at a frequency specified in the corresponding entry in column 2 of that Schedule.

The employer shall keep a suitable record of monitoring carried out for the purpose of the regulation and that record or a suitable summary thereof shall be kept available:

(a) where the record is representative of the personal exposure of identifiable employees, for at least 40 years; and

(b) in any other case, for at least five years.

Regulation 11 – Health surveillance

Where it is appropriate for the protection of the health of his employees who are, or are liable to be exposed to a substance hazardous to health, the employer shall ensure that such employees are under suitable health surveillance.

Health surveillance shall be treated as being appropriate where:

(a)   the employee is exposed to one of the substances specified in column 1 of Schedule 6 and is engaged in a process specified in column 2 of that Schedule, unless the exposure is not significant; or

(b)   the exposure of the employee to a substance hazardous to health is such that an identifiable disease or adverse health effect may be related to the exposure, there is a reasonable likelihood that the disease or effect may occur under the particular conditions of his work and there are valid techniques for detecting indications of the disease or that effect.

The employer shall ensure that a health record, containing particulars approved by the HSE, in respect of each of his employees to whom paragraph 1 relates is made and maintained and that that record is kept in a suitable form for at least 40 years from the date of the last entry.

Where an employer who holds records in accordance with the above paragraph ceases to trade, he shall forthwith notify the HSE in writing and offer those records to the HSE.

The remainder of this regulation covers:

♦   medical surveillance where employees are exposed to substances specified in Schedule 6;

♦   prohibition by an employment medical adviser on engagement in work of employees considered to be at risk;

♦   access by employees to their health records;

♦   duty on employees to present themselves for health surveillance;

♦   access to inspect a workplace or any record kept by employment medical advisers and appointed doctors; and

♦   review by an aggrieved employee or employer of medical suspension by an employment medical adviser or appointed doctor.

Regulation 12 – Information, instruction and training

Any employer who undertakes work that may expose any of his employees to substances hazardous to health shall provide that employee with such information, instruction and training as is suitable and sufficient for him to know:

(a)   the risks to health created by such exposure; and

(b)   the precautions that should be taken.

Without prejudice to the generality of paragraph 1 above of this regulation, the information provided under that paragraph shall include:

(a)   information on the results of any monitoring of exposure at the workplace in accordance with Regulation 10 and, in particular, in the case of a substance hazardous to health specified in Schedule 1, the employee or his representative shall be informed forthwith if the results of such monitoring shows that the MEL has been exceeded; and

(b)   information on the collective results of any health surveillance undertaken in a form calculated to prevent it from being identified as relating to a particular person.

Every employer shall ensure that any person (whether or not his employee) who carries out work in connection with the employer's duties under these regulations has the necessary information, instruction and training.

Regulation 16 – Defence under the regulations

In any proceedings for an offence consisting of contravention of these regulations it shall be a defence for any person to prove that he took all reasonable precautions and exercised all due diligence to avoid the commission of that offence.

Note

To rely on this defence, the employer must establish that, on the balance of probabilities, he has taken all precautions that were reasonable and exercised all due diligence to ensure that these precautions were implemented in order to avoid such a contravention. It is unlikely that an employer could rely on a Regulation 16 defence if:

(a)   precautions were available that had not been taken; or

(b)   that he had not provided sufficient information, instruction and training, together with adequate supervision, to ensure that the precautions were effective.

Schedules to the COSHH Regulations

The regulations incorporate a number of Schedules that provide further detail necessary to ensure compliance with specific regulations as follows:

1.   Other Substances and Processes to which the Definition of "Carcinogen" Relates;
2.   Prohibition of Certain Substances Hazardous to Health for Certain Purposes;
3.   Special Provisions Relating to Biological Agents;
4.   Frequency of Thorough Examination and Test of Local Exhaust Ventilation Plant used in Certain Processes;
5.   Specific Substances and Processes for which Monitoring is Required;
6.   Medical Surveillance;
7.   Fumigations Excepted from Regulation 13; and
8.   Notification of Certain Fumigations.

PREVENTION AND CONTROL STRATEGIES

The more important prevention and control strategies, in order of effectiveness, are:

♦   prohibition;
♦   elimination;
♦   substitution;
♦   enclosure/containment;
♦   isolation/separation;
♦   LEV; and
♦   dilution ventilation

with the provision and use of PPE as the last resort.

PREVENTION STRATEGIES

In considering prevention and control strategies, a number of questions need to be asked.

Prohibition

♦   Should we prohibit use of this substance?

In certain cases a substance may be so inherently dangerous that its use may be prohibited by law or an organisation's policy on hazardous substances.

Elimination

♦ Is the use of this substance still necessary?

Review of the needs of specific processes can often reveal chemicals and processes that are no longer necessary. Where such chemicals can be eliminated from use, control is unnecessary.

Substitution

♦ Can a safer material be used?

There are some substances that should never be used and are prescribed in current legislation. Others may be banned as a matter of organisational policy. Typical examples are the substitution of toluene for benzene, fibreglass for asbestos, or trichoroethane for trichlorethylene.

CONTROL STRATEGIES

Enclosure/containment

♦ Can the materials be handled so that individuals never need to come into contact with them?

Total enclosure or containment of the process may be possible by the use of bulk tanks and pipework to deliver a liquid directly into a closed production vessel. Complete enclosure is practicable if the substances are in liquid form, used in large quantities, and if the range of substances is small.

Ventilation systems

♦ Can the hazard be removed by a system of ventilation?

Ventilation is an important control strategy. Here it is necessary to distinguish between natural and mechanical ventilation systems.

Air may enter a building in one or more of the following ways:

♦ **Infiltration**

Infiltration through the fabric of a building, for example, through gaps around doors and windows, or between roofing panels or tiles, is common.

♦ **Planned natural ventilation**

This takes place through fixed openings and vents, through windows and doors.

♦ **Mechanical ventilation**

This operates through a system of extract fans located in the external wall and/or roof of a building, or by means of a more complex ducted ventilation system designed to remove the contaminant at the point of emission. (LEV system). In certain cases dilution ventilation (see later) may be appropriate, or a system of air conditioning may operate.

Infiltration and planned natural ventilation give no continuing protection wherever toxic gases, fumes, vapours, etc are emitted from processes. LEV systems must, therefore, be operated.

LEV systems

LEV systems take two principal forms, receptor systems and captor systems.

See **FIG. 17 Examples of LEV systems.**

LOCAL EXHAUST VENTILATION SYSTEMS FIG. 17

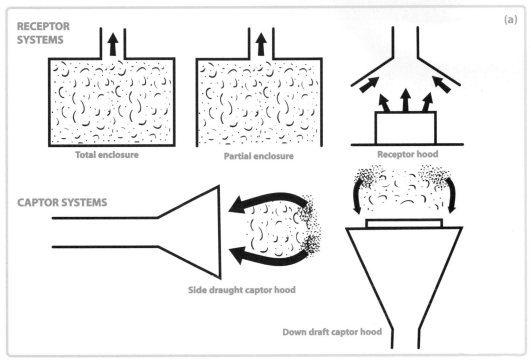

LOCAL EXHAUST VENTILATION SYSTEM FOR A CIRCULAR SAW

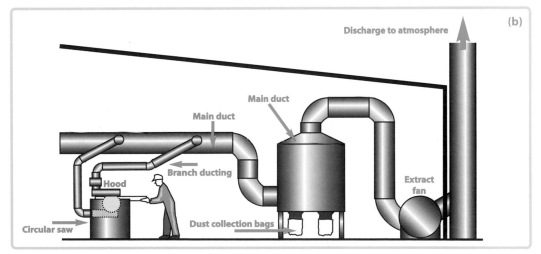

Receptor systems

In a receptor system, the contaminant enters the system without inducement. The fan in the system is used to provide air flow to transport the contaminant from the hood/enclosure through the ducting to a collection system. The hood may form a total enclosure around the source, for example, with highly toxic contaminants, such as beryllium or radioactive sources, or a partial enclosure, as with spray booths, in which all spraying takes place within the three-sided booth, and laboratory fume cupboard. Receptor hoods receive contaminants as they flow from their origin under the influence of thermal currents.

Captor systems

With a captor system, the air that flows into the hood captures the contaminant at some point outside the hood and induces its flow into the system. The rate of air flow into the hood must be sufficient to capture the contaminant at the furthermost point of origin, and the air velocity induced at this point must be high enough to overcome any tendency the contaminant may have to go in any direction other than into the hood.

Contaminants emitted with high energy, ie large particles with high velocities, will require high velocities in the capturing stream.

Dilution ventilation

♦   Could we use a dilution ventilation system?

In certain cases, it may not be possible to extract a contaminant close to the point of origin. If the quantity of the contaminant is small, uniformly evolved and of low toxicity, it may be possible to dilute the contaminant by inducing large volumes of air to flow through the contaminated region. Dilution ventilation is most successfully used to control vapours, for example, vapours from low toxicity solvents, but is seldom successfully applied to dust and fumes, as it will not prevent inhalation.

PPE

♦   What about the use of PPE?

The use of various forms of PPE, including RPE is never a perfect solution to preventing exposure to hazardous substances. As a control strategy it relies heavily on the operator wearing the correct PPE and/or RPE all the time he is exposed to the risk, and people simply will not do this. In the majority of cases the provision and use of PPE should be seen as an additional form of protection where other forms of protection are in operation.

Health surveillance

The operation of a health surveillance programme directed at monitoring the on-going state of health of the people who might be exposed to substances hazardous to health is an important support strategy. However, it should not be used as the sole strategy in protecting people from the risk of exposure to such substances.

HEALTH RISK ASSESSMENT

The management of hazardous substances

All hazardous substances, whether they are directly hazardous to health or otherwise, for example, flammable substances, can be managed safely provided that a suitable prevention or control strategy has been established and is operated effectively and conscientiously. Such a strategy incorporates the five principal elements of occupational hygiene practice.

1. **Identification/Recognition**
   Obtaining and passing on information and knowledge about the substance.
2. **Measurement**
   The assessment of hazards posed by the substance in terms of its use, by-products, disposal and storage.
3. **Evaluation**
   Evaluation of the measured hazards against recognised standards, such as OELs.
4. **Control**
   Control of the substance using various engineering techniques, safe systems of work and with the use of PPE as an extra form of protection, not the sole form of protection.
5. **Monitoring**
   Monitoring the effectiveness of control strategies, for example, LEV systems.

The above principles apply in most cases of health risk assessment. The COSHH Regulations use the term 'assessment' in a very broad sense, which encompasses not only the identification and assessment of the hazards and risks involved, but also the subsequent development of control strategies applicable to the substance in question.

An assessment under the regulations can, therefore, be regarded as a written strategy, rather than a simple hazard and risk analysis. The assessment of risk needs a review of the hazardous properties of substances in terms of the way these substances are handled, used or encountered at work and a judgement as to whether the risk to people, property and the environment is tolerable.

Hazardous substances at work

There are four main ways in which hazardous substances may be encountered at work.

1. **Raw materials**
   For manufacturing and service processes, for example, chemical feedstocks, solvents for degreasing or dry cleaning plants, paints, fertilisers for agricultural use, toners for dry copiers.
2. **Engineering and cleaning materials**
   These include lubricants, cutting oils, water treatment chemicals, paints, toilet cleaners and bleaches.
3. **Service functions**
   For example, materials such as adhesives and correcting fluids.
4. **Products of the process**
   This could include Legionella bacteria, vehicle exhaust fumes or ozone from photocopiers.

A structured approach to health risk assessment

Assessment under the regulations should take a structured approach, commencing with the completion of an inventory of hazardous substances stored and used on site. On completion of the inventory, the various phases of this structured approach can commence.

Phase 1 – Obtaining and passing on knowledge

1. Prepare lists of substances, mixtures and compounds that are used, bought in,

produced in the location or work operation, or to which employees are otherwise exposed at work.

2. Consolidate the lists and prepare a matrix chart in tabular form indicating the substances and their various uses.
3. Marshal information from suppliers, such as safety data sheets, external data sources, industry associations, etc on the properties and hazards.
4. Summarise the basic hazards of each substance in terms of use, storage and specific properties.
5. Prepare in-house data sheets to a standard pattern, brief employees and advise of the action necessary to reduce the risks.

Phase 2 – Assessment of the risks in practice

1. Assess each process using the substances listed.
2. Identify those substances defined as hazardous to health under the COSHH Regulations.
3. Review all chemicals and associated hazards on the list to identify further hazards, or rule against unacceptable processes or practices.
4. Assess likely exposure to substances listed, including any potential exposure of non-employees.
5. Compare this exposure with a known standard, ie MEL or OES.
6. Decide on the need for air monitoring to assist in 4 and 5 above.

Phase 3 – Control of hazards and risks

1. For each chemical, decide and record how it is to be controlled.
2. Produce, or review, safe operating procedures, in written form for each chemical deemed to be hazardous, to cover processes and control measures.
3. Ensure that specific reference is made to the PPE necessary by type and/or British Standard.

Phase 4 – Monitoring effectiveness

1. Establish a written procedure for reviewing control measures.
2. Establish the frequency of required air monitoring as an on-going check.
3. Set up the necessary arrangements for the maintenance, examination and testing of LEV systems and other appropriate control measures.
4. Establish procedures for supplying and maintaining PPE.
5. Establish a procedure for incorporating new safety data information and for dealing with changes to work processes in the assessment.
6. Identify training needs and establish the information, instruction and training process.
7. Indicate the frequency with which the assessment will be reviewed in full or in part.
8. Sign and date the finished assessment record and distribute copies to all interested parties.

SPECIMEN HEALTH RISK ASSESSMENT FIG. 18

HEALTH RISK ASSESSMENT
CONTROL OF SUBSTANCES HAZARDOUS TO HEALTH REGULATIONS
This health risk assessment should be undertaken taking into account the supplier's safety data information provided in accordance with the CHIP Regulations.

Assessment No.

Location   **Process/Activity/Use**

Substance information

Name of substance   Chemical composition

Supplier

Risk information

Risk classification   Stated OELs

Toxic/Corrosive/Harmful/Irritant   **MEL/OES**

                                                LTEL   **STEL**

Route of entry   **Acute/Chronic/Local/Systemic**

Exposure situations

Exposure effects

Estimate of potential exposure   Frequency of use

Quantities used   Duration of use

Storage requirements

Air monitoring requirements and standards

First aid requirements

Health surveillance requirements

Routine disposal requirements

Procedure in the event of spillage:
Small scale spillage

Large scale spillage

Information, instruction and training requirements/arrangements

General conclusions as to risk

High/Medium/Low risk

Special precautions

Supervision requirements

HEALTH RISK ASSESSMENT SUMMARY

General comments as to the extent of the health risk

ACTION

1.   Immediate action

2. **Short-term action (7days)**

3. **Medium-term action (3 months)**

4. **Long-term action (12 months)**

Date of reassessment

Assessor_____**Date**_____

KEY POINTS

♦ All substances are classified according to the categories of danger detailed in Schedule 1 to the CHIP Regulations.

♦ Safety data sheets produced by suppliers must incorporate the heading outlined in Appendix 1 to the CHIP Regulations.

♦ The form taken by a substance is significant in its potential for harm.

♦ Substances may enter the body by different routes, inhalation being the principal route.

♦ The COSHH Regulations provide a strategy for ensuring the safe use of substances hazardous to health.

♦ The term 'substance hazardous to health' is very broadly defined in the regulations.

♦ Under the COSHH Regulations employers must undertake a health risk assessment wherever there is a chance that employees may be exposed to substances hazardous to health.

♦ OELS are used to determine the accuracy of control of exposure by inhalation of substances hazardous to health.

- Employers must either prevent or control exposure to substances hazardous to health.
- LEV systems are a common form of controlling exposure to hazardous substances.
- PPE as a means of protecting people from exposure to substances hazardous to health must be seen:
    - as the last resort; or
    - as an interim measure until a more appropriate control measure can be installed; or
    - as an additional means of protecting people from exposure and not the sole means of protection.

15 Personal Protective Equipment

The provision and use of a range of PPE, such as safety boots, hearing protection, chain mail gloves and eye protectors is common practice in most organisations. In some organisations, this may be the only form of protection provided.

However, this is never the perfect solution to controlling hazards at work. The use of PPE does have some value, however, and must be viewed as an extra form of protection where people may be exposed to hazards.

This chapter examines the range of PPE available, recommendations for selection, the limitations of PPE and the duties of employers and employees under the Personal Protective Equipment at Work Regulations 1992.

WHAT IS PERSONAL PROTECTIVE EQUIPMENT?

The term is generally defined as including equipment worn and used by people at work to protect them from both general and specific risks.

Under the Personal Protective Equipment at Work Regulations, 'personal protective equipment' is defined as meaning 'all equipment (including clothing affording protection against the weather) that is intended to be worn or held by a person at work and that protects him against one or more risks to his health or safety, and any addition or accessory designed to meet that objective'. These regulations are accompanied by HSE Guidance that provides extensive information on the subject.

CLASSIFICATION OF PERSONAL PROTECTIVE EQUIPMENT

A wide range of PPE is available for use by people at work. The various forms of PPE can be classified as follows.

Head protection

Head protection is designed to protect the head against contact with fixed objects, falling objects and the risk of entanglement and scalping. According to HSE Guidance, there are four principal types of head protection:

(a) Crash helmets, cycling helmets, riding helmets and climbing helmets, which are intended to protect the user in falls.

(b) Industrial safety helmets which can protect against falling objects or impact with fixed objects.

(c) Industrial scalp protectors (bump caps) which can protect against striking fixed obstacles, scalping or entanglement.

(d) Caps, hairnets, etc, which can protect against scalping and entanglement.

Eye protection

The selection of the correct form of eye protection is important. Eye protection serves to protect the wearer against the hazards of impact, splashes from chemicals or molten metal, liquids (chemical mists and sprays), dust, gases, welding arcs, non-ionising radiation and the light from lasers.

There are several forms of eye protection:

(a) safety spectacles, which are similar to prescription spectacles but may incorporate side shields to give extra protection to the wearer;

(b) eye shields designed with a one-piece moulded lens; and

(c) safety goggles, which incorporate a flexible plastic frame, a one-piece lens and an elastic headband, giving total protection from all angles.

Face protection

This takes the form of a face shield, which incorporates an adjustable head harness or can be hand-held, and protects the face only.

Respiratory protection

This field is particularly broad, depending on the airborne particulates the protective equipment is designed to protect against, such as dusts, gases, vapours, fumes, together with the risk associated with working in confined and enclosed spaces. This classification also includes respiratory protection used in emergency situations.

Respiratory protection includes:

(a) simple face masks;

(b) general purpose dust respirators;

(c) positive pressure-powered dust respirators;

(d) helmet-contained positive pressure respirators;

(e) gas respirators;

(f) emergency escape respirators;

(g) airline breathing apparatus; and

(h) self-contained breathing apparatus.

Much will depend on the circumstances as to the type of respiratory protection used.

Hearing protection

Hearing protection should be used to protect against the risk of occupational deafness. It includes:

(a) acoustic wool;

(b) various forms of ear plug;

(c) ear defenders;

(d) ear muffs; and

(e) ear valves.

Body protection

Body protection of varying types needs to be worn in activities such as construction and work outdoors, road work, foundry work, work in laboratories and in low temperatures, such as work in cold stores. The range of body protection is extensive and includes:

(a) one- and two-piece overalls;

(b) donkey jackets;

(c) rubber and PVC-coated aprons;

(d) vapour suits;

(e) splash-resistant suits;

(f)   warehouse coats;

(g)   body warmers;

(h)   thermal and weather protection overclothing;

(i)   oilskin overclothing;

(j)   high visibility clothing; and

(k)   personal buoyancy equipment, such as life jackets.

Hand and arm protection

Hands and arms are exposed to the risk of cuts and abrasions, extremes of temperature, skin irritants and other hazardous substances. Protection includes:

(a)   general purpose fibre gloves;

(b)   PVC fabric gauntlets and gloves;

(c)   leather gloves and sleeves;

(d)   wrist protectors;

(e)   chain mail hand and arm protectors;

(f)   fire-resistant gloves; and

(g)   gloves giving thermal protection.

Leg and foot protection

Injuries to the feet are commonly associated with manual handling operations, construction work, agricultural and forestry work and work involving molten metals, as with work in foundries.

This form of protection includes:

(a)   safety boots and shoes;

(b)   clogs;

(c)   foundry boots;

(d)   anti-static footwear; and

(e)   wellington boots.

together with gaiters and anklets.

RESPIRATORY PROTECTIVE EQUIPMENT

RPE can take a number of forms. The use of RPE is essential when employees may be exposed to dangerous aerosols, such as gases, fumes, dusts and sprays. The various forms of RPE are outlined below.

Face masks

These masks commonly incorporate a filtering medium and light metal holder, which covers the mouth and nose. They may be safe for preventing inhalation of coarse dust particles or non-toxic sprays. Under no circumstances should they be used as a form of respiratory protection against toxic aerosols, such as gases and fumes.

General purpose dust respirator

This form of RPE incorporates an ori-nasal face piece and a particulate filter designed to trap finely divided solids, such as dusts, or liquid particles.

Positive pressure-powered dust respirator

These respirators comprise an ori-nasal face piece linked to a power-driven pack, which is worn by the operator and connected by means of a flexible hose. They use a more efficient form of filtering medium and operate with positive pressure at the face piece. This form of RPE is more efficient than a simple form of dust respirator.

Helmet-contained positive pressure respirator

This is a more sophisticated form of RPE, providing head, eye, face and respiratory protection. The respirator incorporates a helmet and visor with a high efficiency axial fan mounted at the rear of the helmet. The battery-driven fans draw dust-laden air through a coarse filter and, subsequently, a fine filter bag. The filtered air provides a cool airstream over the face and is exhausted at the bottom of the visor at a flow rate sufficient to prevent dust coming near the mouth and nose.

Gas respirators

Gas respirators take two forms – **cartridge** and **canister**.

1. Cartridge respirators incorporate a chemical cartridge filter, which is effective against low concentrations of non-toxic gases or vapours that have an acceptable level of concentration not exceeding 100 ppm.

2. Canister respirators are normally of the full face piece type with exhalation valves, and incorporate goggles and visor. They are connected to a chemical canister filter for protection against low concentrations of specific toxic gases and vapours.

Emergency escape respirators

This form of respiratory protection is specifically designed using a chemical filter that enables people to escape from dangerous atmospheres in an emergency situation. They are intended purely for short-term use and should not be used for normal respiratory protection.

Airline breathing apparatus

This apparatus can take a number of forms. It incorporates a full face mask or half mask connected by a flexible hose either to a source of clean air, for work involving short distances, or to a compressed airline via a filter and demand valve in the case of longer distances. Clearly, its use is limited by the length of the airline.

Self-contained breathing apparatus

This appliances can be of the open or closed circuit type.

In the case of the open circuit type, air is supplied by a lung-governed demand valve or pressure reducer connected to a full face piece and hose supply. The hose is connected to its own compressed air or oxygen supply, which is carried in a harness by the user.

The closed circuit type incorporates a purifier to absorb exhaled carbon dioxide and the purified air is fed back to the respirator after mixing with pure oxygen.

Both types of self-contained breathing apparatus can be used in dangerous atmospheres or where there is an oxygen-deficient atmosphere. They are commonly used for rescue work in confined spaces.

THE SELECTION OF PERSONAL PROTECTIVE EQUIPMENT

A systematic approach to the selection of PPE is essential in ensuring people at risk are adequately protected. Under the Personal Protective Equipment at Work Regulations, PPE must be 'suitable' in terms of protecting or controlling exposure to the risks and for the work being undertaken.

When considering the type and form of PPE to be provided, and its relative suitability, the following factors are relevant:

♦ the needs of the user in terms of comfort, ease of movement, convenience in putting on, use and removal, and individual suitability;

♦ the ergonomic (work-related) requirements and state of health of the persons who may use that PPE;

♦ the capability of the PPE to fit the wearer correctly, if necessary, after adjustments within the range for which it is designed;

♦ the number of personnel exposed to a particular hazard, for instance, noise, dust or risk of hand injury;

♦ the risk or risks involved, the conditions at the place where the exposure to risk may occur, and the relative appropriateness of the PPE in protecting operators against, for example, fume and dust inhalation or molten metal splashes;

♦ its relative effectiveness to prevent or adequately control the risk or risks without increasing overall risk;

♦ the scale of the hazard;

♦ standards representing recognised 'safety limits' for the hazard, for example, HSE Guidance Notes, British Standards;

♦ specific regulations currently in force;

♦ specific job requirements of restrictions, for example, work in confined spaces, roof work;

♦ the presence of environmental stressors that will affect the individual's wearing or use of the equipment, for example, high temperatures, inadequate ventilation, background noise; and

♦ the ease of cleaning, sanitisation, maintenance and replacement of equipment and/or its component parts.

PERSONAL PROTECTIVE EQUIPMENT AT WORK REGULATIONS 1992

These regulations:

(a) amend certain regulations made under the HSWA that deal with PPE, so that they fully implement the European Directive in circumstances where they apply;

(b) cover all aspects of the provision, maintenance and use of PPE at work in other circumstances; and

(c) revoke and replace almost all pre-HSWA legislation that deals with PPE.

Specific requirements of current regulations dealing with PPE, namely, the Control of Lead at Work Regulations, the Ionising Radiations Regulations, the Control of Asbestos at Work Regulations, the COSHH Regulations, the Noise at Work Regulations and the Construction (Head Protection) Regulations take precedence over the more general requirements of the

Personal Protective Equipment at Work Regulations.

In these regulations, **PPE** is defined as meaning all equipment (including clothing affording protection against the weather) that is intended to be worn or held by a person at work and that protects him against one or more risks to his health and safety, and any addition or accessory designed to meet this objective.

Regulation 3 – Disapplication of these regulations

These regulations shall not apply to or in relation to the master or crew of a sea-going ship or to the employer of such persons in respect of normal shipboard activities of a ship's crew under the direction of a master.

Regulations 4 to 12 shall not apply in respect of PPE which is:

(a) ordinary working clothes and uniforms that do not specifically protect the health and safety of the wearer;

(b) an offensive weapon within the meaning of section 1(4) of the Prevention of Crime Act 1953 used as self-defence or deterring equipment;

(c) portable devices for detecting and signalling risks and nuisances;

(d) used for protection whilst travelling on a road; and

(e) equipment used during the playing of competitive sports.

Regulation 4 – Provision of PPE

Every employer shall ensure that suitable PPE is provided to his employees who may be exposed to a risk to their health and safety while at work except where and to the extent that such risk has been adequately controlled by other means that are equally or more effective.

Similar provisions apply in the case of self-employed persons.

PPE shall not be suitable unless:

(a) it is appropriate for the risk or risks involved and the conditions at place the where exposure to the risk may occur;

(b) it takes account of ergonomic requirements and state of health of the person or persons who may wear it;

(c) it is capable of fitting the wearer correctly, if necessary after adjustments within the range for which it is designed; and

(d) so far as is practicable, it is effective to prevent or adequately control the risk or risks involved without increasing overall risk.

Regulation 5 – Compatibility of PPE

Every employer shall ensure that where the presence of more than one risk to health or safety makes it necessary for his employee to wear or use simultaneously more than one item of PPE, such equipment is compatible and continues to be effective against the risk or risks in question.

Similar provisions apply in the case of self-employed persons.

Regulation 6 – Assessment of PPE

Before choosing any PPE that he is required to provide, an employer or self-employed person shall make an assessment to determine whether the PPE he intends to provide is suitable.

The assessment shall comprise:

(a) an assessment of any risk or risks that have not been avoided by other means;

(b) the definition of the characteristics that the PPE must have in order to be effective against the risks referred to above, taking into account any risks which the equipment itself may create; and

(c) comparison of the characteristics of the PPE available with the characteristics referred to in (b) above.

The assessment shall be reviewed forthwith if:

(a) there is reason to suspect that any element of the assessment is no longer valid; or

(b) there has been a significant change in the work to which the assessment relates;

and where, as a result of the review, changes in the assessments are required, these changes shall be made.

SPECIMEN RISK SURVEY TABLE FOR THE USE OF PERSONAL PROTECTIVE EQUIPMENT FIG. 19

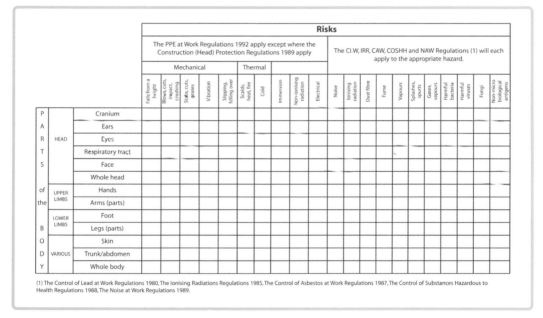

(1) The Control of Lead at Work Regulations 1980, The Ionising Radiations Regulations 1985, The Control of Asbestos at Work Regulations 1987, The Control of Substances Hazardous to Health Regulations 1988, The Noise at Work Regulations 1989.

Regulation 7 – Maintenance and replacement of PPE

Every employer and every self-employed person shall ensure that any PPE provided by them is maintained in relation to any matter that it is reasonably foreseeable will affect the health and safety of any person in an efficient state, in efficient working order, in good repair and in hygienic condition.

Regulation 8 – Accommodation for PPE

Where an employer or self-employed person is required, by virtue of Regulation 4, to ensure PPE is provided, he shall also ensure that appropriate accommodation is provided for that PPE when it is not being used.

Regulation 9 – Information, instruction and training

Where an employer is required to provide PPE to an employee, the employer shall provide that employee with such information, instruction and training as is adequate and appropriate to enable the employee to know:

(a)   the risk or risks that the PPE will avoid or limit;

(b)   the purpose for which and the manner in which the PPE is to be used; and

(c)   any action to be taken by the employee to ensure that the PPE remains in an efficient state, in efficient working order, in good repair and in hygienic condition.

Regulation 10 – Use of PPE

Every employer who provides any PPE shall take all reasonable steps to ensure that it is properly used.

Every employee and self-employed person who has been provided with PPE shall:

(a)   make full and proper use of the PPE; and

(b)   take all reasonable steps to ensure it is returned to the accommodation provided for it after use.

Regulation 11 – Reporting loss or defect

Every employee who has been provided with PPE by his employer shall forthwith report to his employer any loss of or obvious defect in that PPE.

Guidance on the regulations

Detailed HSE Guidance is provided on the requirements of the regulations.

KEY POINTS

♦   PPE includes equipment used and worn by people at work to protect themselves from certain hazards, for example, hand injury.

♦   The use of PPE must be considered a last resort in protecting people from hazards at work or an interim measure until more effective means of protection can be applied.

♦   The limitations of PPE must be appreciated at the selection stage.

♦   When selecting PPE, factors such as the relative comfort, ease of movement and convenience in putting on and removing should be considered.

♦   The Personal Protective Equipment at Work Regulations place duties on employers to ensure PPE is suitable and on employees to use PPE correctly.

♦   Employees must report loss of, or obvious defect in, PPE provided.

16 Noise at Work

Noise is defined as 'unwanted sound'. Exposure to noise from machinery and equipment in the workplace can result in several forms of hearing impairment.

This chapter examines the health hazards associated with exposure to noise, noise control strategies, the human hearing system, noise monitoring techniques and the requirements of the Noise at Work Regulations 1989.

SOUND AND NOISE

'Sound' is defined as any pressure variation in air, water or some other medium that the human ear can detect. 'Noise', on the other hand, is defined as 'unwanted sound'.

Noise nuisance

Noise may be a nuisance at common law and under statute law (Environmental Protection Act 1990 and Noise Act 1996). This form of nuisance, such as noise from a nearby disco, results in disturbance and loss of enjoyment of life, loss of sleep and fatigue.

Noise and accidents

Noise can distract attention and concentration, mask audible warning signals or interfere with work, thereby becoming a causative factor in accidents.

NOISE MONITORING

The range of intensities to which the ear responds is enormous, from the threshold of hearing, at one end of the range, to the threshold of pain. For example, at a frequency of 1,000 Hz, the threshold of pain is 100,000,000,000,000 (10^{14}) times more intense than the threshold of hearing, where sound is just discernible. It is clearly difficult to express such ratios on a simple arithmetic scale, so a logarithmic scale is used to compress the scale for measurement purposes.

Bels and decibels

The unit of sound intensity is the bel. The bel, however, is a very large unit, so it is further split into tenths, ie dB: 1 bel equals 10 dB.

Noise measurement

It is possible to make a single measurement of the overall sound pressure over the entire range of audible frequencies but this measurement, if taken in linear dB, is of limited use since the ear is more sensitive to some frequencies than others.

Use of the 'A' weighted dB scale, which corresponds closest to the performance of the human ear, provides a reasonable means of assessing likely risk to hearing (hence the term dB(A).

However, a knowledge of the way in which the sound is distributed throughout the frequency spectrum provides a much more accurate picture. This can be obtained by dividing the noise into octave bands and measuring the sound pressure level at the centre frequency of each band. An octave represents a doubling of frequency so that the range 90 – 180 Hz is one octave, as is the range 1400 – 2800 Hz. Octave bands are identified by their geometric centre frequencies. For example the geometric centre frequency of the octave 90 – 180 Hz is approximately 125 Hz.

NOISE-INDUCED HEARING LOSS

Exposure to excessive noise can result in hearing impairment, the condition known as 'noise-induced hearing loss' or 'occupational deafness'. Where the intensity and duration of exposure are sufficient, even 'wanted sound', such as loud music, can lead to hearing impairment.

Occupational deafness is a prescribed occupational disease, which is described thus:

♦ substantial sensorineural hearing loss amounting to at least 50 dB in each ear, being due in the case of at least one ear to occupational noise, and being the average of pure tone loss measured by audiometry over the 1, 2 and 3 KHz frequencies'.

Under the Social Security (Industrial Injuries)(Prescribed Diseases) Regulations, this definition goes on to state a wide range of activities and occupations associated with exposure to noise whereby industrial injuries benefit may be payable.

EXPOSURE TO NOISE

Noise dose

For most steady types of industrial noise, intensity and duration of exposure, ie the dose of noise, are the principal factors in the degree of noise-induced hearing loss (sociocusis). Hearing ability also deteriorates with age (presbycusis), and it is sometimes difficult to distinguish between the effects of noise exposure and normal age-related deterioration in hearing.

The risk of noise-induced hearing loss can be related to the total amount of noise energy taken in by the ears over a working lifetime.

The effects of noise exposure

Exposure to noise can affect hearing in three ways.

1. Temporary threshold shift

This is the short-term effect, that is, a temporary reduction in hearing acuity, which may follow exposure to noise. The condition is reversible and the effect depends, to some extent, on an individual's susceptibility to noise.

2. Permanent threshold shift

This takes place when the limit of tolerance is exceeded in terms of time, the level of noise and individual susceptibility to noise. Recovery from permanent threshold shift will not proceed to completion, but will effectively cease at some particular point in time after the end of the exposure.

3. Acoustic trauma

This condition involves ear damage from short-term intense exposure or even from one single exposure. Explosive pressure rises are often responsible, such as that from gunfire, major explosions or even fireworks.

SYMPTOMS OF NOISE-INDUCED HEARING LOSS

Symptoms vary according to whether the hearing loss is mild or severe.

Mild form of hearing loss

Typical symptoms include a difficulty in conversing with people and the wrong answers may be given occasionally due to the individual missing certain key elements of the question. Speech on television and radio seems indistinct. There may also be difficulty in hearing normal domestic sounds, such as a clock ticking.

Severe form of hearing loss

Here there is difficulty in discussion, even when face-to-face with people, as well as hearing what is said at public meetings, unless sitting right at the front. Generally, people seem to be speaking indistinctly and there is an inability to hear the normal sounds of the home and street.

What is important is that it is often impossible for someone with this level of hearing loss to tell the actual direction from which a source of noise is coming and to assess the actual distance from that noise. This can be a contributory factor in accidents and, in particular, pedestrian-related road accidents.

In the most severe cases, there is the sensation of whistling or ringing in the ear (tinnitus).

THE HUMAN HEARING SYSTEM

The human ear incorporates:
- ♦ the outer ear, incorporating the external pinna and the auditory canal terminating at the eardrum;
- ♦ the middle ear, which comprises a chamber containing ossicles, ie three linked bones, the malleus, incus and stapes (hammer, anvil and stirrup bones); and
- ♦ the inner ear, which houses the cochlea, the important organ of hearing and which is, fundamentally, a coiled fluid-filled tube incorporating the Organ of Corti.

Sound is conveyed via the auditory canal to the eardrum and ossicles to the cochlea, and from the cochlea via the auditory nerve to the brain, where the sensation of sound is perceived. Hearing loss takes place in the Organ of Corti and this may be measured by audiometry.

THE HUMAN HEARING SYSTEM FIG. 20

1. Incus
2. Malleus
3. Pinna
4. Stapes
5. Semi-circular canals
6. Auditory nerve (containing basilar membrane and frequency-responsive hair cells)
7. Cochlea
8. Auditory canal
9. Ear drum
10. Middle ear cavity
11. Eustachian tube
12. Fenestra rotunda
13. Fenestra ovalis

OUTER EAR

INNER EAR

MIDDLE EAR

NOISE CONTROL STRATEGIES

In any strategy to reduce or control noise, two factors must be considered:
♦ the actual source or sources of noise, for example, machinery, ventilation systems; and
♦ the transmission pathway taken by the noise to the recipient.

The design stage

The first consideration must be that of tackling a potential noise hazard at the design stage of new projects, rather than endeavouring to control noise once the machinery or noise-emitting plant is installed.

Manufacturers, suppliers and importers of machinery and plant must be required to give an indication of anticipated sound pressure levels from their equipment once installed, and of the measures necessary to reduce noise emission, prior to the ordering of the equipment. Ensuring appropriate reduction of noise emission by manufacturers, suppliers and importers of plant and machinery should feature in any contract to supply.

Existing machinery and plant

In this case, a range of methods of noise control are suitable for dealing with identified sources of noise and the stages in the transmission pathway. These methods are summarised in Table 14 Methods of noise control.

TABLE 14 : METHODS OF NOISE CONTROL

Sources and pathways	Control measures
Vibration produced through machinery operation	Reduction at source eg substitution of metal components by nylon components; use of tapered tools on power presses
Structure-borne noise (vibration)	Vibration isolation on power presses; use of resilient mounts and connections; anti-vibration mounts
Radiation of structural vibration	Vibration damping to prevent resonance
Turbulence created by air or gas flow	Reduction at source or the use of silencers
Airborne noise pathway	Noise insulation – reflection; use of heavy barriers
	Noise absorption – no reflection; use of porous lightweight barriers

Control of the main or primary pathway is the most important strategy in noise control and to ensure compliance with the Noise at Work Regulations 1989.

Hearing protection

The use of hearing protection, such as ear plugs, ear defenders and acoustic wool, may go some way towards preventing people from going deaf at work, but such a strategy must be regarded as secondary since it relies too heavily on exposed persons wearing potentially uncomfortable and inconvenient protection for all the time they are exposed to noise. The majority of employees simply will not do this!

NOISE AT WORK REGULATIONS 1989

These regulations are accompanied by a number of Noise Guides issued by the HSE. The regulations brought in the concepts of 'daily personal noise exposure' and 'action levels'.

Important definitions

Daily personal noise exposure means a level of daily personal noise exposure of an employee ascertained in accordance with Part 1 of the Schedule to the regulations, but taking no account of the effect of any personal ear protector used.

The first action level means a daily personal noise exposure of 85 dBA.
The peak action level means a peak sound pressure of 200 pascals.
The second action level means a daily personal noise exposure of 90 dBA.

Note: Under the SI system, sound pressure is expressed in pascals. A pascal is a unit of pressure corresponding to a force of one Newton acting uniformly upon an area of one square metre. Hence 1 Pa = 1 N/m2.

Regulation 4 – Assessment of exposure

Every employer shall, when any of his employees is likely to be exposed to the first action level or above or to the peak action level or above, ensure a competent person makes a noise assessment that is adequate for the purposes of:

(a) identifying which of his employees are so exposed; and
(b) providing him with such information with regard to the noise to which those employees may be so exposed as will facilitate compliance with his duties under Regulations 7, 8, 9 and 11.

The above noise assessment shall be reviewed when:

(a) there is reason to suspect the assessment is no longer valid; or
(b) there has been a significant change in the work to which the assessment relates,
and where as a result of the review changes in the assessment are required, those changes shall be made.

Regulation 5 – Assessment records

Following any noise assessment, the employer shall ensure that an adequate record of the assessment, and of any review thereof carried out, is kept until a further noise assessment is made.

Regulation 6 – Reducing the risk of damage to hearing

Every employer shall reduce the risk of damage to the hearing of his employees from exposure to noise to the lowest level reasonably practicable.

Regulation 7 – Reducing exposure to noise

Every employer shall, when any of his employees is likely to be exposed to the second action level or above or to the peak action level or above, reduce, so far as is reasonably practicable, (other than by the provision of ear protectors) the exposure to noise of that employee.

Regulation 8 – Ear protection

Every employer shall ensure, so far as is practicable, that when any of his employees is likely to be exposed to the first action level or above in circumstances where the daily personal noise exposure of that employee is likely to be less than 90 dBA, that employee is provided, at his request, with suitable and sufficient ear protectors.

When any of his employees is likely to be exposed to the second action level or above or to the peak action level or above, every employer shall ensure, so far as is practicable, that the employee is provided with suitable ear protectors, which, when properly worn, can reasonably be expected to keep the risk of damage to that employee's hearing to below that arising from exposure to the second action level or, as the case may be, to the peak action level.

Regulation 9 – Ear protection zones

Every employer shall, in respect of premises under his control, ensure, so far as is reasonably practicable, that:

(a) each ear protection zone is demarcated and identified by means of the sign specified in paragraph A.3.3 of Appendix A to Part 1 of BS 5878, which sign shall include such text as indicates:

   (i) that it is an ear protection zone; and

   (ii) the need for his employees to wear personal ear protectors whilst in any such zone; and

(b) none of his employees should enter any such zone unless that employee is wearing personal ear protectors.

In this regulation, **ear protection zone** means any part of the premises referred to above where any employee is likely to be exposed to the second action level or above or to the peak action level or above, and **Part 1 of BS 5378** has the same meaning as in Regulation 2(1) of the Safety Signs Regulations 1980.

Regulation 10 – The maintenance and use of equipment

Every employer shall:

(a) ensure, so far as is practicable, that anything provided by him to or for the benefit of an employee in compliance with his duties under these regulations (other than personal ear protectors provided pursuant to Regulation 8) is fully and properly used; and

(b) ensure, so far is practicable, that anything provided by him in compliance with his duties under these regulations is maintained in an efficient state, in efficient working order and in good repair.

Every employee shall, so far as is practicable, fully and properly use personal ear protectors when they are provided by his employer pursuant to Regulation 7 and any other protective measures provided by his employer in compliance with his duties under these regulations; and if any employee discovers any defect therein, he shall report it forthwith to his employer.

Regulation 11 – Information to employees

Every employer shall, in respect of any premises under his control, provide each of his employees who is likely to be exposed to the first action level or above or to the peak action level or above with adequate information, instruction and training on:

(a) the risk of damage to the employee's hearing that such exposure may cause;

(b) what steps that employee can take to minimise that risk;

(c) the steps that the employee must take to obtain the personal ear protectors referred to in Regulation 8; and

(d) that employee's obligations under these regulations.

Regulation 12 – Duties of manufacturers, designers, etc

Where any article is likely to cause any employee to be exposed to the first action level or above or to the peak action level or above, adequate information must be provided concerning the noise likely to be generated by that article.

KEY POINTS

♦ Noise is defined as 'unwanted sound'.

♦ Occupational deafness arising from specific activities is a prescribed occupational disease.

♦ Exposure to noise can cause temporary threshold shift, permanent threshold shift and acoustic trauma.

♦ Noise dose is significant in hearing risk assessment.

♦ The symptoms of occupational deafness may vary according to whether the hearing loss is mild or severe.

♦ Reliance by an employer on the use of hearing protection, as the sole means of protecting employees from the risk of occupational deafness is not a perfect solution to the problem.

♦ Noise intensity is measured in dBA.

♦ Effective noise measurement entails frequency analysis across the range of geometric centre frequencies.

♦ Noise control strategies should be implemented preferably at the design stage of projects involving machinery and plant.

♦ Deafness takes place in the inner ear, in the Organ of Corti.

♦ The Noise at Work Regulations 1989 require employers to undertake hearing risk assessments and to reduce noise so far as is reasonably practicable.

17 Radiation

Exposure to radiation, as a source of energy, has long been a risk to many groups of workers, to members of the armed forces and even members of the public. Radiological protection legislation is directed at keeping exposures to safe levels as the long-term effects of excessive exposure to radiation can be significant.

This chapter examines the hazards associated with ionising and non-ionising radiation, the effects of exposure, radiological protection strategies and the main requirements of the Ionising Radiations Regulations.

THE STRUCTURE OF MATTER

All matter consists of elements and the basic unit of any element is the atom, which cannot be further sub-divided by chemical means. The atom is an arrangement of three types of particles:

1. **Protons**
   These have unit mass and carry a positive electrical charge.
2. **Neutrons**
   These have unit mass but carry no charge.
3. **Electrons**
   These have unit mass about 2,000 times less than that of protons and neutrons and carry a negative charge.

Protons and neutrons comprise the central part of the nucleus of an atom, with electrons orbiting the nucleus. In an electrically neutral atom, the number of electrons equals the number of protons. The element itself is defined by the number of protons in the nucleus.

Isotopes

For a given element, however, the number of neutrons can vary to form different isotopes of that element. A particular isotope of an element is called a nuclide and is identified by the name of the element and its mass, for example, Carbon - 14.

There are 90 naturally occurring elements. Other elements, such as plutonium, have been created by man in, for example, nuclear reactors.

RADIATION ENERGY

Radiation is a significant form of energy. When an atom is split, these energetic forces are released and are converted to heat, light and other forms of radiation. The subsequent effects, namely, visible light, infrared radiation, ultraviolet light and microwaves, are all forms of released energy. The energy is released in waves, the length and frequency of these waves depending upon how much energy the atom is releasing. The form of energy and its effects are affected by the length and frequency of these waves. (See **The electromagnetic spectrum** later.)

The energy with which some radiations are produced is expressed in units of electron volt. This is equivalent to the energy gained by an electron passing through a potential difference of one volt. Multiples of this unit are commonly used, especially one million or 10^6 electron volts (Mev).

IONISATION

An ion is a charged atom or group of atoms. Where the number of electrons does not equal the number of protons, the atom has a net positive or negative charge and is said to be ionised. Thus if a neutral atom loses an electron, a positively charged ion will result. Ionisation is the process of losing or gaining electrons and occurs in the course of many physical and chemical reactions.

Ionising radiation includes X-rays, gamma rays and alpha particles.

TABLE 15 : THE ELECTROMAGNETIC SPECTRUM

Radiation	Frequency	Wavelength	Energy	Radiation sources
Gamma	10^{21}	Short	High	Cosmic sources
X-ray	10^{18}	|	|	Atomic strike by high energy particles
Ultraviolet light		|	|	Excited gases
Visible light	10^{15}	|	|	Hot bodies
Infra red	$10^{12} - 10^{14}$	|	|	Hot bodies
Microwaves	10^{9}	|	|	Microwave generator
Radio waves	-10^{6}	Long	Low	Radio transmitter

NON-IONISING RADIATION

This includes lasers, ultraviolet, infrared and microwaves.

RADIATION HAZARDS

The effects of exposure to doses of ionising radiation vary according to:

(a) the type of exposure, for instance, whether the dose was local, affecting only a part of the body surface, or general, affecting the whole body; and

(b) the actual duration or length of time of exposure, which determines the severity of the outcome of such exposure.

Local exposure

This is the most common form of exposure and may result in reddening of the skin with ulceration in serious cases. Where exposure is local and the dose small, but of long duration, loss of hair, atrophy and fibrosis of the skin can occur.

General exposure

The effects of acute general exposure range from mild nausea to severe illness, with vomiting, diarrhoea, collapse and, in some cases, death. General exposure to small doses may result in chronic anaemia and leukaemia. The ovaries and testes are particularly vulnerable and there is evidence that exposure to radiation reduces fertility and causes sterility.

Apart from the danger of increased susceptibility to cancer, radiation can damage the genetic structure of reproductive cells, causing increases in the number of stillbirths and malformations.

Biological dose of radiation

The unit of biological dose of radiation is the milliSievert (mSv). Specified dose limits are listed in Schedule 4 to the Ionising Radiations Regulations 1999.

PRINCIPLES OF RADIOLOGICAL PROTECTION

A significant feature in radiological protection is the form taken by the radioactive source. Sources may be sealed or unsealed.

Sealed sources of radiation

The source is contained in such a way that the radioactive material cannot be released as in the case of X-ray machines. The source of radiation can be a piece of radioactive material, such as cobalt, which is sealed in a container or held in another material that is not radioactive. It is usually solid and the container and bonding material are regarded as the source.

Unsealed sources of radiation

Unsealed sources may take many forms, for example, gases, liquids and particulates. As they are unsealed, entry into the body is comparatively easy.

CRITERIA FOR RADIOLOGICAL PROTECTION

These rests on three specific factors, namely, time, distance and shielding. The principal objective is to ensure that no one receives a harmful dose of radiation.

Time

Radiation workers may be protected by limiting the duration of exposure to certain predetermined limits.

Distance

Workers can be protected by ensuring that they do not come within certain distances of radiation sources. This may be achieved by the use of restricted areas, barriers and similar controls. The Inverse Square Law applies in this case.

Shielding

Workers may be shielded by the use of absorbing material, such as lead or concrete, between themselves and the source to reduce the level of radiation to below the maximum dose level. The quality and quantity (thickness) of shielding varies for the radiation type and energy level and varies from no shielding through lightweight shielding, for example, 1cm thick Perspex, to heavy shielding, in terms of centimetres of lead or metres of concrete.

RADIOLOGICAL PROTECTION PROCEDURES

These can be summarised as including:

- pre-employment and follow up medical examinations for classified persons;
- appointment of qualified persons (radiation protection advisers);
- maintenance and retention of individual dose records;
- information, instruction and training, together with hazard awareness;
- continuous and spot check radiation (dose) monitoring by the use of dosemeters and film badges for classified persons;
- use of warning notices, controlled areas and supervised areas; and
- strict adherence to maximum dose limits.

The following additional measures apply in the case of work with unsealed sources:

- appropriate personal protective clothing and equipment, including respiratory protection;
- effective ventilation;
- enclosure/containment to prevent leakage;
- use of impervious surfaces;
- immaculate working techniques; and
- use of remote control systems.

The central objective is the avoidance of radioactive contamination.

IONISING RADIATIONS REGULATIONS 1999

These extensive and specialised regulations deal with the general principles and procedures for ensuring safe working with ionising radiation.

As such, they reinforce the basic principles of radiological protection, namely time, distance and shielding, with specific provisions for classified persons, controlled and supervised areas, the setting of radiation dose limits and rates, the keeping of dose records, the appointment of radiation protection advisers and the provision of medical surveillance.

Important definitions

Classified person means:

- (a) a person designated as such pursuant to Regulation 20(1); and
- (b) in the case of an outside worker employed by an undertaking in Northern Ireland or in another member state, a person who has been designated as a Category A exposed worker within the meaning of Article 21 of the Directive.

Contamination means the contamination by any radioactive substance of any surface (including any surface of the body of clothing) or any part of absorbent objects or materials or the contamination of liquids or gases by any radioactive substance.

Controlled area means:

- (a) in the case of an area situated in Great Britain, an area that has been so designated in accordance with Regulation 16(1); and
- (b) in the case of an area situated in Northern Ireland or in another member state, an area

subject to special rules for the purposes of protection against ionising radiation and to which access is controlled as specified in Article 19 of the Directive.

Dose means, in relation to ionising radiation, any dose quantity or sum of dose quantities mentioned in Schedule 4.

Dose assessment means the dose assessment made and recorded by an approved dosimetry service in accordance with Regulation 21.

Dose limit means, in relation to persons of a specified class, the limit in effective dose or equivalent dose specified in Schedule 4 in relation to a person of that class.

Dose rate, in relation to a place, the rate at which a person or part of a person would receive a dose of ionising radiation from external radiation if he were at that place being a dose rate at that place averaged over one minute.

Dose record means, in relation to a person, the record of doses received by that person as a result of his exposure to ionising radiation, being the record made and maintained on behalf of the employer by the approved dosimetry service in accordance with Regulation 21

Ionising radiation means the transfer of energy in the form of particles or electromagnetic waves of a wavelength of 100 nanometres or less or a frequency of 3×10^{15} Hz or more capable of producing ions directly or indirectly.

Over exposure means any exposure of a person to ionising radiation to the extent that the dose received by that person causes a dose limit relevant to that person to be exceeded or, in relation to Regulation 26(2), causes a proportion of a dose limit relevant to any employee to be exceeded.

Radiation accident means an accident where immediate action would be required to prevent or reduce the exposure to ionising radiation of employees or any other persons.

Radiation employer means an employer who in the course of a trade, business or other undertaking carries out work with ionising radiation and, for the purposes of Regulations 5, 6 and 7, includes an employer who intends to carry out such work.

Sealed source means a source containing any radioactive substance, the structure of which is such as to prevent, under normal conditions of use, any dispersion of radioactive substances into the environment, but it does not include any radioactive substance inside a nuclear reactor or any nuclear fuel element.

Supervised area means an area that has been so designated by the employer in accordance with Regulation 16(3).

PART II – GENERAL PRINCIPLES AND PROCEDURES
Regulation 5 – Authorisation of specified procedures
A radiation employer shall not, except in accordance with a prior authorisation granted by

the HSE in writing, carrying out the following practices:

    (a) the use of electrical equipment intended to produce X-rays for the purpose of:

        (i)   industrial radiography;

        (ii) the processing of products;

        (iii) research; or

        (iv) the exposure of persons for medical treatment; or

    (b) the use of accelerators, except electron microscopes.

An authorisation granted may be subject to conditions.

Regulation 6 – Notification of project work

A radiation employer shall not for the first time carry out work with ionising radiation unless at least 28 days before commencing that work he has notified the HSE of his intention to do so and has provided particulars specified in Schedule 2.

Regulation 7 – Prior risk assessment, etc

Before a radiation employer commences a new activity, he shall make a suitable and sufficient assessment of the risk to any employee or other person for the purposes of identifying the measures he needs to take to restrict exposure of that employee or other person to ionising radiation.

Regulation 8 – Restriction of exposure

Every radiation employer shall, in relation to any work with ionising radiation that he undertakes, take all necessary steps to restrict so far as is reasonably practicable the extent to which his employees and other persons are exposed to ionising radiation.

Restriction of exposure shall, so far as is reasonably practicable, be by:

    (a) engineering controls and design features, together with safety features and warning devices;

    (b) the provision of safe systems of work to restrict exposure; and

    (c) the provision of adequate and suitable PPE (including respiratory equipment.

Regulation 9 – Personal protective equipment

Any PPE shall comply with any provision in the Personal Protective Equipment (EC Directive) Regulations 1992.

Regulation 10 – Maintenance and examination of engineering controls etc and personal protective equipment

A radiation employer shall ensure:

    (a) that any such control feature or device is properly maintained; and

    (b) where appropriate, thorough examinations and tests of controls, features or devices are carried out at suitable intervals.

Every radiation employer shall ensure that all PPE is, where appropriate, thoroughly examined at suitable intervals and is properly maintained and that, in the case of RPE, a suitable record of that examination is made and kept for at least two years.

Regulation 11 – Dose limitation

Every employer shall ensure that his employees are not exposed to ionising radiation to an extent that any dose limit is exceeded in one calendar year.

Regulation 12 – Contingency plans

Where an assessment shows that a radiation accident is reasonably foreseeable, the radiation employer shall prepare a contingency plan designed to secure, so far as is reasonably practicable, the restriction of exposure to ionising radiation and the health and safety of persons who may be affected by such accident.

PART III – ARRANGEMENTS FOR THE MANAGEMENT OF RADIATION PROTECTION

Regulation 13 – Radiation protection adviser

Every radiation employer shall consult such suitable radiation protection advisers as are necessary for the purpose of advising the radiation employer as to the observance of these regulations.

Regulation 14 – Information, instruction and training

Every employer shall ensure that:
(a) those of his employees who are engaged in work with ionising radiation are given appropriate training in the field of radiation protection and receive such information and instruction as is suitable and sufficient for them to know:
  (i) the risks to health created by exposure to radiation;
  (ii) the precautions that should be taken; and
  (iii) the importance of complying with the medical, technical and administrative requirements of these regulations;
(b) adequate information is given to other persons who are directly concerned with the work with ionising radiation carried on by the employer to ensure their health and safety so far as is reasonably practicable; and
(c) those female employees of that employer who are engaged in work with ionising radiation are informed of the possible risks arising from radiation to the foetus and to a nursing infant and of the importance of those employees informing the employer in writing as soon as possible:
  (i) after becoming aware of their pregnancy; or
  (ii) if they are breastfeeding.

Regulation 15 – Cooperation between employers

Where work with ionising radiation is likely to give rise to the exposure to ionising radiation of the employee of another employer, the employers concerned shall cooperate by the exchange of information.

PART IV – DESIGNATED AREAS

Regulation 16 – Designation of controlled or supervised areas

Every employer shall designate as a controlled area any area under his control that has been identified by an assessment as an area in which:
(a) it is necessary for any person to follow special procedures to restrict significant

exposure or to prevent or limit the probability and magnitude of radiation accidents or their effects; and

(b) any person working in the area is likely to receive an effective dose greater than 6mSv a year or an equivalent dose greater than three-tenths of any relevant dose limit in respect of an employee aged 18 years and over.

An employer shall designate as a supervised area under his control;

(a) where it is necessary to keep the conditions of the area under review to determine whether the area should be designated as a controlled area; or

(b) in which any person is likely to receive an effective dose greater than 1mSv a year or an equivalent dose greater than one-tenth of any relevant dose limit in respect of an employee aged 18 years and over.

Regulation 17 – Local rules and radiation protection supervisors

Every radiation employer shall, in respect of any controlled area and supervised area, make and set down in writing such local rules as are appropriate to the radiation risk and the nature of the operations undertaken in that area.

The radiation employer shall take all reasonable steps to ensure local rules are observed and brought to the attention of the appropriate employees and other persons.

The radiation employer shall appoint one or more radiation protection supervisors to ensure compliance with these regulations in respect of any area made subject to local rules.

Regulation 18 – Additional requirements for designated areas

Every employer shall ensure that any designated area is adequately described in local rules and that:

(a) in the case of any controlled area:

    (i) the area is physically demarcated or, where this is not reasonably practicable, delineated by some other means; and

    (ii) suitable and sufficient signs are displayed in suitable positions indicating that the area is a controlled area, the nature of the radiation sources and the risks arising; and

(a) in the case of any supervised area, suitable and sufficient signs are displayed indicating the nature of the sources and the risks arising.

Only persons designated as classified persons shall enter and remain in a controlled area.

No person shall enter a controlled area unless he can demonstrate, by personal dose monitoring or other suitable measurements, that the doses are restricted.

Employers who undertake monitoring or measurements shall keep the results for a period of two years from the date they were recorded.

Where there is a significant risk of the spread of radioactive contamination from a controlled area, the employer shall make adequate arrangements to restrict, so far as is reasonably practicable, the spread of such contamination.

The arrangements shall, where appropriate, include:

♦ the provision of suitable and sufficient washing facilities;

♦ the proper maintenance of such facilities;

♦ the prohibition of eating, drinking or smoking or similar activity; and

♦ the means for monitoring for contamination of any person, article or goods leaving a controlled area.

Regulation 19 – Monitoring of designated areas

The levels of radiation in controlled and supervised areas shall be adequate monitored and the working conditions kept under review.

Monitoring equipment shall be properly maintained and adequately tested and examined, and its accuracy established before initial use under the supervision of a qualified person.

The employer shall make and maintain suitable records of monitoring and testing required above.

PART V – CLASSIFICATION AND MONITORING OF PERSONS

Regulation 20 – Designation of classified persons

The employer shall designate as classified persons those of his employees who are likely to receive an effective dose in excess of 6mSv per year or an equivalent dose that exceeds three-tenths of any relevant dose limit and shall forthwith inform those employees that they have been so designated.

A classified person must be 18 years and over and certified as fit for work with ionising radiation by an appointed doctor or employment medical adviser.

Regulation 21 – Dose assessment and recording

Every employer shall ensure, in the case of classified persons, that an assessment of all doses received by such employees, is made and recorded.

The arrangements that the employer makes with the approved dosimetry service shall include requirements, for instance, that records must be made and maintained until that person has or would have attained the age of 75 years but in any event for at least 50 years from when they were made.

Regulations 22 – 26

These regulations cover procedures in respect of:
♦ estimated doses and special entries in dose records;
♦ dosimetry for accidents;
♦ medical surveillance arrangements;
♦ investigation and notification of overexposure; and
♦ dose limitation for overexposed employees.

PART VI – ARRANGEMENTS FOR THE CONTROL OF RADIOACTIVE SUBSTANCES, ARTICLES AND EQUIPMENT

Regulation 27 – Sealed sources and articles containing or embodying radioactive substances

Whenever reasonably practicable, a radioactive substance shall be in the form of a sealed source.

The design, construction and maintenance of any article containing or embodying a radioactive substance, including its bonding, immediate container and other mechanical protection, must be such as to prevent leakage:
(a) in the case of a sealed source, so far as is practicable; or
(b) in the case of any other article, so far as is reasonably practicable.

Suitable tests shall be carried out at suitable intervals to detect leakage of radioactive substances from any article. Records must be made and maintained for at least two years.

Regulations 28 – 33

These regulations deal with:

♦ procedures for accounting for radioactive substances;

♦ precautions for the moving, transporting or disposing of radioactive substances;

♦ notification of certain occurrences, for example, releases into the atmosphere, spillages;

♦ losses, and evidence of stealing, of radioactive substances;

♦ investigation of occurrences;

♦ duties of manufacturers, etc of articles for use at work with ionising radiation; and

♦ equipment used for medical exposure.

Regulation 33 – Misuse of or interference with sources of ionising radiation

No person shall intentionally or recklessly misuse or without reasonable excuse interfere with any radioactive substance or any electrical equipment to which these regulations apply.

PART VII – DUTIES OF EMPLOYEES AND MISCELLANEOUS

Regulation 34 – Duties of employees

An employee who is engaged in work with ionising radiation shall:

(a) not knowingly expose himself or any other person to ionising radiation to an extent greater than is reasonably necessary for the purposes of the work;

(b) exercise reasonable care while carrying out such work;

(c) make full and proper use of any PPE;

(d) forthwith report any defect in his PPE;

(e) take all reasonable steps to return after use the PPE to the accommodation provided;

(f) comply with any reasonable requirement imposed on him by his employer for the purpose of making the measurements and assessments required under these regulations;

(g) present himself during working hours for such medical examination and tests as may be required;

(h) forthwith notify his employer if he has reasonable cause to believe that:

    (i) he has or some other person has received overexposure;

    (ii) an occurrence has occurred; or

    (iii) an incident has occurred.

SCHEDULE 4

The limits on effective dose (dose to the whole body) are:

♦ 20mSv a year for employees aged over 18;

(In special cases, employers may apply a dose limit of 100mSv in five years with no more than 50mSv in a single year, subject to strict conditions.

♦ 6mSv a year for trainees; and

♦ 1mSv for any other person, including members of the public.

KEY POINTS

♦ Radiation can be a dangerous source of energy.

♦ Where the number of electrons in an atom does not equal the number of protons, the atom has a net positive or negative charge and is said to be ionised.

♦ The hazards associated with radiation depend upon the extent of the dose to which a person could be exposed.

♦ Exposure to radiation may be of a local or general nature.

♦ The form taken by radiation, ie sealed or unsealed source, is significant in its potential for harm.

♦ The principles of radiological protection are based on time, distance and shielding.

♦ The Ionising Radiations Regulations impose extensive requirements on employers for protecting the health of employees working with sources of radiation.

18 Stress at Work

In the last decade, increasing attention has been paid by employers, the enforcement agencies, trade unions and the courts to the question of stress at work. According to the HSE, nearly one in three of Europe's workers, more than 40 million people, report that they are affected by stress at work.

This chapter defines the term, examines the causes of stress and the remedies for reducing stress at work. Reference is also made to the legal implications for employers where employees may complain of stress at work.

WHAT IS STRESS?

'Stress' is a word that is rarely understood. It means different things to different people. Indeed, almost anything anyone can think of, pleasant or unpleasant, has been described as a source of stress, such as getting married, being made redundant, getting older, starting a new job, too much or too little work, an unsuitable working environment or insufficient training to do a job well.

Stress has been defined in a number of ways:

♦ the common response to attack (Selye, 1936);

♦ a psychological response that follows failure to cope with problems;

♦ a psychological state that results from people's perceptions of an imbalance between job demands and their abilities to cope with these demands (Cox, 1993);

♦ pressure and extreme demands placed on a person beyond their ability to cope (HSE, 1995); and

♦ a feeling of sustained anxiety, which, over a period of time, leads to disease.

All these definitions point to a number of common factors surrounding stress, namely, it is a psychological response on the part of the individual associated with being put under pressure coupled with an inability to cope with problems, situations and extreme demands.

Fundamentally, a stressor produces stress, which produces a stress response on the part of the individual. That stress response can include insomnia, loss of appetite, lower back pain, irritability, increased perspiration, asthma, dermatitis, depression, overeating and excessive drinking, high blood pressure and personality change. What is important is that no two people have the same response to stress.

THE CAUSES OF STRESS AT WORK

The more common occupational stressors can be classified thus:

♦ **The physical environment**

Poor working conditions associated with, for instance, insufficient space, lack of privacy, open-plan office layouts, inadequate temperature control, poor levels of illumination and excessive noise are significant contributory factors to stress at work.

♦ **The organisation**

The organisation, its policies and procedures, the culture and style of operation can be a cause of stress due to, for instance, insufficient staff for the size of workload, too many unfilled posts, poor coordination between departments, insufficient training and, in some cases, bullying behaviour on the part of senior managers.

♦ **The way the organisation is managed**

Management styles, philosophies, work systems, approaches and objectives can contribute to individual stress on employees, as a result of inconsistency in style and approach, emphasis on competitiveness and 'crisis management' all the time.

♦ **One's role in the organisation**

Everyone has a role in the organisation. 'Role theory' views large organisations as systems of interlocking roles. These roles relate to what people do and what others expect of them, rather than their individual identities. Stress arises due to:

♦ **Role ambiguity**

This is the situation where the role holder has insufficient information for adequate performance of his role, or where the information is open to more than one interpretation.

♦ **Role conflict**

Role conflict arises where members of the organisation who exchange information with the role holder have different expectations of his role. Each may exert pressure on the role holder and satisfying one expectation could make compliance with other expectations difficult. This is the classic 'servant of two masters' situation.

♦ **Role overload**

This results generally from a combination of role ambiguity and role conflict. The role holder works harder to clarify normal expectations or to satisfy conflicting priorities that are impossible to achieve within the time limits specified.

♦ **Relationships within the organisation**

How people relate to each other within the organisational framework and structure can be a significant cause of stress, due to, perhaps, poor relationships with senior managers, colleagues and subordinates and difficulties in delegating responsibility.

♦ **Career development**

Stress is directly related to progression or otherwise in a career. It may be created by lack of job security, over-promotion, under-promotion or thwarted ambition.

♦ **Personal and social relationships**

The relationships that exist between people on a personal and social basis are frequently a cause of stress arising from, for example, insufficient opportunities for social contact at work, sexism and sexual harassment, racism and racial harassment and conflicts with the demands of the family.

♦ **The equipment provided**

Inadequate, out-of-date and/or unreliable equipment, such as word processing equipment, is frequently associated with stressful conditions amongst workers. The equipment may not be suitable for the task or the environment in which it is used and/or poorly maintained.

♦ **Individual concerns**

All people are different in terms of attitudes, personality, motivation and in their ability to cope with work stressors. People may experience a stress response due to difficulty in coping with change, lack of confidence in dealing with interpersonal problems or through not being assertive enough.

TABLE 16 : THE MORE COMMON OCCUPATIONAL STRESSORS

New work patterns	Increased competition
New technology	Longer working hours
Promotion	Redundancy
Relocation	Early retirement
Deregulation	Acquisition
Downsizing	Merger
Job design	Manning levels
Boredom	Insecurity
Noise	Lighting
Temperature	Atmosphere/ventilation

THE EFFECTS OF STRESS ON JOB PERFORMANCE

Job performance can be directly and indirectly affected as a result of the following factors.

Absenteeism

Absenteeism, especially on Monday mornings or in taking early or extended meal breaks, is a typical manifestation of stress amongst employees.

Accidents

People under stress are more likely to have accidents due to lack of concentration, distraction and, perhaps, as a result of excessive alcohol consumption.

Loss of concentration

Stressful events in people's lives commonly result in a lack of ability to concentrate on the task in hand or an inability to complete one task at a time.

Loss of short-term memory

This leads to arguments about who said, did or decided what.

Errors of judgement

Stress is a classic cause of errors of judgement, which can result in accidents, wastage, reject products and near misses. Such errors are commonly blamed on others.

Poor employee relations

People going through a period of stress frequently become irritable and sensitive to criticism. This may be accompanied by 'Jekyll and Hyde' mood changes, all of which have a direct effect on employee relationships.

PSYCHOLOGICAL EFFECTS OF STRESS

Two common effects of stress are anxiety and depression.

Anxiety

Anxiety is a state of tension coupled with apprehension, worry, guilt, insecurity and a constant need for reassurance. It is commonly accompanied by a number of psychosomatic symptoms, such as profuse perspiration, difficulty in breathing, gastric disturbances, rapid heartbeat, frequent urination, muscle tension or high blood pressure. Insomnia is a reliable indicator of a state of anxiety.

TABLE 17 : PERSONALITY TRAITS

Type	Traits
A, ambitious	Active and energetic, impatient if they have to wait in a queue. Conscientious, maintain high standards, time is a problem – there is never enough, often intolerant of others who may be slower
B, placid	Quiet, very little worries them, often uncompetitive, put their worries into things they can alter and leave others to worry about the rest
C, worrying	Nervous, highly strung, not very confident of self-ability, anxious about the future and being able to cope
D, carefree	Love variety, often athletic and daring, very little worries them, not concerned about the future
E, suspicious	Dedicated and serious, very concerned with others' opinions of them, do not take criticism kindly and remember such criticisms for a long time, distrust most people
F, dependent	Bored with their own company, sensitive to surroundings, rely on others a great deal, people who interest them are oddly unreliable, they find the people that they really need are boring, do not respond easily to change
G, fussy	Punctilious, conscientious and like a set routine, do not like change, any new problems throw them because there are no rules to follow. Conventional and predictable, great believers in authority

Depression

Depression, on the other hand, is much more a mood, characterised by feelings of dejection and gloom, and other permutations, such as feelings of hopelessness, futility and guilt. Severe forms may exhibit biochemical disturbances, and the extreme form may lead to suicide.

PERSONALITY AND STRESS

'Personality' is defined as 'the dynamic organisation within the individual of the psychophysical systems that determine his characteristics behaviour and thought'.
(Allport, 1961)

Research into personality traits has indicated that people fit into one or more of the classifications shown in table 15.

Because most people fit into a combination of the above traits, these definitions can be used only as a guide. The type most at risk to stress is Type A.

STRESS REDUCTION

Organisational level

Organisations need to recognise that the decisions, objectives and actions of the organisation can, in many cases, put employees under stress. Thus, there may be a need for a Stress Management Programme run by an occupational health professional, such as an occupational physician or occupational health nurse.

This programme should take a number of stages:

♦ recognition of the causes and symptoms of stress;
♦ decisions on what the organisation needs to do about it;
♦ decisions as to which groups of employees can least afford to be stressed, for example, key operators, supervisors;
♦ examination and evaluation by interview and/or questionnaire of the specific causes of stress;
♦ analysis of problem areas, for example, shift work; and
♦ decisions as to suitable strategies, such as counselling for specific individuals, social support, training, such as time management training, environmental improvement, redesign of jobs and ergonomic studies.

Individual level

Employees should receive training in dealing with stress at work with a view to:

♦ identifying their work and life objectives and re-evaluating them on a regular basis or as necessary, putting them up where they can be seen;
♦ ensuring a correct time balance;
♦ identifying their stress indicators and planning how these sources of stress can be eliminated;
♦ allowing at least 30 minutes each day for refreshing and recharging;
♦ identifying crisis areas and planning contingency action;
♦ identifying key tasks and priorities and doing the important, not necessarily the urgent; and
♦ keeping their eyes on their objectives and, above all, having fun!

SOURCES OF MANAGERIAL STRESS FIG. 21

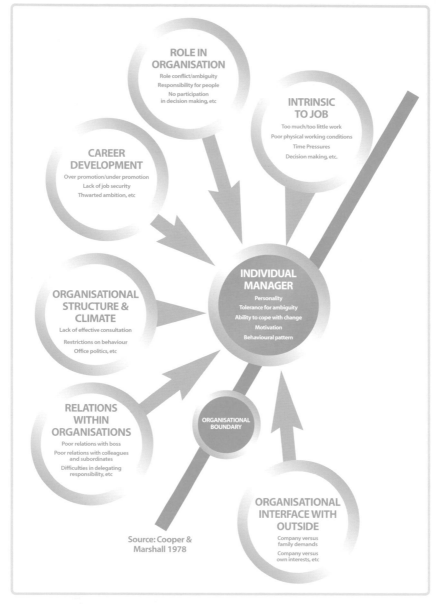

ROLE IN ORGANISATION
Role conflict/ambiguity
Responsibility for people
No participation in decision making, etc

INTRINSIC TO JOB
Too much/too little work
Poor physical working conditions
Time Pressures
Decision making, etc.

CAREER DEVELOPMENT
Over promotion/under promotion
Lack of job security
Thwarted ambition, etc

ORGANISATIONAL STRUCTURE & CLIMATE
Lack of effective consultation
Restrictions on behaviour
Office politics, etc

INDIVIDUAL MANAGER
Personality
Tolerance for ambiguity
Ability to cope with change
Motivation
Behavioural pattern

RELATIONS WITHIN ORGANISATIONS
Poor relations with boss
Poor relations with colleagues and subordinates
Difficulties in delegating responsibility, etc

ORGANISATIONAL BOUNDARY

ORGANISATIONAL INTERFACE WITH OUTSIDE
Company versus family demands
Company versus own interests, etc

Source: Cooper & Marshall 1978

STRESS AND THE LAW

With the increased recognition by the courts of stress at work, employers need to be aware of legal requirements covering this area. Whilst there is no specific legislation dealing with stress, the duty to protect the health, which includes the mental health, of employees under both civil and criminal law is well recognised.

At common law employers have a duty to provide for their employees:

◆ a safe place of work, including safe access and egress;

◆ a safe system of work;

♦ safe plant and appliances; and

♦ competent co-employees to undertake the work.

Employers must take steps to protect employees from risks that are reasonably foreseeable and failure to ensure the provision of any of the above could result in stress on operators. An employer failing to make such provision could be held to be negligent. Although common law has developed almost exclusively in relation to physical injury, recent civil cases dealing with stress-induced injury have demonstrated no specific reason as to why mental illness should be treated differently.

At criminal law, an employer has a general duty under the HSWA to ensure, so far as is reasonably practicable, the safety, health and welfare of all his employees. 'Health' is defined as 'a state of physical and mental well-being' and, on this basis, there is no reason why an employer could not be prosecuted for failing to ensure the mental health of his employees by exposing them to excessive stress. Many organisations that have recognised the risk of stress have well-written policies on stress at work.

More specifically, under the MHSWR 1999 an employer is required to undertake a suitable and sufficient assessment of the risks to the health and safety of his employees to which they are exposed whilst at work.

Where people are exposed to stressful situations, for instance, dealing with members of the public, where they may be required to meet deadlines or undertake mentally exacting work, the potential for stress should be considered in any risk assessment carried out. An outcome of risk assessment may well be the need for information, instruction and training in dealing with stress at work and the implementation of a stress management programme.

KEY POINTS

♦ A stressor produces stress.

♦ 'Stress' is defined as 'the common response to attack' or 'a psychological state that results from people's perceptions of an imbalance between job demands and their abilities to cope with these demands'.

♦ Most people go through varying degrees of stress at work.

♦ Insomnia is a classic manifestation of stress.

♦ The causes of stress at work include the way the organisation is managed, relationships within the organisation, an individual's role in the organisation and the physical environment.

♦ The effects of stress on job performance include absenteeism, loss of concentration, errors and, in some cases, accidents.

♦ Anxiety and depression are common effects of stress.

♦ Type A personalities are particularly prone to stress.

♦ Organisations should recognise the existence of stress and implement strategies for its reduction.

♦ A policy on stress at work may be necessary to draw the attention of managers and employees to the fact that the organisation recognises the existence of stress and has strategies for its reduction.

♦ Employers may be liable under both civil and criminal law for stress-induced injury.

19 First Aid

First aid arrangements are an essential post-accident strategy in safety management. There is a duty on employers to provide 'such facilities and equipment as are adequate and appropriate' with regard to first aid treatment at work.

This chapter examines the principles of first aid and the requirements of the Health and Safety (First Aid) Regulations.

WHAT IS FIRST AID?

First aid is defined as 'the skilled application of accepted principles of treatment on the occurrence of an accident or in the case of sudden illness, using facilities and materials available at the time'.

First aid is rendered:

 ♦ to save life;
 ♦ to prevent deterioration in an existing condition; and
 ♦ to promote recovery.

The principal areas or objectives of first aid treatment are:

 ♦ restoration of breathing (resuscitation);
 ♦ control of bleeding; and
 ♦ prevention of collapse.

All the above measures are directed at saving life.

See **FIG. 22 Resuscitation procedure**

HEALTH AND SAFETY (FIRST AID) REGULATIONS 1981

These regulations apply to the majority of workplaces.

Under the regulations, 'first aid' is defined as meaning:

(a) cases where a person will need help from a medical practitioner or nurse, treatment for the purpose of preserving life and minimising the consequences of injury or illness until such help is obtained; and

(b) treatment of minor injuries that would otherwise receive no treatment or that do not need treatment by a medical practitioner or nurse.

Regulation 3 – Duties of employers

Every employer shall provide, or ensure that there is provided, such equipment and facilities as are adequate and appropriate in the circumstances for enabling first aid to be rendered to his employees if they are injured or become ill at work.

Employers must further inform employees of the first aid arrangements.

Self-employed persons must provide first aid equipment for their own use.

BASIC ADVICE ON FIRST AID AT WORK FIG. 22
What to do in an emergency

PRIORITIES
- Assess the situation – do not put yourself in danger.
- Make the area safe.
- Assess all casualties and attend first to any unconscious casualties.
- Send for help – do not delay.
- Follow the advice given below.

CHECK FOR CONSCIOUSNESS

If there is no response to gentle shaking of the shoulders and shouting, the casualty may be unconscious. The priority is then to check the **A**irway, **B**reathing and **C**irculation. This is the **ABC** of resuscitation.

Ⓐ Airway

To open the airway:
- place one hand on the casualty's forehead and gently tilt the head back;
- remove any obvious obstruction from the casualty's mouth;
- lift the chin with two fingertips.

Ⓑ Breathing

Look along the chest, listen and feel at the mouth, for signs of normal breathing, for no more than ten seconds.

If the casualty is breathing:
- place in the recovery position and ensure the airway remains open;
- send for help and monitor the casualty until help arrives.

If the casualty is **not** breathing:
- send for help;
- keep the airway open by maintaining the head tilt and chin lift;
- pinch the casualty's nose closed and allow the mouth to open;
- take a full breath and place your mouth around the casualty's mouth, making a good seal;
- blow slowly into the mouth until chest rises;

Ⓑ Breathing cont

- remove your mouth from the casualty and let the chest fall fully;
- give a second slow breath, then look for signs of a circulation;
- if signs of a circulation are present, continue breathing for the casualty and recheck for signs of a circulation about every ten breaths;
- if the casualty starts to breathe but remains unconscious, put them in the recovery position, ensure the airway remains open and monitor until help arrives.

Ⓒ Circulation

Look, listen and feel for normal breathing, coughing or movement by the casualty, for no more than ten seconds.

If there are no signs of a circulation, or you are at all unsure, immediately start chest compressions:
- lean over the casualty and with straight arms, press vertically down 4-5cm on the breastbone, then release the pressure;
- give 15 rapid chest compressions (a rate of about 100 per minute) followed by two breaths;
- continue alternating 15 chest compressions with two breaths until help arrives or the casualty shows signs of recovery.

APPROVED CODE OF PRACTICE

This ACOP emphasises the duty of employers to consider a number of factors in determining for themselves what is 'adequate and appropriate' first aid in all the circumstances.

Moreover, where there are particular risks associated with the operation of an enterprise, the employer must ensure that first aiders receive training to deal with these specific risks.

First aid provision

Factors to be considered in assessing first aid provision include:

♦ the number of employees;
♦ the nature of the undertaking;
♦ the size of the establishment and the distribution of employees;
♦ the location of the establishment and the locations to which employees go in the course of their employment;
♦ use of shift working (each shift should have the same level of first aid cover/protection); and
♦ the distance from external medical services, for example, local accident and emergency department.

First aid boxes

There should be at least one first aid box, the contents of which are listed in the HSE (1981): First Aid at Work: ACOP Guidance accompanying the regulations.

First aid rooms

The ACOP stresses the fact that the need for a first aid room is not solely dependent upon the number of persons employed in an undertaking.

Where an establishment presents a high-risk from hazards the employer should provide a suitably equipped and staffed first aid room. In situations where access to accident and emergency facilities is difficult, or where there is dispersed working, a first aid room may also be necessary.

Where a first aid room is considered appropriate for an establishment, the following conditions should be met:

♦ a 'suitable' person should be responsible for the room and its contents;
♦ a suitable person should be available at all times when employees are at work;
♦ the room should be readily available at all times when employees are at work and should not be used for any purposes other than the rendering of first aid or health screening;
♦ the room should be positioned as near as possible to a point of access for transport to hospital, taking into account the location and layout of the establishment;
♦ the room should be large enough to hold a couch, with space for people to work around it, and a chair;
♦ the room's entrances should be wide enough to accommodate a stretcher, wheelchair or carrying gear;
♦ the room should contain suitable facilities and equipment, have impervious floor covering and should be effectively ventilated, heated, lighted and maintained;

- the room should be cleaned each working day and suitable arrangements for refuse disposal should be provided; all surfaces should be easy to clean;
- suitable facilities, for example, one or more chairs, should be provided close to the first aid room if employees have to wait for treatment;
- the room should be clearly identified as a first aid room by means of a sign complying with the Safety Signs Regulations 1980; and
- a notice should be attached to the door of the first aid room clearly showing the names and locations of the nearest first aiders or appointed persons.

When siting a new first aid room the necessity to have toilets nearby and for the room to be on the ground floor should be considered. Corridors, lifts, doors, etc that lead to the first aid room should allow access for a stretcher, wheelchair or carrying chair. Emergency lighting should be provided.

HEALTH AND SAFETY EXECUTIVE GUIDANCE

The Guidance makes recommendations for the contents of first aid boxes and the equipment for first aid rooms.

Contents of first aid boxes

A first aid box should contain the following items:
- one guidance card;
- 20 assorted individually wrapped sterile adhesive dressings;
- two sterile eye pads with attachment;
- six individually wrapped triangular bandages;
- six safety pins;
- six medium sized individually wrapped sterile unmedicated wound dressings;
- two large individually wrapped sterile unmedicated wound dressings; and
- three extra large individually wrapped sterile unmedicated wound dressings
and NOTHING ELSE.

A minimum 300ml sterile water container should be provided where mains water is not available.

Equipment for first aid rooms

The following equipment and other items are recommended for first aid rooms:
- a sink with running hot and cold water always available;
- drinking water when not available on tap, together with disposable cups;
- soap;
- paper towels;
- smooth-topped work surfaces;
- a suitable store for first aid materials;
- suitable refuse containers lined with a disposable plastic bag;
- a couch with waterproof surface, together with frequently cleaned pillows and blankets;
- clean protective garments;
- an appropriate record (for example, Form BI 510 Accident Book); and
- a bowl.

Travelling first aid kits

Where employees travel regularly as part of their work, for example, drivers of all sorts of vehicles, they must be provided with a travelling first aid kit.

The minimum contents for a travelling first aid kit are:

- one guidance card;
- six individually wrapped sterile adhesive dressings;
- one large sterile unmedicated dressing;
- two triangular bandages;
- two safety pins; and
- individually wrapped moist cleaning wipes.

FIRST AIDERS

Depending upon the risks associated with an undertaking, employers may need to appoint 'suitable persons' to render first aid treatment. A suitable person, for the purposes of the regulations, is:

(a) a first aider who holds a current first aid certificate issued by an organisation whose training and qualifications were, at the time of the issue of the certificate, approved by the HSE for the purposes of the regulations (in certain circumstances, a first aider will need additional or specific training to be classed as a 'suitable person'); and

(b) any other person who has undergone training and obtained qualifications approved by the HSE for the purposes of the regulations.

Practising registered medical practitioners and nurses may be regarded as first aiders for the purposes of the ACOP.

APPOINTED PERSONS

In establishments with relatively low risks, for example, offices, shops, banks, libraries, there need normally be no first aider where there are fewer than 150 employees, but there should be at least one first aider for 150 employees or more.

Where there are fewer than 150 employees at work, an employer must assign an appointed person whose principal function is to take charge of the situation until emergency services arrive.

RECORDS OF FIRST AID TREATMENT

Whilst there is no formal duty under the regulations to record first aid treatments by first aiders, it is strongly recommended that a suitable record be maintained in the first aid room. A record of treatment given may be significant in a civil claim made by an injured employee months or years later following an accident at work.

This record should incorporate the following details:

- full name and address of the person receiving first aid treatment;
- occupation;
- date of treatment;
- circumstances of the accident;
- injuries suffered and treatment provided; and
- name and signature of first aider providing treatment.

KEY POINTS

- First aid is rendered to sustain life, to prevent deterioration of an existing condition and to promote recovery.
- The principal objectives of first aid treatment are to restore breathing, control bleeding and prevent collapse.
- Employers must appoint suitable persons to render first aid.
- The contents of first aid boxes are specified in the ACOP to the Health and Safety (First Aid) Regulations 1981.
- Where employees work regularly away from base, they must be provided with a travelling first aid kit.
- Employers must decide on the scale of first aid provision necessary.
- In low risk establishments, where a first aider is not required, the employer must assign one or more appointed persons.

20 Construction, Contracting & Maintenance Operations

Construction work can be particularly dangerous. Hazards arise during work on scaffolds and on roofs, in work below ground, in demolition operations, where services are being installed and during maintenance operations.

This chapter reviews the health and safety issues in a range of construction and maintenance situations, the duties of clients, contractors and others under construction safety law, the procedures for regulating the activities of contractors and the use of method statements to ensure safe working practices.

HAZARDS IN CONSTRUCTION WORK

Traditionally, the construction industry has ranked as one of the more dangerous industries. This can be related to a number of factors, such as work at heights and below ground level, adverse weather conditions, the temporary nature of the work, a lack of safety supervision in some cases, and the pressing need to complete projects on time, which can result in safety considerations not being given high priority.

THE PRINCIPAL HAZARDS

The use of ladders

The risks associated with falls from ladders are common due to ladders slipping outwards at the base or falling away at the upper resting place. Failure to follow the '1 out: 4 up' rule (which means a ratio of 1:4 with respect to the distance from the vertical surface and the height of the top of the ladder respectively) when resting a ladder against a vertical surface, the use of defective wooden and aluminium ladders and over-reaching situations when working off ladders are common causes of falls from a height.

Falls from working platforms

Unfenced and inadequately fenced working platforms to scaffolds, inadequate, missing and defective boarding to working platforms, the overloading of platforms with building materials, together with the absence of toe boards, are common causes of people falling from a height.

Falls of materials

Small objects, such as bricks and hand tools, dropped from a height can kill or severely injure people working below. These hazards are commonly associated with poor standards of housekeeping on working platforms, unsafe working practices, inadequate or absent toe boards and barriers, incorrect assembly of gin wheels for raising and lowering materials, incorrect or careless hooking and slinging of loads, the failure to install catching platforms (fans) for falling materials, particularly during demolition, and the practice of demolition materials being thrown to the ground.

Falls from pitched roofs and through fragile roofs

Unsafe working practices on pitched roofs, including the use of inappropriate or unsuitable footwear, the failure to provide eaves protection and verge protection and to work off crawl boards, frequently result in people sliding or falling off the edge of a roof.

In the case of fragile roofs, such as those constructed in corrugated asbestos cement sheeting, which can be very fragile, or corrugated iron sheeting, which may be severely corroded, the risk of falling through a roof is significant.

Moreover, the stacking of materials on a fragile roof often results in partial collapse of the roof with the risk of workers falling through the gap created.

Falls through openings in flat roofs and floors

When working on flat roofs or floors that have recently been constructed, failure to cover openings, which may have been created for ducting or lift shafts, may result in falls. The absence of edge protection and covers to floor openings, or where covers are not clearly marked to indicate floor openings below, can have the same consequences.

Collapses of excavations

Every year people get buried alive in excavations due to a failure of adequate support. Excavation collapses may be caused by inadequate timbering or shoring, shifting sand situations, the presence of water in large quantities following, for example, a flash flood, timbering failures due to the pressure of materials and equipment located too close to the edge of an excavation, or the failure to reinstate supports after damage by, for instance, excavating equipment.

Site transport

The risk of falls from vehicles not designed to carry passengers, such as dumper trucks, and crushing by reversing lorries and trucks, can arise during construction operations. Hazards may further arise due to poor maintenance of site vehicles, for example, braking and reversing systems. The operation of vehicles and machinery, particularly lifting appliances, such as mobile cranes, static cranes, hoists and winches, by inexperienced people can be a further contributory factor in accidents.

Other hazardous situations associated with site transport include the overloading of passenger-carrying vehicles, dangerous parking, poor standards of driving on site roads and the problem of mud on roads, causing skidding.

Machinery and power hand tools

Extensive use is made of machinery during construction operations. Failure to adequately guard all moving and dangerous parts of machinery, such as power take-offs, cooling fans and belt drives and woodworking machinery, particularly circular saws, can result in major injuries, such as amputations and scalpings. In particular, the operation of portable hand tools, such as angle grinders, can result in both amputations and eye injuries.

Defective and uninsulated electrically operated hand tools, such as drills and sanders, may expose operators to the risk of electrocution.

Housekeeping

Poor housekeeping is a contributory factor in many trips and falls during construction. It is common for people to fall over debris that has accumulated during construction work.

Fire

Serious escalating fires have been known to arise on construction sites due to inadequate fire protection measures, such as ensuring that adverse weather covering to working platforms is flameproof. Poor site supervision, particularly in respect of the activities of sub-contractors, is a contributory factor here.

Ignition sources can be created by uncontrolled 'hot work', such as welding and soldering. The burning of site refuse should be prohibited.

Personal protective equipment

Failure to provide and enforce the wearing and use of PPE, such as safety helmets, full-face protection, eye protection, safety boots, gloves and overalls, can result in serious injuries to heads, eyes, hands and feet in particular.

The requirements of the Personal Protective Equipment at Work Regulations and the Construction (Head Protection) Regulations must be complied with.

Work over water and transport across water

Where people are exposed to risk of drowning, there is a need to provide barriers, life jackets or buoyancy aids and rescue equipment. The use of defective and inadequately sized boats for conveying workers to workplaces, together with the overcrowding of boats, has had fatal consequences in the past. Before requiring workers to undertake this type of work it would be reasonable for an employer to check that everyone can swim.

Work involving hazardous substances

Many hazardous substances are used in construction work. The failure to prevent or adequately control risks from exposure to and/or use of hazardous substances, such as lead and asbestos, have resulted in workers contracting lead poisoning and asbestosis in the past. Dermatitis, commonly associated with poor levels of personal hygiene, such as thorough washing after the use of certain substances, such as cement, is common amongst construction workers.

The failure by employers to comply with the COSHH Regulations with regard to the undertaking of health risk assessments, air monitoring, the use of LEV systems and health surveillance, together with the provision of inadequate prevention and control arrangements, can result in exposure to health risks.

Manual handling injuries

Manual handling injuries, such as prolapsed intervertebral discs, hernias and back and ligamental strains, are common in the construction industry. In many cases, the failure to provide mechanical handling aids has contributed to these injuries.

Underground services

Damage to underground services using mechanical excavation plant in particular can arise through failure to consult existing service plans and to establish the location of service lines. Those operating excavating plant may well be at risk of electrocution, gas-related fires and even explosion in this case.

Similarly, the failure to use cable and service locators, together with unsafe digging and excavating practices, can result in employees suffering burns or even being electrocuted.

Confined spaces

Confined spaces can arise or be created below and above ground, exposing employees to the risk of asphyxiation and anoxia. The Confined Spaces Regulations place a duty on employers to operate a safe system of work, for example, a Permit to Work system, in these cases.

Hazards in confined spaces may further arise due to inadequate ventilation, the failure to provide and/or use breathing apparatus, inadequate air monitoring and poor communication systems where people have entered confined spaces.

CONSTRUCTION SAFETY LAW

Employers in the construction industry must comply not only with the HSWA and MHSWR in particular, but also with specific legislation, namely the (CDM) Regulations, Construction (Health, Safety and Welfare) Regulations and the Construction (Head Protection) Regulations.

CONSTRUCTION (DESIGN AND MANAGEMENT) REGULATIONS 1994

The CDM Regulations implemented the design and management features of the Temporary or Mobile Construction Sites Directive and apply to 'construction work', a term that is very broadly defined.

The regulations do not apply to construction work if:

(a) the work will last for 30 days or less and involves four or less people on site at any one time; and

(b) the work is carried out for a domestic client.

Objectives of the regulations

The main objectives and underlying principles of the CDM Regulations are:

(a) to consider the health and safety aspects of construction projects from the outset, systematically by ensuring proper planning and coordination of all work involved;

(b) to involve those who can contribute, that is clients, designers, planning supervisors, the principal contractor and other contractors;

(c) to ensure that health and safety will be adequately resourced by competent persons;

(d) to share and communicate information; and

(e) to record information for the future in order to help promote the safety of future projects.

Joint consultation

The regulations incorporate a procedure or mechanism for ensuring consultation on health and safety issues amongst all persons concerned on a site – employers, employees, the self-employed, etc.

Responsibilities of clients

The regulations place considerable responsibilities on clients, namely, a person who negotiates a project with a contractor.

The responsibilities of clients include:

♦ the appointment of a planning supervisor and principal contractor;

- making reasonable checks as to the competence from a health and safety viewpoint of those being appointed, including designers, and of the resources they make available for health and safety;
- ensuring that an adequate health and safety plan is in place before commencement of the work;
- passing on information about the land and premises being developed; and
- ensuring, so far as is reasonably practicable, that the health and safety file, which has to be prepared at the end of the project work, is kept readily available for use by those subsequently undertaking construction work.

Appointment of an agent by the client

Regulation 4 of the regulations enables a client to appoint an agent, or another client to act as the only client in respect of a project, provided these persons are competent to perform the duties imposed on a client under the regulations.

Duties on designers

Designers must pay proper attention to health and safety requirements in the early design stages of a project. This would include consideration of matters such as general site layout, the actual layout of the buildings on site, the range and type of construction materials to be used, including finishing materials, and the manner in which services, such as gas, electricity and water, are installed.

Designers have a duty to:

- take reasonable steps to alert clients to their duties under the regulations and the Guidance provided by the HSE;
- ensure, so far as is reasonably practicable, that any design either avoids foreseeable risks or includes control measures for reducing that risk at source in a way that will protect everyone subsequently carrying out the work;
- pass on information about aspects of the structural design and materials that subsequently might be important to the health and safety of any person carrying out the work; and
- cooperate with the planning supervisor and other designers in carrying out their functions.

Functions of planning supervisors

The planning supervisor has a particular role to play at the planning stage of a construction project. His principal functions are to:

- ensure notification of the intended construction work to the HSE;
- review the design work carried out by the designer;
- ensure cooperation between designers;
- advise both clients and contractors of their respective duties with regard to design work, the appointment by the client of a principal contractor and the adequacy of the health and safety plan;
- ensure that a health and safety file is prepared for the project, this file to be a record of information relating to the construction of the building on a stage-by-stage basis and that can subsequently be used to promote correct planning of subsequent project work;

♦ ensure any appropriate amendment of the health and safety file and its subsequent delivery to the client; and

♦ ensure there is an adequate pre-tender health and safety plan available at the time when construction work is being let or tenders sought or arrangements made.

Generally, the planning supervisor has the duty of ensuring, so far as is reasonably practicable, that the task is fulfilled, allowing some degree of latitude as to how and which particular people undertake the work.

Notifiable projects

A project is notifiable (on Form 10) to the HSE if the construction phase:

(a) will be longer than 30 days; or

(b) will involve more than 500 person days of construction work.

Duties of principal contractor and contractors

Both these groups have the duty to ensure that the theme of coordination of health and safety is given practical effect when the work actually starts and during the operation of the project. The principal contractor is responsible for ensuring cooperation between individual contractors and for ensuring implementation of the more general duties for shared work sites, as required under the MHSWR, and for shared work equipment, as required under the PUWER.

The principal contractor has the following duties:

♦ to develop the construction phase health and safety plan;

♦ to promote cooperation between the various contractors;

♦ to ensure that only authorised persons gain access to the site; and

♦ to act as a focus for information passing to and from the planning supervisor.

Contractors must:

♦ cooperate with the principal contractor; and

♦ provide relevant information on the risks to health and safety arising from their work and on the means of control.

Health and safety plans

Health and safety plans must be produced at two stages of a project:

1. **Pre-tender stage**

This must include a general description of the work, timings, details of risks to workers and information for the principal contractor on welfare arrangements in particular. This document is prepared by the planning supervisor.

2. **Construction phase**

The Construction Phase Health and Safety Plan is prepared by the principal contractor. It must include the arrangements for health and safety of all those affected by the construction work, the arrangements for the management of the work and for monitoring legal compliance, and information about welfare arrangements.

3. **Health and safety file**

This document contains information for the client or user of the premises on the risks that may be present during maintenance, repair or renovation. The health and safety file should be handed to the client by the principal contractor at the completion of the project.

CONSTRUCTION (HEALTH, SAFETY AND WELFARE) REGULATIONS 1996

These regulations apply to:
- (a) every employer whose employees are carrying out construction work (as defined);
- (b) every self-employed person carrying out construction work;
- (c) every person who controls the way in which construction work is carried out;
- (d) every employee carrying out construction work; and
- (e) every person at work.

Competent persons

As with former 'Construction Regulations', considerable emphasis is placed on the need for competent persons to be appointed, with a view to supervising some of the more dangerous activities and for ensuring safety, such as the erection and inspection of scaffolds, excavations and demolition work.

Principal requirements

These regulations are concerned with:
- ◆ accident prevention;
- ◆ welfare arrangements; and
- ◆ environmental working conditions

on construction sites. As such, they lay down absolute requirements, in most cases, on employers with regard to:
- ◆ a safe place of work;
- ◆ the prevention of falls from heights and protection against falling objects;
- ◆ stability of structures;
- ◆ safe demolition and dismantling, including the use of explosives;
- ◆ safe excavation work;
- ◆ provisions in respect of coffer dams and caissons;
- ◆ the prevention of drowning when working over water;
- ◆ control of site traffic;
- ◆ provisions for doors and gates;
- ◆ prevention of injury from fire or explosion, flooding or any substance likely to cause asphyxiation;
- ◆ emergency routes and exits;
- ◆ arrangements for dealing with foreseeable emergencies;
- ◆ provision, maintenance, examination and testing of fire detection and alarm systems and fire fighting equipment;
- ◆ welfare facilities – sanitation, washing facilities, clothing storage and changing clothing;
- ◆ ventilation, temperature control, weather protection and site housekeeping;
- ◆ safe plant and equipment;

- training and supervision; and
- procedures for inspection by a competent person of working platforms, personal suspension equipment, excavations, coffer dams and caissons.

RULES FOR THE SAFE CONDUCT OF PROJECT WORK (CONTRACTORS' REGULATIONS)

The relationship between occupiers of land and premises, clients and contractors can be tenuous in terms of both criminal and civil liability of the parties concerned. There is a need, therefore, for occupiers, employers and clients to regulate the activities of contractors, whether large or small, through clearly documented rules and procedures.

The Construction (Health, Safety and Welfare) Regulations lay down strict requirements for the safe conduct of construction work. The detailed requirements of the above regulations should be incorporated in any 'rules for the safe conduct of project work' (or Contractors' Regulations) issued to an intending principal contractor at the pre-tender stage of a notifiable project and, indeed, when inviting tenders for other forms of construction work not notifiable under the CDM Regulations, such as window cleaning, external painting, electrical installation work and internal modifications to premises.

The following matters might be incorporated in an organisation's Contractor's Regulations.
- definitions of the titles of the parties concerned, for example, site manager, designer, principal contractor;
- the relevant statutory provisions applying to construction work;
- consultation prior to commencement of contract work;
- use of on-site services, for example, electricity, gas;
- safe systems of work;
- reporting, recording and investigation of injuries, diseases and dangerous occurrences;
- first aid and ambulance arrangements;
- welfare provisions;
- transport on site and parking arrangements for vehicles;
- housekeeping and waste disposal;
- security on site;
- PPE;
- hazardous substances;
- manual handling operations;
- use of the organisation's equipment; and
- procedures in the event of unsafe behaviour.

CONSTRUCTION (HEAD PROTECTION) REGULATIONS 1989

These regulations impose requirements for the provision of suitable head protection for, and the wearing of same by, people at work on building operations or works of engineering construction.

'Suitable head protection' means head protection that:
- is designed to provide protection, so far as is reasonably practicable, against foreseeable risks of injury to the head to which the wearer may be exposed;

◆ after any necessary adjustment fits the wearer; and
◆ is suitable with regard to the work or activity in which the wearer may be engaged.

Employers must provide suitable head protection for their employees, and self-employed persons must provide their own head protection. Head protection must be maintained and replaced if it becomes defective. Employees are required to report to their employers any loss of, or defect in, their head protection.

METHOD STATEMENTS

A safety method statement is a formally written safe system of work, or series of integrating safe systems of work, agreed between a client and principal contractor or principal contractor and sub-contractor, and produced where work with a foreseeably high-risk is to be undertaken.

A method statement may be required to ensure safe working in activities involving:
◆ the use of hazardous substances in large quantities;
◆ the use of explosives;
◆ lifting operations using cranes or road cranes;
◆ potential fire risk situations;
◆ electrical risk situations;
◆ the use of sources of radiation;
◆ the risk of dust explosions or the inhalation of hazardous dusts, gases, vapours, etc;
◆ certain types of excavation, particularly those adjacent to existing buildings;
◆ demolition work; and
◆ the stripping and removal of asbestos.

Contents of a method statement

The following elements may be incorporated in a method statement:
◆ techniques to be used;
◆ access provisions;
◆ safeguarding existing work locations and positions;
◆ structural stability requirements, for example, shoring;
◆ procedures to ensure the safety of others, for example, members of the public;
◆ health precautions, including the use of LEV systems and PPE;
◆ plant and equipment to be used;
◆ procedures to prevent area and internal pollution;
◆ physical segregation of certain areas;
◆ procedures for the disposal of, particularly, toxic wastes; and
◆ procedures to ensure compliance with specific legislation, such as the Environmental Protection Act, COSHH Regulations, Control of Asbestos at Work Regulations.

Further information is provided in the ACOP to the CDM Regulations.

MAINTENANCE WORK

Under the WHSWR there is an absolute duty on employers to maintain the workplace, equipment, systems and devices in an efficient state, in efficient working order and in good repair.

Maintenance work may be of a planned and routine nature (planned preventive maintenance). Other forms of maintenance, however, may be required in crisis situations (crisis maintenance).

Hazards in maintenance work

The principal hazards associated with maintenance work, whether undertaken by employees or the employees of contractors, include the following.

Mechanical

Machinery traps, entanglement, contact and ejection hazards; the unexpected start-up of machinery due to electrical faults.

Electrical

The risk of electrocution, shock, fire and burns.

Pressure

Unexpected pressure releases, explosion.

Physical

Exposure to extremes of temperature, noise and vibration; dust and fume inhalation.

Chemical

The risk of inhaling airborne contaminants; contact with strong acids, alkalis, etc.

Structural

Physical contact with obstructions; falls through dangerous floor openings.

Access

The risk of falling during work at heights; hazardous work in confined spaces.

The precautions necessary

The following precautions should be considered:

♦ operation of safe systems of work, including Permit to Work systems;
♦ training and designation of competent persons for certain inspections, examinations and tests;
♦ use of method statements by contractors for high-risk activities;
♦ enforcement of the organisation's Contractors' Regulations consistently and effectively;
♦ designation of controlled areas;
♦ access control at limited points;
♦ the provision of information, instruction and training and supervision; signs, marking and labelling; and
♦ ensuring regular and correct use of PPE, in particular safety helmets.

KEY POINTS

- Traditionally, construction work has always been ranked as one of the most hazardous activities.
- Falls of people and materials from a height are the most common form of serious accident in construction.
- Dermatitis is a common disease amongst construction workers.
- Under the CDM Regulations clients, designers, planning supervisors, principal contractors and contractors have a range of duties.
- In the case of a notifiable project, a health and safety plan must be prepared at the commencement of the pre-tender stage and prior to the construction phase of the project.
- The Construction (Health, Safety and Welfare) Regulations lay down extensive requirements with regard to safety, health and welfare in construction work.
- Employers must pay particular attention to the health and safety arrangements of contractors.
- Competent persons must be appointed for a range of activities under construction health and safety law.
- Maintenance work can be particularly dangerous and employers must ensure the operation of safe systems of work at all times.

Questions

CHAPTER 1
Question

There are a number of sources of health and safety law that employers have to take into account to ensure the protection of their employees whilst at work.

(a)	Explain the purpose and relevance of:	
	(i) Statutes (Acts of Parliament)	5 marks
	(ii) Regulations	5 marks
	(iii) ACOPs	5 marks
	(iv) HSE Guidance Notes	5 marks

under health and safety law.

(b)	Explain the meaning of the term 'negligence'	5 marks

Answer

Statutes (Acts of Parliament) outline the general principles of the legislation applying to a particular matter, for example, health and safety at work, environmental protection, and are the principal form of law, their requirements taking precedence over regulations. A Statute generally gives the Minister or Secretary of State power to make regulations.

(a) **Regulations** give substance to the provisions detailed in statutes and contain more specific details of requirements.

Approved Codes of Practice are commonly produced by the HSC in conjunction with regulations, detailing the way the regulations should be interpreted and put into operation. Failure to comply with an ACOP may be construed as failure to comply with the requirements of regulations unless the defendant can show that 'works of an equivalent nature' were carried out, which met the requirements of the regulation in question.

HSE Guidance Notes are produced for guidance purposes only and have no legal status.

(b) **Negligence** is defined as 'careless conduct injuring another'.
In order to establish negligence in a civil court, a claimant must be able to show that:

      (i)   the defendant owed the claimant a duty of care;

      (ii) the defendant had been in breach of that duty of care; and

      (iii) the claimant suffered injury, damage or loss as a result.

CHAPTER 2
Question

(a)	Outline the powers of inspectors under the HSWA 1974.	15 marks
(b)	State the circumstances where any enforcement authority may instigate proceedings against an employer in the Magistrates' Court	10 marks

Answer

(a) Section 20 of the HSWA outlines the powers of inspectors thus:
- enter premises at any reasonable time;
- take with him a constable if any serious obstruction is anticipated;
- take with him:
  - (i) any other person duly authorised;
  - (ii) any equipment or materials required;
- make such examination and investigation;
- direct that premises remain undisturbed;
- take measurements and photographs and make recordings;
- take samples of articles and substances;
- cause dangerous articles or substances to be dismantled or subject to any process or test;
- to take possession of and detain the above articles and substances:
  - (i) for examination;
  - (ii) to prevent tampering;
  - (iii) to ensure they are available for use as evidence in any proceedings;
- require persons to sign a declaration of truth;
- require the production of, inspect and take copies of:
  - (i) books or documents required to be kept;
  - (ii) any other books or documents necessary;
- require any person to afford facilities and assistance; and
- any other power necessary in the circumstances.

(b) An inspector may decide to instigate proceedings in one or more of the following situations:
- flagrant disregard for the law;
- failure to heed advice or to cooperate with an inspector with a view to bringing about improvement;
- where there may be imminent or serious risk to personal injury to employees, non-employees and members of the public; and
- where there is clear-cut evidence of a breach of one or more of the relevant statutory provisions that has resulted in an accident at work.

CHAPTER 3

Question

(a) Outline the factors to be considered by an employer in order to establish an effective health and safety management system   20 marks

(b) Describe the principal features of a Statement of Health and Safety Policy   5 marks

Answer

(a) Reference to duty on employers to establish such 'arrangements' for the effective planning, organisation, control, monitoring and review of the preventive and protective measures arising from risk assessment.

These arrangements include:

- ♦ safety monitoring systems and accident investigation procedures;
- ♦ risk assessment procedures;
- ♦ planned preventative maintenance systems;
- ♦ cleaning schedules;
- ♦ emergency procedures;
- ♦ health surveillance, where appropriate;
- ♦ appointment of competent persons;
- ♦ provision of information, instruction and training;
- ♦ assessment of human capability for certain tasks; and
- ♦ joint consultation procedures.

(b) The principal features of a Statement of Health and Safety Policy are:
- ♦ a general statement of intent stating the basic objectives of the organisation with regard to health and safety at work;
- ♦ the organisation for health and safety, including the chain of command, individual accountabilities and arrangements for monitoring implementation of the policy; and
- ♦ the arrangements for putting the policy into practice, including procedures, systems, rules and training systems.

CHAPTER 4

Question
(a)	Define the terms 'risk' and 'hazard'	5 marks
(b)	Describe the factors to be considered by an employer when undertaking a risk assessment of his supermarket	20 marks

Answer

(a) A risk is the probability or likelihood of harm arising.
A hazard is something with the potential to cause harm.

(b) The risk assessment should take into account the significant hazards to customers, employees and other persons, such as people delivering goods. These hazards include those associated with:
- ♦ slips, trips and falls due to, for example, obstructed aisles;
- ♦ items falling from a height;
- ♦ fire;
- ♦ manual handling injuries;
- ♦ contact with hazardous cleaning materials;
- ♦ contact with glass doors and partitions;
- ♦ inadequate lighting;
- ♦ unsafe storage of waste materials;
- ♦ unsafe window cleaning;
- ♦ dangerous doors and gates; and
- ♦ people using escalators and staircases.

In each case, the following risk variables should be considered:

♦ the probability or likelihood of human injury, disease, damage or other forms of loss;
♦ the predicted severity of the outcome;
♦ the number of people exposed to the risk at any one time; and
♦ the frequency of the risk arising.

The outcome of the risk assessment should indicate future action, taking into account current legal requirements.

CHAPTER 5

Question

   (a) Explain the meaning of the term 'human factors'   10 marks
   (b) Explain the factors to be considered in matching the employee to his job   5 marks
   (c) Describe those characteristics of an organisation that influence safety-related behaviour   10 marks

Answer

   (a) 'Human factors' covers a range of issues including:

♦ the perceptual, physical and mental capabilities of people and the interaction of individuals with the job and working environments;
♦ the influence of equipment and system design on human performance; and
♦ those organisational characteristics that influence safety-related behaviour.

   (b) 'Physical match' includes the design of the whole workplace and the working environment.

♦ 'Mental match' involves the individual's information and decision-making requirements, as well as his perception of tasks.

   (c) Organisational characteristics that influence safety-related behaviour include:

♦ the promotion of a positive safety climate;
♦ policies and systems that take account of human capabilities and fallibilities;
♦ commitment to the achievement of progressively higher standards;
♦ demonstration by senior management of their active involvement in health and safety;
♦ leadership, where an environment is created that encourages safe behaviour.

CHAPTER 6

Question

   (a) Explain the meaning of the term 'ergonomics'   5 marks
   (b) Discuss the factors to be considered by an employer when taking an ergonomics-based approach to health and safety at work   20 marks

Answer

   (a) Ergonomics is the study of the interrelationships between people and their work. It is concerned with the design and specification of working environments in which people receive prime consideration.

- ♦ The factors to be considered by an employer include:
    - ♦ the human system – physical and psychological elements;
    - ♦ environmental factors – the effects on the human system of the working environment, ie layout, workspace, extremes of temperature, lighting, ventilation, noise and vibration;
    - ♦ the man-machine interface – design of controls and displays on work equipment;
    - ♦ task characteristics – frequency of operation, repetitiveness of the task, actual work load, criticality of the task, duration of the task and its interaction with other tasks;
    - ♦ task demands – the physical and mental demands of the task;
    - ♦ instructions and procedures – the quality of verbal and written instructions
    - ♦ task stressors – factors of the task that may be stressful to the operator, for example, a high mental workload, repetitive nature of the task; and
    - ♦ socio-technical factors – relationships between operators and groups of operators, working practices, manning levels, provision of breaks, communication systems, rewards and benefits.

CHAPTER 7

Question

Environmental stress is a feature of many workplaces.

(a) Discuss the various forms of environmental stressor   15 marks

(b) Outline the duties on employers for ensuring the provision and maintenance of a healthy working environment   10 marks

Answer

(a) Environmental stressors include:

- ♦ extremes of temperature, in many cases, from winter to summer months;
- ♦ high temperatures from process activities;
- ♦ the nature of the work involved, ie active physical work or sedentary work;
- ♦ inadequate ventilation including comfort ventilation and means for removing airborne contaminants;
- ♦ extremes of humidity;
- ♦ inadequate lighting, both generally and at a particular task;
- ♦ the problems of glare;
- ♦ correct distribution of light;
- ♦ dirty working areas;
- ♦ inadequate space to do the work safely;
- ♦ unsuitable workstations, including seats; and
- ♦ noise that may cause distraction or be so intense as to cause occupational deafness.

(b) Duties of employers under the WHSWR 1992 to provide and maintain:

- effective and suitable ventilation;
- a reasonable temperature during working hours;
- suitable and sufficient lighting, together with emergency lighting where necessary;
- a clean workplace with adequate control over waste materials;
- sufficient floor area and work space for employees; and
- suitable workstations, both indoors and outdoors;
- suitable seats for people and in terms of the work undertaken.

CHAPTER 8

Question

Fire is one of the greatest causes of death, injury and loss in workplaces.

  (a) Outline the principal causes of fire in workplaces.   10 marks

  (b) Describe the factors to be considered in a fire risk assessment of a two-storey office block.   15 marks

Answer

  (a) The principal causes of fire in workplaces are:

- defective and dangerous electrical equipment;
- spontaneous ignition of certain highly flammable liquids;
- spontaneous combustion caused by exothermic reactions between substances;
- people smoking, particularly in flammable material storage areas;
- sparks from friction between machinery surfaces;
- hot work, such as welding, soldering and brazing activities;
- static electricity;
- vehicle emissions and hot surfaces on vehicles, such as exhausts;
- open flames from portable and fixed heating appliances, furnaces and misused or badly maintained equipment; and
- lightning.

  (b) The factors to be considered in the fire risk assessment of a two-storey office block include:

- the identification of fire hazards, in particular, sources of ignition and the presence of flammable substances;
- the identification of persons at risk, including members of the public and other people, such as cleaners, who may be present when the premises are closed;
- measuring and evaluating the risks, together with the control measures necessary;
- preventing or controlling exposure to risks, such as segregation of high fire risk processes;
- recording the findings, including current control measures and future actions necessary; and
- reviewing the assessment, particularly on the introduction of other flammable substances and where there have been modifications to the layout of the offices.

CHAPTER 9

Question

A review of accident reports has indicated a high level of machinery-related accidents in a workshop.

  (a)   Describe the principal hazards associated with machinery operation   10 marks
  (b)   Outline the various forms of guarding that may be applied to
        the dangerous parts of machinery to control these hazards   15 marks

Answer

  (a)   The principal hazards associated with machinery operation are:

   ◆   traps – reciprocating traps, for example, with power presses, shearing traps on guillotines, in-running nips between belts and conveyors, rollers and gears;
   ◆   entanglement – of hair and clothes in rotating machinery, such as shafts, drills and augers;
   ◆   ejection – items being emitted from machines; and
   ◆   contact – with hot surfaces, sharp projections on machines.

  (b)   The various forms of machinery guarding are, in order of relative safety:

   ◆   fixed guards, ie guards that can be removed only by the use of a tool;
   ◆   interlocking guards – guards incorporating an interlock mechanism that prevents access to a danger point until the moving parts have come to rest;
   ◆   automatic guards – those that are associated with, and dependent on, the mechanism of the machinery and operate so as to remove physically from the danger area a person exposed to danger, as in the case of large power presses;
   ◆   distance guards – those guards that place a danger point out of normal reach;
   ◆   adjustable guards – those that incorporate an adjustable element, which, once adjusted, remains in position during a particular operation, for example, circular saws.

CHAPTER 10

Question

A contractor is renewing the electrical installation in a large warehouse.

  (a)   Outline the hazards that the contractors' employees could
        encounter during this work   10 marks
  (b)   Describe the precautions necessary on the part of the occupier
        and the contractor to ensure safe working   15 marks

Answer

  (a)   Typical hazards during electrical installation work include:

   ◆   risk of electric shock through contact with live conductors;
   ◆   risk of burns through contact with hot conductors;
   ◆   explosion where an electrical short circuit may cause sparking in a flammable atmosphere;
   ◆   risk of eye injury through exposure to ultraviolet rays from accidental arcing;

  (b)   Precautions necessary include:

   ◆   protection against direct contact, for example, by suitable insulation for parts of equipment liable to be charged with electricity;

◆ protection against indirect contact, for example, by providing effective earthing for metallic enclosures;
◆ earthing of appliances;
◆ use of fuses of the correct type and rating for appliances;
◆ use of circuit breakers;
◆ use of earth leakage circuit breakers (residual current devices)
◆ use of reduced voltage systems; and
◆ the operation of safe systems of work, including Permit to Work systems.

CHAPTER 11

Question

Employers have a duty to protect employees from health risks whilst at work.

(a) Describe the health risks to employees working in a large supermarket   10 marks
(b) Discuss the methods available for protecting employees against these identified health risks   15 marks

Answer

(a) Typical health risks to supermarket workers include:
    ◆ manual handling injuries through excessive handling of loads including:
        ◆ prolapsed intervertebral discs;
        ◆ hernia;
        ◆ ligamental strains; and
        ◆ rheumatic disorders;
    ◆ dermatitis through contact with hazardous cleaning compounds.

(b) Methods available for protecting employees against manual handling injuries include:
    ◆ provision and use of mechanical handling aids, such as trolleys, sack trucks, etc wherever possible;
    ◆ training in manual handling techniques;
    ◆ adequate supervision during manual handling operations; and
    ◆ provision and use of hand and foot protection.

(c) Methods available for protecting employees against dermatitis include:
    ◆ depending upon the quantities used, the employer may need to undertake health risk assessments for substances classified as toxic, corrosive, harmful and irritant under the CHIP Regulations;
    ◆ provision of information, instruction, training and supervision in the correct use of hazardous cleaning compounds;
    ◆ health surveillance and medical surveillance in certain cases; and
    ◆ careful control by management over the issue of hazardous chemical cleaning compounds.

CHAPTER 12
Question
You are the manager of a parcel-handling depot.
- (a) Explain the health risks to employees arising from manual handling operations   10 marks
- (b) Describe the measures necessary for an employer to ensure compliance with the Manual Handling Operations Regulations   15 marks

Answer
- (a) Employees undertaking manual handling operations are exposed to the risks of:
  - ♦ prolapsed intervertebral disc – due to displacement of the intervertebral disc from its normal position;
  - ♦ hernia – where a loop of intestine breaks through into the groin;
  - ♦ muscular and ligamental strains – due to overloading of muscles and extension of ligaments beyond their extremes of movement; and
  - ♦ rheumatic disorders – painful disorders of the joints and muscles.

- (b) Under the Manual Handling Operations Regulations employers must, wherever reasonably practicable, avoid the need for manual handling operations by the provision of mechanical handling aids for their employees.

Where such provision is not reasonably practicable, they must undertake a manual handling risk assessment, take appropriate steps to reduce the risk of injury to the lowest level reasonably practicable, and provide those undertaking manual handling with general indications and, where reasonably practicable, precise information on the weight of each load and the heaviest side of a load, the centre of gravity of which is not positioned centrally.

A manual handling risk assessment covers four aspects, namely, the load, the task, the working environment and individual capability.

Employees must be provided with information, instruction, training and supervision on safe manual handling techniques.

Specific precautions may need to be taken in respect of pregnant workers and young persons.

CHAPTER 13
Question
- (a) Describe the hazards associated with the use of DSE   10 marks
- (b) Explain the methods that can be used to reduce the likelihood of these hazards resulting in ill-health   15 marks

Answer
- (a) The principal hazards associated with the use of DSE are:
  - ♦ visual fatigue – eye strain associated with excessive periods working at a screen;
  - ♦ postural fatigue – neck, back and shoulder pains caused by constrained postures while using DSE; and
  - ♦ RSI (work-related upper limb disorders) affecting the hands, fingers, wrists, elbows, shoulders and neck of DSE users. These disorders include

epicondylitis, peritendinitis, carpal tunnel syndrome, tenosynovitis, tendonitis, Dupuytren's contracture and writer's cramp.

(b)   Methods to reduce the likelihood of these conditions arising are:
  ◆   advising employees of the need to take regular breaks away from the screen;
  ◆   vision screening of users on a regular basis and provision of suitable corrective appliances;
  ◆   the provision and use of document holders at workstations;
  ◆   improving the design of workstations and working areas, with particular reference to the positioning of keyboards and screens, the height of chairs and the effectiveness of back supports on chairs;
  ◆   provision of wrist supports at keyboards;
  ◆   health surveillance to detect early stages of RSI; and
  ◆   the provision of information, instruction and training in the correct use of workstations and DSE.

CHAPTER 14

Question

A workplace inspection has identified a wide range of hazardous substances being used and stored in various locations.

(a)   Explain the duties on employers for ensuring the safe use of substances hazardous to health   15 marks

(b)   Describe methods for preventing or controlling the exposure of employees to substances hazardous to health   10 marks

Answer

(a)   There is a general duty on employers under the HSWA to provide arrangements for ensuring, so far as is reasonably practicable, the absence of risks to health in connection with the use, handling, storage and transport of substances hazardous to health.

More specifically, under the COSHH Regulations, where a substance is classified as a 'substance hazardous to health', for example, a substance classified as 'toxic', 'corrosive', 'harmful' or 'irritant', or where a substance has a specified MEL or occupational standard, an employer must make a suitable and sufficient assessment of the risks of using that substance and the steps that need to be taken to meet the requirements of the regulations.

The employers must then ensure that the exposure of employees to a substance hazardous to health is either prevented or, where this is not reasonably practicable, adequately controlled. Any control measure must be properly used or applied and employees must make full and proper use of any control measure.

Control measures must be maintained, examined and tested on a regular basis.

In certain cases, an employer must make arrangements for monitoring exposure at the workplace and provide health surveillance for employees who are liable to be exposed.

Employees must be provided with information, instruction and training.

(b) The methods for preventing or controlling exposure to substances hazardous to health, in order of effectiveness, are:
- ♦ prohibition – a total ban on the use of the substance;
- ♦ elimination – ceasing use of the substance altogether;
- ♦ substitution – replacing the substance with a less hazardous substance;
- ♦ enclosure/containment – enclosing or containing the substance in such a way that access is prevented;
- ♦ ventilation – the use of mechanical ventilation systems, particularly LEV systems, to remove the contaminant from the working area;
- ♦ PPE – provision of respiratory protection in particular, the last resort when all other measures have failed or an interim measure until, for instance, exhaust ventilation is installed; and
- ♦ health surveillance – as a support strategy, monitoring the health of exposed employees on a regular basis.

CHAPTER 15

Question
Prior to the installation of a new working procedure, an employer has decided that certain employees will need PPE.
- (a) Describe the factors to be considered in the selection of PPE   20 marks
- (b) Outline the duties of employers under the PPE at Work Regulations 1992 with regard to:
  - (i) maintenance of PPE; and
  - (ii) the provision of information, instruction and training for employees   5 marks

Answer
(a) Under the Personal Protective Equipment at Work Regulations, any PPE must be suitable in terms of preventing or controlling exposure to risks and for the work being undertaken.
- ♦ In the selection of PPE the following aspects must be considered:
- ♦ the needs of the user in terms of comfort, ease of movement, etc;
- ♦ the ergonomic requirements of the task and the state of health of people using or wearing the PPE;
- ♦ the capability of the PPE to fit the wearer correctly, if necessary after any adjustments are made;
- ♦ the number of people exposed to a particular hazard;
- ♦ the risk(s) involved, the conditions at the particular workplace and the relative appropriateness of the PPE;
- ♦ the relative effectiveness to prevent or adequately control the risk(s) without increasing the overall risk;

♦ the scale of the hazard;
♦ standards representing recognised 'safety limits' for the hazard, for example, British Standards;
♦ specific regulations in force;
♦ specific job requirements or restrictions;
♦ environmental stressors that could affect the individual user; and
♦ ease of cleaning, sanitisation, maintenance and replacement of component parts.

(b) Under the Personal Protective Equipment at Work Regulations, employers must ensure PPE is maintained in an efficient state, in efficient working order and in good repair.

Employers must provide such information, instruction and training as is adequate and appropriate to enable the employee to know:
    (a) risk(s) the PPE will avoid or limit;
    (b) the purpose for which and the manner in which the PPE is to be used; and
    (c) any action to be taken by the employee to ensure the PPE remains in an efficient state, in efficient working order, in good repair and in hygienic condition.

CHAPTER 16

Question
    (a) Explain how exposure to noise can affect hearing   10 marks
    (b) Describe the methods available for controlling the exposure
        of employees to noise   15 marks

Answer
    (a) Exposure to noise may affect hearing thus:
♦ temporary threshold shift – the temporary and short-term effect in hearing ability that may follow exposure to noise. The condition is reversible and the effect depends, to some extent, on an individual's susceptibility to noise;
♦ permanent threshold shift – this takes place when the limit of tolerance is exceeded in terms of time, the level of noise and individual susceptibility. Recovery from permanent threshold shift does not proceed to completion, but effectively ceases at some particular point in time after the end of the exposure; and
♦ acoustic trauma – this condition involves ear damage from short-term intense exposure to noise or from even one single exposure. Explosive pressure rises are often responsible, such as that from gunfire, fireworks and major explosions.

    (b) In any strategy for reducing exposure to noise, two factors must be considered, namely, the source of the noise, for example, machinery, and the pathway taken by the noise to the recipient.
The following noise control strategies are available:
♦ vibration produced through machinery operation – reduction at source, for example, substitution of metal components for nylon components where practicable;

- structure-borne noise (vibration) – vibration isolation, for example, use of resilient mounts and connections to machinery;
- radiation of structural vibration – vibration damping to prevent resonance;
- turbulence created by air or gas flow – reduction at source and/or the use of silencers; and
- airborne noise pathway – noise insulation through the use of heavy barriers, noise absorption through the use of porous lightweight barriers.

CHAPTER 17

Question

Employees use a range of radioactive sources in a laboratory.

(a) Outline the essential criteria for ensuring radiological protection of the employees   10 marks

(b) Describe the various radiological protection procedures   15 marks

Answer

(a) Radiological protection criteria are:

- Time – protection by limiting the duration of exposure to certain predetermined limits;
- Distance – ensuring that workers do not come within prescribed distances of radiation sources the Inverse Square Law applies in this case;
- Shielding – the use of absorbing material, such as lead or concrete, between operators and sources of radiation. The density of materials varies according to the radiation type and energy level.

(b) Radiological protection procedures include:

- pre-employment and follow-up medical examinations for classified workers;
- appointment of qualified persons (radiation protection advisers);
- maintenance and retention of individual dose records;
- information, instruction and training;
- continuous and spot check dose monitoring;
- use of warning notices, demarcated areas and supervised areas;
- strict adherence to maximum dose limits;
- additionally for the use of unsealed sources:
    - appropriate PPE, including respiratory protection;
    - effective ventilation of working areas;
    - enclosure/containment of the source to prevent leakage;
    - use of impervious working surfaces;
    - immaculate working techniques; and
    - the use of remote control systems.

CHAPTER 18

Question

Many employees suffer stress at work.

(a) Explain the meaning of the term 'stress'   5 marks

(b) Describe four causes of stress at work   10 marks

(c) Describe steps an organisation should take to deal with stress ⠀⠀⠀10 marks

Answer

(a) Stress is defined as 'the common response to attack', 'pressure and extreme demands placed on a person beyond his ability to cope' or 'a feeling of sustained anxiety, which, over a period of time, leads to disease'. Stress is commonly concerned with changes in people's lives ⠀Everyone has their own particular stress response, such as insomnia.

(b) Four causes of stress at work are:
- the way the organisation is managed – management styles, philosophies, work systems, approaches, etc can result in stress as a result of inconsistency of style and approach by management, emphasis on competitiveness;
- role ambiguity – the situation where the role holder has insufficient information for adequate performance of his role, or where the information is open to more than one interpretation;
- career development – the degree of progression or otherwise in a career, stress may be created by lack of job security, over-promotion or thwarted ambitions;
- individual concerns – people may experience a stress response due to difficulty in coping with change, lack of confidence in dealing with interpersonal problems or through not being assertive enough.

(c) The principal features of a stress management programme include:
- recognition of the causes and symptoms of stress;
- decisions on what the organisation needs to do about it;
- decisions as to which groups of employees can least afford to be stressed, for example, key operators, supervisors;
- examination and evaluation by interview and/or questionnaire of the specific causes of stress;
- analysis of problem areas, for example, shift work;
- decisions as to suitable strategies, such as counselling for specific individuals, social support, training, environmental improvement, redesign of jobs and ergonomic studies.

CHAPTER 19

Question

Employers have a duty to provide 'adequate first did arrangements' for employees.
- (a) Define the term 'first aid' ⠀⠀⠀5 marks
- (b) State the principal objectives of first aid treatment ⠀⠀⠀5 marks
- (c) Describe the factors to be considered by an employer in the design of a first aid room

Answer

(a) The skilled application of accepted principles of treatment on the occurrence of an accident or in the cause of sudden illness, using facilities and equipment as are adequate and appropriate.

(b) The principal objectives of first aid treatment are:
- restoration of breathing;
- control of bleeding; and
- prevention of collapse.

(c) When considering the design and arrangements for a first aid room, the following points must be taken into account:
- the appointment of a 'suitable person' with responsibility for the room and its contents;
- the availability of the suitable person when employees are at work;
- the availability of the room when all persons are at work and a prohibition on the use of the first aid room for other purposes;
- location of the first aid room adjacent to a point of access for transport to hospital;
- the size of the room with adequate space for a couch, space for people to work around the couch, and a chair;
- entrances should be wide enough to accommodate a stretcher, wheelchair and carrying gear;
- the room should have suitable facilities and equipment, an impervious floor covering, should be effectively heated and ventilated and all surfaces should be easy to clean;
- suitable seating facilities should be provided outside the room; and
- the room should be suitably marked as the first aid room.

CHAPTER 20

Question

Traditionally, construction work has had a poor safety record.

| (a) | Describe four hazards associated with construction work | 10 marks |
| (b) | Outline the management systems necessary to ensure safe working on construction sites | 15 marks |

Answer

(a) Four hazards associated with construction work are:
- the use of ladders – falls from ladders, use of defective ladders, over-reaching situations, incorrect pitch of ladders, failure to secure ladders;
- collapses of excavations – caused by inadequate shoring, the presence of water in large quantities, timbering failures, equipment and materials stored too close to the edge of a trench;
- site transport arrangements – hazards to site employees due to failure to provide adequately designed traffic routes for dumpers, excavating equipment and other site vehicles, the unsafe operation of vehicle-mounted cranes and the overloading of passenger-carrying vehicles; and
- fire – serious escalating fires due to inadequate storage of flammable substances, hot work, inadequate storage of waste, burning of site refuse.

(b) The following management systems are necessary to ensure safe working on construction sites:

- clear indication of the system for management with particular reference to the on site responsibilities of the client, principal contractor, design specialists, contractors and other persons on site;
- the appointment of competent persons for certain inspection and examination functions, for example, inspections of scaffolds and excavations;
- joint consultation by all parties on health and safety issues;
- the provision of information, instruction and training for all persons working on site;
- consultation between client and principal contractor prior to commencement of contract work;
- the use of safe systems of work, including written Method Statements and Permits to Work where appropriate;
- procedures for the reporting, recording and investigation of injuries, diseases, accidents involving gas appliances and scheduled dangerous occurrences;
- first aid arrangements;
- arrangements for housekeeping and waste disposal;
- fire protection arrangements and action in the event of fire;
- security procedures;
- transport on site and vehicle parking arrangements;
- the use of PPE, particularly safety helmets by all personnel;
- the use and storage of hazardous substances, including flammable materials and explosives;
- procedures for safe manual handling operations; and
- disciplinary procedures to be followed in the event of unsafe or dangerous behaviour by employees.

Glossary

ABSOLUTE DUTIES Certain duties under health and safety law are of an absolute or strict nature. These duties are qualified by the terms 'shall' or 'must'. For instance, under the Workplace (Health, Safety and Welfare) Regulations (WHSWR) 1992 a workplace and the equipment, devices and systems shall be maintained in an efficient state, in efficient working order and in good repair.

ACCIDENT The term 'accident' can be defined in a number of ways:
- an unforeseeable event, often resulting in injury;
- an unplanned and uncontrolled event, which has led to or could have caused injury to persons, damage to plant or other loss;
- a deviation from the normal, the expected or the planned, usually resulting in injury.

ACCIDENT STATISTICS Accident statistics, as a reactive form of safety monitoring, generally take the form of a number of standard indices:

(a) Frequency rate = $\dfrac{\text{Total number of accidents} \times 100{,}000}{\text{Total number of man hours worked}}$

(b) Incidence rate = $\dfrac{\text{Total number of accidents} \times 1{,}000}{\text{Number of persons employed}}$

(c) Severity rate = $\dfrac{\text{Total number of days lost} \times 1{,}000}{\text{Total number of man hours worked}}$

(d) Mean duration rate = $\dfrac{\text{Total number of days lost}}{\text{Total number of accidents}}$

(e) Duration rate = $\dfrac{\text{Number of man hours worked}}{\text{Total number of accidents}}$

Accident incidence rate is the most commonly used index.

ACTIVE MONITORING This form of monitoring entails the carrying out of a range of proactive safety monitoring exercises directed at preventing accidents, such as safety audits and safety inspections.

ACT OF PARLIAMENT (STATUTE) This is the principal form of legislation that has gone through the parliamentary process to become a statute, eg the Health and Safety at Work etc Act 1974 (HSWA).
The HSWA enables the Secretary of State for Employment to make regulations on a range of health and safety related matters, eg the Noise at Work Regulations 1989.

ADJUSTABLE GUARD A guard incorporating an adjustable element, which, once adjusted, remains in that position during a particular operation.
[BS 5304: Safeguarding of machinery.]

ALTERNATIVE MEANS OF ESCAPE

This is a second route, usually in the opposite direction to the first means of escape in the case of fire, which may join the first means of escape.

APPROVED CODE OF PRACTICE (ACOP)

The Health and Safety Commission (HSC) is empowered under the HSWA to approve and issue codes of practice for the purpose of supplementing information contained in statute and regulations. A code of practice can be drawn up by the HSC or some other body. In every case, however, any relevant government department or other body must be consulted beforehand and the approval of the Secretary of State for Employment must be obtained.
Failure to comply with an ACOP can raise the presumption that the offender was in breach of the legislation unless 'works of an equivalent nature' are undertaken, which satisfy the requirements of the ACOP.

ARM PROTECTION

This may take the form of gauntlets, chain mail and leather arm protectors. This form of protection is commonly used where operators are using knives or other implements where there is a risk of arm injury.

ARTICLE FOR USE AT WORK

This means:
♦ any plant designed for use or operation (whether exclusively or not) by persons at work, or persons who erect or install any fairground equipment; and
♦ any article designed for use as a component in any such plant or equipment.
[Health and Safety at Work etc Act 1974.]

ATTITUDE

Variously defined as:
♦ a predetermined set of responses built up as a result of experience of situations;
♦ a tendency to respond favourably or unfavourably to certain persons, objects or situations.

AUTOMATIC GUARD

A guard that is associated with, and dependent upon, the mechanism of the machinery and operates so as to remove physically from the danger area any part of a person exposed to the danger.
[BS 5304: Safeguarding of machinery.]

BODY PROTECTION

This form of protection may include one-piece and two-piece overalls, donkey jackets, aprons, warehouse coats, foul weather clothing, and clothing to protect against machinery, together with high visibility clothing, life jackets and buoyancy aids.
Certain forms of body protection can be of the washable, semi-disposable or disposable type, such as overalls.

BREACH OF STATUTORY DUTY

In certain situations a breach of a criminal duty may give rise to civil liability. In many cases, a statute or regulations will state that a breach of them shall not give rise to civil liability for injury, damage or loss, but where such a disclaimer is not made, civil liability is implied. The standard test adopted by the courts has been to ask the question:

Was the duty imposed specifically for the protection of a particular class of person, or was it intended for the benefit of the public at large?

If the answer to the first part of the question is 'Yes', then a civil claim may be allowed.

Whilst a breach of the HSWA 1974 and the Management of Health and Safety at Work Regulations (MHSWR)1992 does not give rise to civil liability, a breach of other regulations, such as the WHSWR 1992, does give rise to civil liability, ie a claim of breach of statutory duty.

BREATHING APPARATUS

This is generally taken to mean apparatus that replaces the surrounding air supply and provides the user with sufficient air to breathe normally. The use of breathing apparatus may be necessary in atmospheres contaminated with smoke and other airborne pollutants.

There are two forms of breathing apparatus, namely airline breathing apparatus and self-contained breathing apparatus.

CARBON DIOXIDE EXTINGUISHER

This extinguisher consists of a pressure cylinder filled with liquid carbon dioxide. On operation of the trigger the liquid is discharged through the horn under its own pressure, being converted to carbon dioxide snow prior to application. Carbon dioxide can be used for extinguishing both class A and class B fires.
(See FIRE CLASSIFICATION.)

CHEMICAL FOAM EXTINGUISHER

These appliances incorporate a cylinder containing two solutions that are mixed on inversion of the cylinder, namely, aluminium sulphate and sodium bicarbonate. The cylinder is filled with sodium carbonate solution and the inner compartment contains about 13% aluminium sulphate. The foaming mixture is expelled in the inverted position by carbon dioxide generated in the chemical reaction.

Some chemical foam extinguishers incorporate a cylinder with a seal that must be broken with a plunger prior to inversion.
(See FIRE CLASSIFICATION.)

CIVIL LIABILITY

This refers to the 'penalty' that can be imposed by a civil court, eg county court, High Court.

A civil action generally involves individuals, with a plaintiff suing a defendant for a remedy or remedies. In most cases, the remedy takes the form of damages, a form of financial compensation.

Civil actions commonly include allegations of negligence and/or breach of statutory duty.

COMFORT VENTILATION

This is the process of providing sufficient air for people to breathe and, to some extent, regulating temperature. It is directly related to the number of air changes per hour in a workplace according to the external ambient air temperature and the actual rate of air movement. Rates of air change will, in most cases, vary from summer to winter to maintain comfort ventilation.

COMPETENT PERSONS

The appointment by an employer of suitable competent persons to undertake a range of examinations, inspections, operations and supervisory duties is well-recognised in health and safety law. Generally, a competent person should have the appropriate skill, knowledge and experience to deal with the particular circumstances and be appointed by the employer.

Under the MHSWR 1992, an employer must:

♦ appoint one or more competent persons to assist him in undertaking the measures he needs to take to comply with the requirements and prohibitions imposed by or under the relevant statutory provisions; and

♦ appoint competent persons to oversee the emergency evacuation procedures.

'CORROSIVE' CLASSIFICATION

Substances and preparations that may, on contact with living tissue, destroy them.

CRIMINAL LIABILITY

A crime is an offence against the state.
Criminal liability refers to the responsibilities of persons under statutes and regulations and the penalties that can be imposed by the criminal courts, eg Magistrates' Court and Crown Court.
The burden of proving a criminal charge 'beyond reasonable doubt' rests with the prosecution.
Where a person is found guilty, a court will impose some form of punishment, namely, a fine and/or imprisonment.

DANGER

Liability or exposure to harm; a thing that causes peril.

DANGEROUS OCCURRENCE

An event listed in Schedule 2 of the Reporting of Injuries, Diseases and Dangerous Occurrences Regulations 1995 (RIDDOR). Such events must be notified immediately to the enforcing authority and reported on Form 2508. Examples of dangerous occurrences are the collapse or overturning of lifting machinery, unintentional explosions, gassing accidents and boiler explosions.

DEADSTOP DEVICE

A form of safety trip device, incorporating a trip bar or arm, an electrical switch and brake, located in close proximity to a danger point on a machine. When the trip arm, eg a telescopic arm to a vertical drill, is touched, the machine motor automatically cuts out.

DISABILITY GLARE

The visually disabling effect produced by bright bare lamps directly in the line of sight (dazzle).

DISCOMFORT GLARE

A form of glare caused by too much contrast of brightness between an object and its background.

DISPLAY SCREEN EQUIPMENT

Any alphanumeric or graphic display screen, regardless of the display process involved.
[Health and Safety (Display Screen Equipment) Regulations 1992.]

DISTANCE GUARD

A guard that does not completely enclose a danger point or area but that places it out of normal reach.
[BS 5304, Safeguarding of machinery.]

DRY POWDER CHEMICAL EXTINGUISHER

These appliances are of two types, stored pressure and gas cartridge. In both cases, the cylinder is fed with dry powder.
In the stored pressure type, the cylinder is pressurised to 10 bar with dry air or nitrogen, and the operation of the trigger allows the pressure to expel the dry powder through the hose.
With the gas cartridge type, the seal on the cartridge is broken by a plunger and the flow of powder is controlled by a trigger valve on the hose.
(**See FIRE CLASSIFICATION.**)

EAR PROTECTION Ear or hearing protection is designed to protect people from the risk of noise-induced hearing loss (occupational deafness). It takes three principal forms:

- ear plugs: fitted into the auditory canal and manufactured in plastic, rubber, glass down or a combination of these materials;
- ear defenders, muffs and pads: cover the whole ear and can reduce exposure by up to 50 dBA at certain frequencies;
- ear valves: inserted into the auditory canal, allowing normal conversation to take place while preventing harmful noise reaching the ear.

EMERGENCY LIGHTING This is provided to ensure safety when a normal lighting installation fails, and may take the form of standby lighting or escape lighting.

Standby lighting enables essential work to continue, the level of illuminance depending upon the nature of the work. This may be between 5 and 100% of the illuminance provided by the normal installation,.

Escape lighting enables a building to be evacuated safely and may take the form of battery or generator-powered installations.

EMPLOYEES' DUTIES Under the HSWA 1974, employees must:

- take reasonable care for the safety of themselves and other persons who may be affected by their acts or omissions whilst at work;
- cooperate with their employer so far as is necessary for him to comply with any duty or requirement under any of the relevant statutory provisions; and
- not intentionally or recklessly interfere with or misuse anything provided for the purposes of health and safety at work in furtherance of a statutory requirement.

Under the MHSWR 1992, employees must:

- use any machinery, equipment, dangerous substance, transport equipment, means of production or safety device provided to him by his employer in accordance with any training received by him in the use of the equipment concerned and the instructions regarding that use that have been provided to him by his employer in compliance with the requirements and prohibitions imposed upon that employer by or under the relevant statutory provisions;
- inform their employer or any other employee with specific responsibility for the health and safety of his fellow employees:
    - of any work situation that represents a serious and immediate danger to health and safety; and
    - of any matter that represents a shortcoming in the employer's protection arrangements for health and safety.

EMPLOYER'S DUTIES Under the HSWA 1974 it is the duty of every employer, so far as is reasonably practicable, to ensure the health, safety and welfare at work of all his employees. More particularly, this includes:

- the provision and maintenance of plant and systems of work that are, so far as is reasonably practicable, safe and without risks to health;
- arrangements for ensuring, so far as is reasonably practicable, safety and absence of health risks in connection with the use, handling, storage and transport of articles and substances;
- the provision of such information, instruction, training and supervision as is necessary to ensure, so far as is reasonably practicable, the health and safety of all employees;

♦ so far as is reasonably practicable as regards any place of work under the employer's control, the maintenance of it in a condition that is safe and without health risks, and the provision and maintenance of means of access to and egress from it that are safe and without health risks; and

♦ the provision and maintenance of a working environment for their employees that is, so far as is reasonably practicable, safe, without risk to health and adequate as regards facilities and arrangements for their welfare at work. Employers must prepare and, as often as is necessary, revise a written Statement of Health and Safety Policy, and bring the Statement and any revision of it to the notice of all their employees.

Every employer must consult appointed safety representatives with a view to making and maintaining arrangements that will enable them and their employees to cooperate effectively in promoting and developing measures to ensure the health and safety at work of the employees, and in checking the effectiveness of such measures.

Under the MHSWR 1992 every employer must:

♦ make a suitable and sufficient assessment of the risks to his own employees and other persons affected by his activities in order to identify the measures he needs to take to comply with the requirements and prohibitions imposed on him by or under the relevant statutory provisions;

♦ review and revise risk assessments and implement changes where necessary;

♦ ensure the effective planning, organisation, control, monitoring and review of the preventive and protective measures arising from the risk assessment;

♦ provide health surveillance, where necessary;

♦ appoint one or more competent persons to assist him in complying with his duties under the relevant statutory provisions;

♦ establish and, where necessary, give effect to procedures to be followed in the event of serious or imminent danger, and nominate competent persons to implement these procedures;

♦ provide employees with comprehensible and relevant information on specific aspects;

♦ where a workplace is shared, cooperate with other employers, take all reasonable steps to coordinate safety procedures, and inform other employees of the risks arising out of or in connection with his own undertaking;

♦ provide comprehensible information to employees from an outside undertaking on the risks and measures he has taken to comply with the relevant statutory provisions;

♦ take into account health and safety capabilities when allocating tasks;

♦ ensure health and safety training of employees:
  ♦ on recruitment; and
  ♦ on being exposed to new or increased risks due to transfer, change of responsibility, introduction of new work equipment, change in existing work equipment, introduction of new technology, introduction of a new system of work or change of an existing system;

♦ provide temporary workers with certain comprehensible information; and

♦ consult with safety representatives in specified circumstances.

EMPLOYER'S LIABILITY

Under the Employers' Liability (Compulsory Insurance) Act 1969 employers are required to carry insurance against common law liability to their employees resulting in injury, disease and/or death. Failure to do so is a criminal offence.

A current employer's liability insurance certificate must be displayed in a prominent position at the workplace.

The policy must state that any person under a contract of service or apprenticeship who sustains injury, disease or death caused during the period of insurance and arising out of the course of employment will be covered for any legal liability on the part of the employer to pay compensation.

Under the Employers' Liability (Defective Equipment) Regulations 1969 employers have been strictly liable for injuries to employees caused by defective equipment.

An injury suffered by an employee is to be attributable to negligence by the employer in the following situations:

♦ where an employee suffers personal injury (including death) in the course of employment in consequence of a defect in equipment;

♦ where the equipment was provided by the employer for use in his business;

♦ where the defect is attributable, wholly or in part, to a fault of a third party, whether identified or not, such as a manufacturer, supplier, distributor or importer.

ENFORCING AUTHORITY

The enforcing authorities are:

♦ the Health and Safety Executive (HSE);

♦ local authorities; and

♦ fire authorities for certain delegated matters.

Enforcement of health and safety legislation is undertaken by inspectors appointed under section 20 of the HSWA and authorised by written warrant from the enforcing authority.

ESCAPE LIGHTING **(see EMERGENCY LIGHTING)**

EVACUATION

The process of moving people from a building or area to an identified assembly point.

'EXPLOSIVE' CLASSIFICATION

Solid, liquid, pasty or gelatinous substances and preparations that may react exothermically without atmospheric oxygen, thereby quickly evolving gases and that, under defined test conditions, detonate, quickly deflagrate or, upon heating, quickly explode when partially confined.

[Schedule 1, Chemicals (Hazard Information and Packaging for Supply) Regulations 1994.]

'EXTREMELY FLAMMABLE' CLASSIFICATION

Liquid substances and preparations having an extremely low flashpoint and a low boiling point and gaseous substances and preparations that are flammable in contact with air at ambient temperature and pressure.

[Schedule 1, Chemicals (Hazard Information and Packaging for Supply) Regulations 1994.]

EYE PROTECTION

Eye protection is designed to prevent injury arising from flying particles, dust, fumes, welding glare and splashes of hazardous substances, such as acids.

Eye protection may take a number of forms:

♦ safety spectacles: with toughened glass or plastic lenses with plastic or metal frames and, in some cases, incorporating side shields;

♦ safety goggles: which incorporate a cup surrounding each eye; and

♦ eye and face shields: which can be hand-held, fixed to a helmet or strapped to the head.

FACE MASKS These generally incorporate a metal frame for holding a filtering medium against the nose and mouth to protect against inhalation of coarse dust particles or non-toxic paint sprays only. They afford no protection against gases, fumes, mists and other forms of airborne contamination.

FACE SHIELDS These provide protection to the eyes and face and can be hand-held, fixed to a helmet or strapped to the head. They are manufactured in toughened polycarbonate materials.

FIRE 'Fire' can be defined in several ways:
- A spectacular example of a fast chemical reaction between a combustible substance and oxygen accompanied by the evolution of heat.
- A mixture in gaseous form of a combustible substance and oxygen with sufficient energy put into the mixture to start a fire.
- An unexpected combustion generating sufficient heat or smoke resulting in loss of life, damage to plant, equipment, goods and buildings.

FIRE ALARM The most effective fire alarm is the human voice. Fire alarm systems can range from a simple hand bell to electronically actuated systems. Systems are commonly linked with heat and/or smoke detection systems, the detection system actuating the audible alarm and sprinkler systems.

FIRE CERTIFICATE Under the Fire Precautions Act 1971 certain classes of industrial and commercial premises must hold a fire certificate.
A fire certificate specifies:
- the use or uses of the premises it covers;
- the means of escape in case of fire indicated on a plan of the premises;
- the means for ensuring the safety and effectiveness of the means of escape, such as fire and smoke stop doors, emergency lighting and direction signs;
- the means of fighting fire for the use of persons on the premises;
- the means of raising the alarm; and
- in the case of factories, particulars of explosive or highly flammable substances stored and used on the premises.

A fire certificate may also impose requirements relating to:
- the maintenance of the means of escape and for keeping it free from obstruction;
- the maintenance of other fire precautions;
- the training of people and the keeping of records;
- limitations on numbers of persons in the premises at any time; and
- any other relevant fire precautions.

FIRE CLASSIFICATION Fires are commonly classified in four categories according to the fuel type and means of extinction.

Class A fires involve solid materials, normally of an organic nature, in which combustion occurs with the formation of glowing embers, eg wood, paper, coal and natural fibres. Water applied as a jet or spray is the most effective means of extinction.

Class B fires involve liquids and liquefiable solids. Liquids fall into two groups:
(i) miscible with water, eg methanol, acetone, acetic acid;

(ii) immiscible with water, eg petrol, benzene, fats and waxes.

Foam, vaporising liquid, carbon dioxide and dry powder can be used on both B(i) and B(ii) type fires. Water spray can be used on type B(i) but not on type b(ii) fires. There may also be some type of restriction on the type of foam that can be used as some foams break down in contact with alcohols. In all cases, extinction is mainly achieved by smothering.

Class C fires involve gases or liquefied gases, eg methane, propane and butane. Both foam and dry powder can be used on small liquefied gas spillage fires, particularly when backed up by water to cool the leaking container.

Class D fires involve metals, eg magnesium and aluminium. They can only be extinguished by the use of dry powders which include talc, soda ash, limestone and dry sand. All extinguishers work by smothering.

FIRE DOOR	A door forming part of a designated means of escape and/or giving direct access to the open air.
FIRE DRILL	A planned or unplanned evacuation of a building or area in order to train and familiarise occupants with the means of escape.
FIRE ESCAPE	A commonly used term to indicate the structural means of escape from a building, such as an external metal staircase or fire-protected internal staircase.
FIRE EXIT	A designated door giving direct access to the open air and forming part of a means of escape in the event of fire.

FIRE EXTINGUISHERS

These are appliances designed to be carried and operated by hand. They contain an extinguishing medium that can be expelled by the action of internal pressure and directed at a fire.
The pressure may be stored, or obtained through a chemical reaction, or by the release of gas from a cartridge.
All portable extinguishers must be coloured red and display a distinguishing label thus:

Water	Red
Foam	Cream
Carbon dioxide	Black
Dry chemical powder	Blue
Vaporising liquid	Green

(See FIRE CLASSIFICATION, CHEMICAL FOAM EXTINGUISHER, DRY POWDER CHEMICAL EXTINGUISHER, FOAM EXTINGUISHERS, GAS CARTRIDGE EXTINGUISHER, SODA ACID EXTINGUISHER, STORED PRESSURE EXTINGUISHER, VAPORISING LIQUID EXTINGUISHER and WATER-CONTAINING EXTINGUISHER.)

FIRE INSTRUCTIONS	A fire instruction is a notice informing people of the action they should take on either hearing a fire alarm or discovering a fire.
FIRE TRIANGLE	There are three requirements for the propagation of a fire, commonly known as the 'fire triangle', namely:

♦ Oxygen or air;

♦   A fuel or combustible substance;

♦   A source of energy.

The removal of one of the three elements of the fire triangle results in combustion failing to take place.

FIRST AID

The skilled application of accepted principles of treatment on the occurrence of an accident or in the case of sudden illness, using facilities and materials available at the time.

First aid is defined by law as follows:

♦   In cases where a person will need help from a medical practitioner or nurse, treatment for the purpose of preserving life and minimising the consequences of injury or illness until such help is obtained; and

♦   treatment of minor injuries that would otherwise receive no treatment or that do not need treatment by a medical practitioner or nurse.

[Health and Safety (First Aid) Regulations 1981.]

FIXED GUARD

A guard that has no moving parts associated with it, or dependent upon the mechanism of any machinery and that, when in position prevents access to a danger point or area.

[BS 5304: Safeguarding of machinery.]

FOAM EXTINGUISHERS

These extinguishers take the form of chemical foam and stored pressure foam extinguishers.

(**See FIRE CLASSIFICATION, CHEMICAL FOAM EXTINGUISHER** and **STORED PRESSURE EXTINGUISHER.**)

FOOT PROTECTION

Foot protection includes safety boots, shoes, clogs, foundry boots, wellington boots, anti-static footwear and ankle protection. Foot protection should be waterproof, resistant to acids, alkalis, oils and other substances. It should incorporate steel toecaps where there is a risk of foot injury. With wet processes, wellington boots, incorporating a steel toecap, should be provided.

GAS CARTRIDGE EXTINGUISHER

This type of fire extinguisher operates on the basis of a plunger breaking the seal of a pressure cylinder. In the case of a gas cartridge water extinguisher, carbon dioxide is contained in a small pressure cylinder, the seal being broken by the plunger. The gas so released expels the water from the appliance.

With a gas cartridge foam extinguisher, a type of stored pressure extinguisher, the foam concentrate is expelled as a result of breaking the seal on a carbon dioxide cartridge.

(**See FIRE CLASSIFICATION.**)

GENERIC (MODEL) RISK ASSESSMENT

A risk assessment produced once only for an identified type of activity, workplace or work group. For generic risk assessments to be effective:

♦   'worst case' situations must be considered; and

♦   provision must be made in the assessment document to monitor the implementation of the controls that are or are not relevant in the case of a particular activity, workplace or work group.

GLARE

The effect of light that causes discomfort or impaired vision, which is experienced when parts of the visual field are excessively bright compared with the general surroundings.

(**See DISABILITY GLARE, DISCOMFORT GLARE** and **REFLECTED GLARE.**)

GUARD

A physical barrier to protect persons from danger.
(**See FIXED GUARD, ADJUSTABLE GUARD, DISTANCE GUARD, INTERLOCKING GUARD and AUTOMATIC GUARD**)

HAND PROTECTION

This includes gloves and gauntlets, principally concerned with protecting the hands from injuries, such as cuts, abrasions and burns and those arising during manual handling operations and in extremes of temperature.

'HARMFUL' CLASSIFICATION

Substances and preparations that may cause death or acute or chronic damage to health when inhaled, swallowed or absorbed via the skin.
[Schedule 1, Chemicals (Hazard Information and Packaging for Supply) Regulations 1994.]

HAZARD

Something with the potential to cause harm. This can include substances or machines, methods of work and other aspects of work organisation.

HEAD PROTECTION

This form of protection includes:
♦ safety helmets to protect the head from falling objects and overhead hazards;
♦ industrial scalp protectors (bump caps) to protect against striking fixed obstacles, scalping or entanglement; and
♦ caps and hairnets to prevent the hair from coming into contact with moving machinery.

HEALTH AND SAFETY AT WORK etc ACT 1974

The HSWA covers all people at work except domestic workers in private employment and extends to the prevention of risks to the health and safety of the general public. The general objectives of the HSWA are:
♦ to secure the health, safety and welfare of all persons at work;
♦ to protect others from the risks arising from workplace activities;
♦ to control the obtaining, keeping and use of explosive or highly flammable substances; and
♦ to control emissions into the atmosphere of noxious or offensive substances.
All duties are qualified by the term so far as is reasonably practicable.
(**See EMPLOYEES' DUTIES, EMPLOYERS' DUTIES, REASONABLY PRACTICABLE.**)

HEALTH AND SAFETY EXECUTIVE

This is the national health and safety enforcing authority. HSE inspectors have wide-ranging powers, including the power to serve Improvement Notices and Prohibition Notices.
(**See POWER OF INSPECTORS.**)

HERNIA

A protrusion of an organ from one compartment of the body into another, eg a loop of intestine into the groin or through the frontal abdominal wall.
Both these forms of hernia can result from incorrect manual handling techniques and particularly from the adoption of bent back stances, which produce compression of the abdomen and lower intestines.

'HIGHLY FLAMMABLE' CLASSIFICATION

The following substances and preparations, namely:
♦ substances and preparations that may become hot and finally catch fire in contact with ambient temperature without any application of energy;
♦ solid substances and preparations that may readily catch fire after brief contact with a source of ignition and that continue to burn or to be consumed after removal of the source of ignition;

♦ liquid substances and preparations that have a very low flashpoint;
♦ substances and preparations that, in contact with water or damp air, evolve highly flammable gases in dangerous quantities.
[Schedule 1, Chemicals (Hazard Information and Packaging for Supply) Regulations 1994.]

HOISTS AND LIFTS

General requirements for hoists and lifts are incorporated in the Lifting Operations and Lifting Equipment Regulations 1998.
Every hoist or lift shall be:
♦ of good mechanical construction, sound material, adequate strength and properly maintained;
♦ examined by a competent person every six months at least, recorded and, where defects are found, a report must be sent to the HSE.

♦ Every hoistway or liftway shall be efficiently protected by a substantial enclosure fitted with gates of such design and layout as to prevent, when the gates are shut, any person falling down the way or coming into contact with any moving part of the equipment. Any such gate must be fitted with an efficient interlocking device.
♦ Every hoist or lift and every enclosure shall be so constructed as to prevent any part of any person or any goods carried from being trapped between any part of the hoist or lift and any fixed structure or between the counterbalance weight or any other moving part.
♦ The safe working load of the hoist or lift must be conspicuously marked and must not be exceeded.

HSE GUIDANCE NOTES

The HSE issues Guidance Notes that have no legal status and are purely of an advisory nature, sometimes to supplement information in an ACOP.
HSE Guidance Notes are issued in six specific series:
♦ General Safety (GS).
♦ Chemical Safety (CS).
♦ Environmental Hygiene (EH).
♦ Medical Series (MS).
♦ Plant and Machinery (PM).
♦ Health and Safety Guidance (HS(G)).

HUMAN ERROR

Limitations in human capacity to perceive, attend to, remember, process and act on information are all relevant in the context of human error.
Typically, human error is associated with:
♦ lapses of attention;
♦ mistaken actions;
♦ misperceptions;
♦ mistaken priorities; and
♦ in some cases, wilfulness.

HUMAN FACTORS

This term is used to cover a range of issues, including:
♦ the perceptual, physical and mental capabilities of people and the interaction of individuals with their job and working environments;
♦ the influence of equipment and system design on human performance; and
♦ the organisational characteristics that influence safety-related behaviour.

These issues are affected by:

♦ the system for communication within the organisation; and
♦ the training systems and procedures in operation,
all of which are directed at preventing human error.

[HSE Guidance Note: Human factors and industrial safety.]

HYGIENE	The science of health; rules for health.
IGNITION	Ignition of a substance is brought about by the introduction of energy sufficient to raise a volume of the substance to its ignition temperature. Ignition sources include open flames, electrical equipment, friction, matches, lighters, static electricity, lightning, welding and other hot work, engines and spontaneous ignition of certain flammable substances.
IMPROVEMENT NOTICE	An Improvement Notice is served on an employer and other persons when, in the opinion of an enforcement officer, a person, business or undertaking is not complying with the relevant statutory provisions and where action is required by a certain date. There is a right of appeal to an industrial tribunal against the notice, which suspends its enforcement until a decision is reached by the tribunal.
IMPULSE NOISE	Noise that is produced by widely spaced impacts between, for instance, metal parts, such as drop hammers.
INCIDENT	An event that does not result in injury, damage or loss but that may cause interruption of the work process.
INGESTION	The taking into the body of substances through the mouth.
INHALATION	The principal route of entry of hazardous substances, such as gases, dusts and vapours, into the body via the nose, mouth and respiratory tract.
INJECTION	A forceful breach of the skin, perhaps as a result of injury, which can transmit hazardous substances past the skin barrier.
INJURY	Damage to the body, commonly as a result of an accident.
INTERLOCKING GUARD	A guard that has a movable part so connected with the machinery controls that: ♦ the part(s) of the machinery causing danger cannot be set in motion until the guard is closed; ♦ the power is switched off and the motion braked before the guard can be opened sufficiently to allow access to the dangerous parts; and ♦ access to the danger point or area is denied while the danger exists. [BS 5304: Safeguarding of machinery.]
'IRRITANT' CLASSIFICATION	Non-corrosive substances and preparations that through immediate, prolonged or repeated contact with the skin or mucous membrane may cause inflammation. [Schedule 1, Chemicals (Hazard Information and Packaging for Supply) Regulations 1994]

JOB SAFETY ANALYSIS

A technique that identifies all the accident prevention measures appropriate to a particular job or area of work activity, and the behavioural factors that most significantly influence whether or not these measures are taken.

LOW VOLTAGE

This is a protective measure against electric shock; the most commonly used reduced low voltage system is the 110 volt centre point earthed system. With this system the secondary winding of the transformer providing the 110 volt supply is centre tapped to earth, thus ensuring that at no part of the 110 volt circuit can the voltage to earth exceed 55 volts.

MACHINE

An apparatus for applying power, having fixed and moving parts, each with definite functions.
[BS 5304: Safeguarding of machinery.]

MANAGEMENT

The effective use of resources in the pursuit of organisational goals. 'Effective' implies achieving a balance between the risk of being in business and the cost of eliminating or reducing those risks.

MANDATORY SIGNS

Signs that indicate that a specific course of action is required, eg EYE PROTECTION MUST BE WORN. These signs are blue in colour, circular in shape, with a symbol or text in white.

MANUAL HANDLING OPERATIONS

This means any transporting or supporting of a load (including the lifting, putting down, pushing, pulling, carrying or moving thereof) by hand or by bodily force.
[Manual Handling Operations Regulations 1992.]

MEANS OF ESCAPE IN CASE OF FIRE

A continuous route by way of a space, room, corridor, staircase, doorway or other means of passage, along or through which persons can travel from wherever they are in a building to the safety of the open air at ground level by their own unaided efforts.

NEAR MISS

An unplanned and unforeseeable event that could have resulted, but did not result, in human injury, property damage or other form of loss.

NEGLIGENCE

'Negligence' can be defined as 'careless conduct injuring another'. It has been defined at common law as:
♦ the existence of a duty of care owed by the defendant to the plaintiff;
♦ breach of that duty; and
♦ injury, damage or loss resulting or caused by that breach.
All the above circumstances must be established by an injured employee before a civil claim for damages can be considered by a court.

NOISE

Noise is generally defined as 'unwanted sound'.

NOISE-INDUCED HEARING LOSS (OCCUPATIONAL DEAFNESS)

Exposure to noise may affect hearing in three ways:
♦ temporary threshold shift: a short-term effect, ie a temporary reduction in the ability to hear, which may follow exposure to excessive noise, such as that from firework explosions;
♦ permanent threshold shift: a permanent effect where the limit of tolerance is exceeded in terms of the duration and level of exposure to noise and individual susceptibility;

♦ acoustic trauma: a condition that involves sudden damage to the ear from short-term intense exposure or even from one single exposure, eg gunfire, major explosions.

OPINION	A statement of something at a point in time that may be subject to change.
'OXIDISING' CLASSIFICATION	Substances and preparations that give rise to an exothermic reaction in contact with other substances, particularly flammable substances. [Schedule 1, Chemicals (Hazard Information and Packaging for Supply) Regulations 1992.]
PERMIT TO WORK	A form of safe system of work operated where there is a high degree of foreseeable risk. A formal safety control system designed to prevent accidental injury to personnel, damage to plant, premises and product particularly when work with a foreseeably high hazard content is undertaken and the precautions required are numerous and complex.
PERVASION	The route of entry of hazardous substances through the skin.
PERSONAL PROTECTIVE EQUIPMENT	All equipment (including clothing affording protection against the weather) that is intended to be worn or held by a person at work and which protects him against one or more risks to his health and safety. Any addition or accessory designed to meet this objective. [Personal Protective Equipment at Work Regulations 1992.]
POSTURAL FATIGUE	A range of symptoms frequently experienced by users and operators of display screen equipment, in particular including lumbar, arm and shoulder pains, due to the adoption of unsuitable postures at a workstation. Generally, the more abnormal the posture, the greater the potential for postural fatigue and even long-term injury.
POWERS OF INSPECTORS	Inspectors have the following powers:

♦ to enter premises at any reasonable time accompanied, if necessary, by a police officer;
♦ to take with them any duly authorised person, equipment or materials required;
♦ to make examinations and investigations;
♦ to direct that any premises, any part thereof or anything therein shall remain undisturbed for the purposes of examination and investigation;
♦ to take measurements, photographs, recordings and samples;
♦ to cause any article or substance to be dismantled or subjected to any process or test;
♦ to take possession of any article or substance and detain for as long as is necessary;
♦ to require any person to give information, answer questions and sign a declaration of truth;
♦ to require production of, inspect and take copies of books and documents required to be maintained or otherwise;
♦ to require any person to afford appropriate facilities and assistance;
♦ to inform safety representatives of matters they have found following an

investigation or examination;

♦ to serve Improvement Notices and Prohibition Notices; and

♦ to prosecute offenders.

PRACTICABLE DUTIES

A level of duty qualified by the term 'so far as is practicable' implies that the duty holder must take all measures necessary 'in the light of current knowledge or invention' or 'in the light of the current state of the art' to comply with the duty. 'So far as is practicable' implies a higher level of duty than 'so far as is reasonably practicable'. Cost or sacrifice cannot be considered in this case.

PROHIBITION NOTICE

These are served by enforcement officers where they are of the opinion that a work activity involves or will involve a risk of serious personal injury.

The notice places a prohibition on specified activities until remedial measures are implemented.

It is not necessary for a legal requirement to have been contravened, but that there is an immediate threat to life.

A Prohibition Notice may be served with immediate effect or suspended for a period of time.

An appeal to an industrial tribunal does not suspend the implementation of the requirements outlined in the notice.

PROLAPSED INTERVERTEBRAL DISC

A prolapsed or 'slipped' disc occurs when one of the intervertebral discs is displaced from its normal position and is no longer performing its function properly. In other cases, there may be squashing or compression of a disc. Slipped discs are associated with incorrect manual handling techniques.

PROSECUTION

The bringing of a person before a court to answer a charge involving an alleged breach of the law. It is normal for the person charged to be served with a summons to attend court to answer to the charge or charges in question.

REACTIVE MONITORING

This includes a range of techniques, such as the investigation of accidents, ill-health and near misses, emergency and disaster planning, interpretation of statistical information and the implementation of a range of strategies to prevent recurrences of accidents and incidents.

REASONABLY PRACTICABLE

A level of duty qualified by the term "so far as is reasonably practicable" implies that a computation must be made by the employer or owner in which the quantum of risk is placed on one scale and the sacrifice involved in the measures necessary for averting the risk (whether in money, time or trouble) is placed in the other, and that, if it be shown that there is a gross disproportion between them, the defendants discharge the onus on them.

[Edwards v National Coal Board (1949) 1 AER 743.]

REFLECTED GLARE

The reflection of bright light sources on shiny or wet work surfaces, such as glass or plated metal, which can almost entirely conceal the detail in or behind the object that is glinting.

RELEVANT STATUTORY PROVISIONS

The HSWA is an umbrella Act of general duties over, in some cases, former legislation, such as the Factories Act 1961 and the Offices, Shops and Railway Premises Act 1963. Both Acts and any regulations made under them are deemed to be the 'relevant statutory provisions' with regard to the HSWA.

Schedule 1 of the HSWA lists regulations deemed to be the relevant statutory provisions. The Secretary of State for Employment may make regulations that are part of the relevant statutory provisions, eg the Control of Substances Hazardous to Health (COSHH) Regulations 1994.

Regulations implementing various European Directives in the UK form part of the relevant statutory provisions, eg the MHSWR 1992.

REPETITIVE STRAIN INJURY

This covers well-known conditions such as tennis elbow, flexor tenosynovitis and carpal tunnel syndrome, and is usually caused or aggravated by work associated with repetitive and over-forceful movement, excessive workloads, inadequate rest periods and sustained or constrained postures. This results in pain or soreness due to inflammation of muscles and the synovial lining of the tendon sheath.

Signs and symptoms include pain, tenderness, swelling and a grating sensation in the joint (crepitus) aggravated by pressure or movement.

(See WORK-RELATED UPPER LIMB DISORDER.)

REPORTABLE DISEASE

A disease or condition affecting a person at work and listed in Schedule 3 to the RIDDOR 1995. On diagnosis by a registered medical practitioner, such a disease or condition must be reported to the relevant enforcing authority by an employer on Form 2508A.

REPORTABLE INJURY

Under the RIDDOR 1995 where any of the following events arise out of work activities it must be notified by the quickest practicable means and subsequently reported within ten days on the appropriate form to the enforcing authority. These events are:

♦ the death of any person as a result of an accident, whether or not they are at work;

♦ someone who is at work suffering a major injury as a result of an accident;

♦ someone who is not at work (eg a member of the public) suffering an injury as a result of an accident and is taken from the scene to a hospital for treatment, or if the accident happens at a hospital, suffering a major injury;

♦ someone at work Is unable to do their normal work for more than three days as a result of an injury caused by an accident at work;

♦ the death of an employee, if this occurs some time after a reportable injury which led to the employee's death, but not more than one year afterwards;

♦ a person at work suffering one of a number of specified diseases, provided that a doctor diagnoses the disease and the person's job involves a specified work activity.

A major injury is:

♦ any fracture, other than to the fingers, thumbs or toes;

♦ any amputation;

♦ dislocation of the shoulder, hip, knee or spine;

♦ loss of sight, whether temporary or permanent;

♦ a chemical or hot metal burn to the eye and any penetrating injury to the eye;

♦ any injury resulting from electric shock (including any electrical burn caused by arcing or arcing products) leading to unconsciousness or requiring resuscitation or admittance to hospital for more than 24 hours;

♦ any other injury:
  ♦ leading to hypothermia, heat-induced illness or to unconsciousness;
  ♦ requiring resuscitation; or
  ♦ requiring admittance to hospital for more than 24 hours;
  ♦ leading to loss of consciousness caused by asphyxia or by exposure to a harmful substance or biological agent;

- either of the following conditions that result from the absorption of any substance by inhalation, ingestion or through the skin:
  - acute illness requiring medical treatment; or
  - loss of consciousness;
- acute illness that requires medical treatment where there is reason to believe that this resulted from exposure to a biological agent or its toxins or infected material.

RESPIRATORS

Respirators are designed to protect the respiratory system of the wearer against harmful dusts, gases, fumes and other forms of airborne contamination.
The correct selection of respiratory protection is vital, and management should decide on the respiratory protection required in individual circumstances on the basis of a formal risk assessment required under the Personal Protective Equipment at Work Regulations 1992.
Respirators may take the form of:
- general purpose dust respirators;
- positive pressure powered dust respirators;
- helmet-contained positive pressure respirators;
- gas respirators:
  - cartridge type; and
  - canister type; and
- emergency escape respirators.

RISK

Risk expresses the likelihood or probability that the harm from a particular hazard will be realised.

RISK ASSESSMENT

A risk assessment should usually involve identifying the hazards present in an undertaking (whether arising from work activities or from other factors, eg the layout of the premises) and then evaluating the risks involved, taking into account whatever precautions are being taken.
A suitable and sufficient risk assessment:
- should identify the significant risks arising out of the work;
- should enable the employer to identify and prioritize the measures that he needs to take to comply with the relevant statutory provisions; and
- should be appropriate to the nature of the work and such that it remains valid for a reasonable period of time.
[ACOP, Management of Health and Safety at Work Regulations 1992.]

RISK RATING

A risk rating is used as part of the risk assessment process and, in most cases, is the numerical product of probability (likelihood) and the severity of the outcome in terms of injury, damage or loss. Probability and severity may be measured on a scale, usually 1 to 5.

SAFE SYSTEM OF WORK

The integration of people, machinery and equipment in a correct environment to provide the safest possible conditions in a work situation.

SAFETY AUDIT

The systematic measurement and validation of an organisation's management of its health and safety programme against a series of specific and attainable standards. A safety audit subjects each area of an organisation's activities to a systematic critical examination with the principal objective of minimising loss. It is an on-going process aimed at ensuring effective health and safety management.

SAFETY CULTURE The development of the right safety culture in an organisation is an important feature of the health and safety management process. This entails:
- ◆ acceptance of responsibility at and from the top, accompanied by the appropriate leadership and commitment;
- ◆ conviction that high standards are achievable;
- ◆ the setting and monitoring of relevant objectives/targets;
- ◆ systematic identification and assessment of hazards, installation and regular review of protective measures;
- ◆ immediate rectification of deficiencies;
- ◆ promotion and reward of enthusiasm and good results;
- ◆ acceptance that it is a long-term strategy that requires sustained effort and interest; and
- ◆ ownership at all levels of the organisation.

SAFETY DEVICE A protective appliance, other than a guard, that eliminates or reduces danger before access to a danger point or area can be achieved.
[BS 5304: Safeguarding of machinery.]
Safety devices can take the form of trip devices, pressure sensitive mats, ultrasonic devices, two-hand control devices, overrun devices and mechanical restraint devices.
[See TRIP DEVICE, TWO HAND CONTROL DEVICE, DEADSTOP DEVICE.]

SAFETY INSPECTION A safety inspection is generally taken to mean a scheduled inspection of a workplace or premises, or part of same, to examine current levels of safety, working practices and compliance with the relevant statutory provisions at a particular time.
Safety inspections can be undertaken by managers, health and safety specialists, safety representatives and enforcement officers.

SAFETY REPRESENTATIVE An employee appointed by his trade union to represent the members of that trade union in consultation with his employer on all matters affecting health and safety at work.
Legal requirements relating to safety representatives and safety committees are covered in the Safety Representatives and Safety Committees Regulations 1977.

SAFETY SIGN Under the Safety Signs Regulations 1980 safety signs must conform to a system with regard to colours and shapes:
- ◆ Prohibition signs – circular with a red band enclosing a crossed out symbol on a white background, such as 'NO SMOKING'.
- ◆ Warning signs – triangular in shape with a yellow background and black borders, symbols and text, such as 'LPG – HIGHLY FLAMMABLE'.
- ◆ Mandatory signs – rectangular in shape, incorporating a blue mandatory symbol and/or text on a white background, such as 'WEAR EYE PROTECTION'.
- ◆ Safe Condition signs – a green square or rectangle with symbols or lettering in white, such as 'FIRE EXIT'.

Under the Health and Safety (Safety Signs and Signals) Regulations 1996 employers must use a safety sign wherever there is a risk to health and safety that cannot be avoided or properly controlled by other means.
Signs must contain a pictogram instead of relying solely on text. Fire safety signs and signals are included and FIRE EXIT signs must incorporate the 'Running Man' pictogram.

Pipework containing dangerous substances must be marked, by fixing labels or signs at sampling and discharge points, together with small stores containing dangerous substances.

SLIPPED DISC — **(SEE PROLAPSED INTERVERTEBRAL DISC).**

SODA ACID EXTINGUISHER — The original form of water-containing extinguisher that is gradually being replaced by other types of appliance. With this type of extinguisher, gas is generated in the cylinder when the acid phial is broken by the plunger; water is then expelled from the discharge tube.
(See FIRE CLASSIFICATION.)

STATEMENT OF HEALTH AND SAFETY POLICY — There is a general duty under the HSWA for an employer to prepare and, as often as may be necessary, revise a written statement of his general policy with regard to health and safety at work of his employees and the organisation and arrangements for the time being in force for carrying out that policy, and to bring the statement and any revision of it to the notice of his employees.
The principal features of a statement of health and safety policy are:
♦ a statement of intent;
♦ the organisation, in terms of accountability and responsibility; and
♦ the arrangements that detail the systems and procedures for monitoring performance and overall implementation of the objectives detailed in the statement of intent.

STORED PRESSURE EXTINGUISHER — These are of two types, containing either water or foam.
A water type stored pressure extinguisher contains carbon dioxide under pressure, the water being released when the trigger is pulled.
A foam type stored pressure extinguisher contains foam concentrate and is pressurised to 10 bar with air or nitrogen. Operation of the trigger valve allows the pressure to expel the foam concentrate through the exit pipe, where foam is generated at the end of the hose.
(See FIRE CLASSIFICATION.)

STRESS — Stress can be defined in a number of ways:
♦ the common response to attack (Selye, 1936);
♦ a psychological response that follows failure to cope with problems;
♦ a feeling of sustained anxiety that, over a period of time, leads to disease;
♦ the non-specific response of the body to any demands made upon it.

SUBSTANCE HAZARDOUS TO HEALTH — This means any substance (including any preparation) that is:
♦ listed in Part 1 of the approved supply list as dangerous for supply within the meaning of the Chemicals (Hazard Information and Packaging for Supply) (CHIP) Regulations 1994 and for which an indication of danger specified for the substance in Part V of that list is very toxic, toxic, harmful, corrosive or irritant;
♦ specified in Schedule 1 (which lists substances assigned maximum exposure limits) or for which the HSC has approved an occupational exposure standard;
♦ a biological agent;
♦ dust of any kind when present at a substantial concentration in air; and
♦ not mentioned above, which creates a hazard to the health of any person that is comparable with the hazards created by, substances the above-mentioned. [Control of Substances Hazardous to Health Regulations 1994.]

'TOXIC' CLASSIFICATION

Substances and preparations that in low quantities can cause death or acute or chronic damage to health when inhaled, swallowed or absorbed via the skin.
[Schedule 1, Chemicals (Hazard Information and Packaging for Supply) Regulations 1994.]

TRAINING

The systematic development of attitude, knowledge and skill patterns required by an individual to perform adequately a given task.
[Department of Employment and Productivity (1978) Glossary of Training Terms: HMSO London]

TRAINING NEED

A training need exists when the optimum solution to an organisation's problem is through some form of training.

TRIP DEVICE

A means whereby any approach by a person beyond the safe limit of working machinery causes the device to actuate and stop the machinery or reverse its motion.
[BS 5304: Safeguarding of machinery]

TWO-HAND CONTROL DEVICE

A device that requires both hands to operate the machinery controls, thus affording a measure of protection from danger only to the machinery operator and not other persons.

USE (DISPLAY SCREEN EQUIPMENT)

This means use for or in connection with work.
[Health and Safety (Display Screen Equipment) Regulations 1992]

USER (DISPLAY SCREEN EQUIPMENT)

An employee who habitually uses display screen equipment as a significant part of his normal work.
[Health and Safety (Display Screen Equipment) Regulations 1992]

VAPORISING LIQUID EXTINGUISHER

This type of fire extinguisher consists of a cylinder containing the liquid that is pressurised to 10 bar with dry carbon dioxide or nitrogen. Striking a knob allows the pressure to expel the liquid.
Vaporising liquid extinguishers should not be used in confined spaces as the liquids and their combustion products are toxic.
(See FIRE CLASSIFICATION)

VENTILATION

Ventilation implies the movement of air through a building. This may be by natural or mechanical means or by a combination of both.
The principal features of a ventilation system are:
♦ the provision and maintenance of the circulation of fresh air in every occupied part of a workplace (comfort ventilation); and
♦ the rendering harmless of all potentially injurious airborne contaminants, eg dusts, fumes, gases (exhaust ventilation).

'VERY TOXIC' CLASSIFICATION

Substances and preparations that in very low quantities can cause death or acute or chronic damage to health when inhaled, swallowed or absorbed via the skin.
[Schedule 1, Chemicals (Hazard Information and Packaging for Supply) Regulations 1994]

VISUAL FATIGUE	Eye strain and discomfort experienced by many people using display screen equipment, which may be due to a combination of both eyesight defects and poor workstation design. Vision screening of display screen equipment users should be undertaken on a regular basis and where users are experiencing the symptoms of visual fatigue.
WARNING SIGNS	**(See SAFETY SIGN)**
WATER-CONTAINING EXTINGUISHER	There are three types of water-containing extinguisher. **(SEE SODA ACID EXTINGUISHER, GAS EXTINGUISHER AND STORED PRESSURE EXTINGUISHER.)** The interior of the vessel must be protected against corrosion and the water contained may need treatment with antifreeze. These extinguishers must be operated in the upright position and should not be used for Class B(ii), C or D type fires or where fires involve electrical installations. **(See FIRE CLASSIFICATION)**
WORK EQUIPMENT	Under the Provision and Use of Work Equipment Regulations 1992, 'work equipment' is defined as including any machinery, appliance, apparatus or tool and any assembly of components that, in order to achieve a common end, are arranged and controlled so that they function as a whole.
WORK-RELATED UPPER LIMB DISORDER	A group of conditions occasionally experienced by keyboard operators, formerly referred to as repetitive strain injury. These disorders affect the soft tissues of the hand, wrist, arm and shoulder. Typical symptoms include pain, restriction of joint movement and swelling of the soft tissues.
WORKSTATION	This means an assembly comprising:

- display screen equipment (whether provided with software determining the interface between the equipment and its operator or user, a keyboard or any other input device);
- any optional accessories to the display screen equipment;
- any disk drive, telephone, modem, printer, document holder, work chair, work desk, work surface or other item peripheral to the display screen equipment; and
- the immediate environment around the display screen equipment.
  [Health and Safety (Display Screen Equipment) Regulations 1992]

Abbreviations

Commonly used abbreviations in Health & Safety for Management

ACOP	Approved Code of Practice
AER	All England Reports
CDM	Construction (Design and Management)
CHIP	Chemicals (Hazard Information and Packaging for Supply)
CIEH	Chartered Institute of Environmental Health
COSHH	Control of Substances Hazardous to Health
db	decibel
DSE	display screen equipment
ERA	Employment Rights Act
FPWR	Fire Precautions (Workplace) Regulations
HSC	Health & Safety Commission
HSE	Health & Safety Executive
HSWA	Health & Safety at Work Act
IOSH	Institute of Occupational Safety & Health
JP	Justice of the Peace
LEV	local exhaust ventilation
LPG	liquified petroleum gas
LTEL	long-term exposure limit
MEL	maximum exposure limit
Mev	million electron volts
mg/m^3	milligrams per cubic metre
MHSWR	Management of Health & Safety at Work Regulations
mSv	milliSievert
NEBOSH	National Examination Board in Occupational Safety & Health
OEL	occupational exposure limit
OES	occupational exposure standard
OLA	Occupiers' Liability Act
PACE	Police & Criminal Evidence Act
PAT	portable appliance testing
PPE	personal protective equipment
ppm	parts per million
PUWER	Provision and Use of Work Equipment Regulations
RCD	residual current device
REHIS	Royal Environmental Health Institute of Scotland
RIDDOR	Reporting of Injuries, Diseases and Dangerous Occurrences Regulations
RoSPA	Royal Society for the Prevention of Accidents
RPE	respiratory protective equipment
RSI	repetitive strain injury
RSPH	Royal Society for the Promotion of Health
SR	safety representative
SRSCR	Safety Representatives and Safety Committees Regulations
STEL	short-term exposure limit
VCM	vinyl chloride monomer
WATCH	Working Group on the Assessment of Toxic Chemicals
WHO	World Health Organisation
WHSWR	Workplace (Health, Safety and Welfare) Regulations

Figures & Tables

LIST OF FIGURES

LIST OF TABLES

Bibliography & further reading

CHAPTER 1

Peter, R & Gill, T [1995]: *Health and Safety: Liability and Litigation.* FT Law & Tax, London

Stranks, J [2001]: *Health and Safety Law* (fourth edition). Pearson Education Limited, London

Walker, D [1982]: *Law of Tort.* Celtic Revision Aids, London

CHAPTER 2

Health and Safety Commission [2000]: *Management of health and safety at work. Management of Health and Safety at Work Regulations 1999, Approved Code of Practice and Guidance.* HSE Books

Health and Safety Executive [1990]: *A guide to the Health and Safety at Work etc Act 1974. Guidance on the Act.* HMSO, London

Secretary of State for Employment [1974]: *Health and Safety at Work etc Act 1974.* HMSO, London

Stranks, J [2001]: *Health and Safety Law* (fourth Edition]. Pearson Education Limited, London

CHAPTER 3

Bird, FE & Loftus, RG [1984]: *Loss Control Management.* RoSPA, Birmingham

British Standards Institution [1996]: *Guide to Occupational Health and Safety Management systems (BS 8800).* BSI, London

Confederation of British Industries [1991]: *Developing a safety culture.* CBI, London

Department of Employment [1977]: *Safety Representatives and Safety Committees Regulations 1977.* HMSO, London

Health and Safety Executive [1996]. *A Guide to the Health and Safety (Consultation with Employees) Regulations 1996.* HSE Books

Health and Safety Executive [1996]: *Consulting employees on health and safety.* HSE Books

Health and Safety Executive [1980]: *Effective Policies for Health and Safety at Work.* HSE Books

Health and Safety Executive [1989]: *Essentials of health and safety at work.* HMSO, London

Health and Safety Executive [1999]: *Health and Safety Law. What you should know. Health and Safety (Information for Employees) 1998.* HMSO, London

Health and Safety Executive [1988]: *Safety representatives and safety committees.* HMSO, London

Health and Safety Executive [1989]: *Safe systems of work.* HSE Enquiry Points

Health and Safety Executive [1991]: *Successful health and safety management.* HMSO, London

Rimington, JR [1989]: *The Onshore Safety Regime:* HSE Director General's submission to the Piper Alpha Inquiry, December 1989

Stranks, J [2001]: *A Manager's Guide to Health and Safety at Work* (fifth edition). Kogan Page, London

Stranks, J [1994]: *Management Systems for Safety.* Pitman Publishing, London

Stranks, J [2000]: *The Handbook of Health and Safety Practice* (fifth edition). Pearson Education Limited, London

CHAPTER 4

Health and Safety Executive [1999]: *5 Steps to Risk Assessment.* HSE Books

Health and Safety Executive [1996]: *Guide to the Reporting of Injuries, Diseases and Dangerous Occurrences Regulations 1995.* HMSO, London

Health and Safety Commission [2000]: *Management of health and safety at work. Management of Health and Safety at Work Regulations 1999, Approved Code of Practice and Guidance.* HSE Books

Health and Safety Executive [1996]: *Reporting a Case of Disease.* HSE Information Centre

Health and Safety Executive [1996]: *Reporting an Injury or Dangerous Occurrence.* HSE Information Centre

Health and Safety Executive [1996]: *The Reporting of Injuries, Diseases and Dangerous Occurrences.* HMSO, London

Saunders, R [1992]: *The Safety Audit.* Financial Times Pitman Publishing, London

Stranks, J [2000]: *The Handbook of Health and Safety Practice* (fifth edition). Pearson Education Limited, London

Stranks, J [1996]: *The Law and Practice of Risk Assessment.* Pitman Publishing, London

CHAPTER 5

Health and Safety Executive [1996]: *A Guide to Information, Instruction and Training. Common Provisions in Health and Safety Law.* HSE Information Centre

Health and Safety Executive [1989]: *Human factors in industrial safety.* HMSO, London

Stranks, J 1994]: *Human Factors and Safety.* Pitman Publishing, London

Warr, PB [1971]: *Psychology at Work.* Penguin Books, Harmondsworth

CHAPTER 6

Bell, CR [1974]: *Men at Work.* George Allen & Unwin Ltd, London

Health and Safety Executive [1997]: *If the task fits: Ergonomics at work.* HSE Books

Stranks, J [1995]: *Occupational Health and Hygiene.* Pitman Publishing, London

CHAPTER 7

Health and Safety Executive [1987]: *Lighting at work.* HMSO, London

Health and Safety Executive [1988]: *Specialist Inspector Reports - No.10 'Sick Building Syndrome: A Review' by J.M. Sykes, BSc, CEng, MIOH, Principal Specialist Inspector.* HMSO, London.

Health and Safety Executive [1992]: *Workplace Health, Safety and Welfare: Workplace (Health, Safety and Welfare) Regulations 1992, Approved Code of Practice.* HMSO, London

Lyons, S [1984]: *Management Guide to Modern Industrial Lighting.* Butterworths, Oxford

CHAPTER 8

Department of Employment [1972]: *Highly Flammable Liquids and Liquefied Petroleum Gases Regulations 1972.* HMSO, London

Fire Protection Association: *Compendium of Fire Safety Data.* FPA, London

Home Office [1984]: *Manual of Firemanship.* HMSO, London

Home Office and Scottish Home and Health Department [1977]: *Guide to the Fire Precautions Act 1971: No 2 Factories.* HMSO, London

Secretary of State for Employment [1997]: *The Fire Precautions (Workplace) Regulations 1996.* HMSO, London

Underdown, GW [1979]: *Practical Fire Precautions.* Gower Press, Farnborough

CHAPTER 9

British Standards Institution [1998]: *Code of Practice: Safeguarding of machinery.* BSI, London

Health and Safety Commission [1998]: *Safe use of work equipment: Provision and Use of Work Equipment Regulations 1998, Approved Code of Practice and Guidance.* HSE Books

Health and Safety Executive [1998]: *Buying New Equipment.* HSE Books

Health and Safety Executive [1999]: *Simple Guide to the Provision and Use of Work Equipment Regulations 1998.* HSE Books

Stranks, J [1996]: *Safety Technology.* Pitman Publishing, London

CHAPTER 10

Institution of Electrical Engineers [1996]: *IEE Regulations for Electrical Installations (The 'Wiring Regulations').* IEE, Hitchin

Health and Safety Executive [1996]: *Electrical Safety and You.* HSE Books

Health and Safety Executive [1990]: *Guidance Note PM32: The Safe Use of Portable Electrical Apparatus (Electrical Safety).* HMSO, London

Health and Safety Executive [1989]: *Memorandum of Guidance on the Electricity at Work Regulations 1989: Guidance on Regulations.* HMSO, London

Secretary of State for Employment [1989]: *Electricity at Work Regulations 1989.* HMSO, London

CHAPTER 11

Department of Social Security [1983]: *Notes on the Diagnosis of Occupational Diseases.* HMSO, London

Financial Times [1995]: *Health in the Workplace.* Financial Times, London

Health and Safety Executive [1996]: *Good Health is Good Business. Employers Guide.* HSE Books

Health and Safety Executive [1996]: *Good Health is Good Business. Managing Health Risks in Manufacturing Industry.* HSE Books

Health and Safety Executive [1996]: *Preventing dermatitis at work.* HSE Information Centre

Health and Safety Executive [1998]: *Preventing hand-arm vibration.* HSE Books

Health and Safety Executive [1993]: *Protecting your health at work.* HSE Information Centre

Health and Safety Executive [1994]: *Upper Limb Disorders. Assessing the Risks.* HSE Books

Stranks, J. [1995]: *Occupational Health and Hygiene.* Pitman Publishing, London

CHAPTER 12

Health and Safety Executive [1993]: *Getting to Grips with Manual Handling.* HSE Information Centre

Health and Safety Executive [1992]: *Lighten the Load: Guidance for Employers on Musculoskeletal Disorders.* HSE Information Centre

Health and Safety Executive [1992]: *Manual handling. Guidance on the Manual Handling Operations Regulations 1992.* HMSO, London

CHAPTER 13

Health and Safety Executive [1992]:
Computer Control: A question of safety.
HSE Books

Health and Safety Executive [1992]: *Display Screen Equipment at Work: Guidance on the Health and Safety (Display Screen Equipment) Regulations 1992.* HMSO, London

Health and Safety Executive [1992]:
Working with VDUs. HSE Information Centre

CHAPTER 14

Department of Employment [1994]:
Chemicals (Hazard Information and Packaging for Supply) Regulations 1994.
HMSO, London

Department of Employment [1999]:
Control of Substances Hazardous to Health Regulations 1999. HMSO, London

Health and Safety Commission [1994]:
Approved Guide to the Classification and Labelling of Substances and Preparations Dangerous for Supply: Chemicals (Hazard Information and Packaging for Supply) Regulations 1994: Guidance on Regulations. HSE Books

Health and Safety Commission [1994]:
Safety Data Sheets for Substances and Preparations Dangerous for Supply: Guidance on Regulation 6 of the Chemicals (Hazard Information and Packaging for Supply) Regulations 1994, Approved Code of Practice. HSE books

Health and Safety Executive: *A Step-by-Step Guide to COSHH Assessment.* HMSO, London

Health and Safety Executive: [Various]
Guidance Notes in the Environmental Hygiene and Medical Series. HMSO, London

Health and Safety Executive [1987]:
Introduction to Local Exhaust Ventilation.
HMSO, London

Health and Safety Executive [1989]:
Monitoring Strategies for Toxic Substances.
HMSO, London

Health and Safety Executive [2000]:
Occupational Exposure Limits. HMSO, London

Health and Safety Executive [1995]: *The complete idiot's guide to CHIP 2.* HSE Books

Health and Safety Executive [1990]: *The Maintenance, Examination and Testing of Local Exhaust Ventilation.* HMSO, London

Stranks, J [1995]: *Occupational Health and Hygiene.* Pitman Publishing, London

CHAPTER 15

Health and Safety Executive [1996]: *A short guide to the Personal Protective Equipment at Work Regulations 1992.* HSE Books

Health and Safety Executive [1992]: *Personal Protective Equipment at Work: Guidance on the Personal Protective Equipment at Work Regulations.* HMSO, London

Health and Safety Executive [1992]:
Respiratory Protective Equipment: Legislative Requirements and Lists of HSE Approved Standards and Type Approved Equipment.
HMSO, London

Stranks, J [2000]: *The Handbook of Health and Safety Practice.* Pearson Education Limited, London

CHAPTER 16

Bilsom International Limited [1992]: *In Defence of Hearing.* Bilsom International, Henley-on-Thames

British Standard Institute [1980]: *BS 5378 Part 1: Safety Signs and Colours - Specification for Colour and Design.* BSI, London

Department of Employment [1989]: *Noise at Work Regulations 1989.* HMSO, London

Health and Safety Executive [1995]: *Health surveillance in noisy industries.* HSE Books

Health and Safety Executive [1995]: *Listen up.* HSE Books

Health and Safety Executive [1992]: *The Noise at Work Regulations: A brief guide to the requirements for controlling noise at work.* HSE Information Centre

Health and Safety Executive [1989 & 1990]: *Noise Guides 1 – 8: Noise at Work Regulations 1989.* HSE Books

CHAPTER 17

Department of Employment [1999]: *Ionising Radiations Regulations 1999.* HMSO, London

National Radiological Protection Board [1981]: *Living with radiation.* HMSO, London

Stranks, J [2000]: *The Handbook of Health and Safety Practice.* Pearson Education Limited, London

CHAPTER 18

Allport, GW [1961]: *Pattern and Growth in Personality.* Holt, Rinechart and Winston

Cox, Professor T [1993]: *Stress Research and Stress Management - Putting the Theory to Work: HSE Contract Research Report.* HSE Books

Health and Safety Executive [1998]: *Help on work-related stress: a short guide.* HSE Information Centre

Health and Safety Executive [1996]: *Homeworking.* HSE books

Health and Safety Executive [1995]: *Stress at work.* HSE Books

Health and Safety Executive [1999]: *Violence at work: A guide for employers.* HSE Books

Selye, H [1936]: *The Stress of Life.* McGraw-Hill, New York

CHAPTER 19

Health and Safety Commission [1990]: *First Aid at Work: Health and Safety (First Aid) Regulations 1981, Approved Code of Practice and Guidance.* HMSO, London

Health and Safety Executive [1981]: *First Aid at Work: Approved Code of Practice and Guidance to the Health and Safety (First Aid) Regulations 1981.* HMSO, London

Health and Safety Executive [1997]: *First Aid at Work: Your questions answered.* HSE Information Centre

CHAPTER 20

Health and Safety Executive [1996]: *A guide to the Construction (Health, Safety and Welfare) Regulations 1996.* HSE Books

Health and Safety Commission [1995]: *A guide to managing health and safety in construction.* HSE Books

Health and Safety Executive [1989]: *Construction (Head Protection) Regulations 1989: Guidance on Regulations.* HMSO, London

Health and Safety Commission [1995]: *Designing for health and safety in construction; A guide for designers on the Construction (Design and Management) Regulations 1994.* HSE Books

Health and Safety Executive [1997]: *Electrical Safety: Electrical Safety on Construction Sites.* HSE Books

Health and Safety Executive [1997]: *Guidance for Everyone in Construction Work: Health and Safety in Construction.* HSE Books

Health and Safety Executive [1997]: *Guidance on How to Protect the Public: Protecting the Public – Your Next Move.* HSE Books

Health and Safety Executive [1996]: *Health and safety in construction.* HSE Books

Health and Safety Executive [1995]: *Health and safety for small construction sites.* HSE Books

Health and Safety Executive [1996]: *Managing Asbestos in Workplace Buildings.* HSE Information Centre

Health and Safety Commission [1995]: *Managing construction for health and safety: Construction (Design and Management) Regulations 1994, Approved Code of Practice.* HSE Books

Index